F. S. Catn

D0871253

THEORY OF FUNCTIONS

OF REAL VARIABLES

PRENTICE-HALL MATHEMATICS SERIES

ALBERT A. BENNETT, Editor

THEORY OF FUNCTIONS

OF REAL VARIABLES

HENRY P. THIELMAN

Professor of Mathematics
Iowa State College

PRENTICE-HALL, INC.,

Englewood Cliffs, N. J.

Library of Congress Catalog Number: 53-8763

Printed in the United States of America

First printing................*May, 1953*
Second printing................*July, 1959*

PREFACE

THE OBJECT of this course is to familiarize the reader with the fundamental concepts and methods of the theory of functions of real variables and to introduce him to the postulational approach to various mathematical theories.

Problems are included in the body of the book, wherever they arise naturally. For their solutions no more theory is usually required than that which precedes the problems. Such an arrangement gives the reader an opportunity to test the extent to which he has absorbed the material up to any particular point in the book. Special emphasis has been placed on existence proofs.

The topics considered are those which are generally included in standard mathematics courses for first-year graduate students and advanced undergraduates. A natural prerequisite for the study of this book would be a course in *Advanced Calculus* as developed by David V. Widder (Prentice-Hall, Inc., 1947).

The author acknowledges his indebtedness to the following persons: To his teacher, the late Professor Henry Blumberg, whose inspiring and challenging lectures supplied the initial stimulus for this book; to Professor H. F. Bohnenblust, whose lecture notes "Real Variables" were consulted during the early stages of the preparation of the manuscript; to H. D. Block, Frederick Chong, and Carl E. Langenhop for valuable suggestions; to Professor D. L. Holl, Head of the Department of Mathematics at Iowa State College, and the clerical staff of that department for help and encouragement received. To Professor E. S. Allen of Iowa State College and Professor A. A. Bennett of Brown University for their suggestions on reading the manuscript.

Finally, the author's appreciation and thanks are extended to the staff of Prentice-Hall, Inc., for its cooperation and efficiency.

HENRY P. THIELMAN

Ames, Iowa

To Lydia

CONTENTS

THEORY OF FUNCTIONS

OF REAL VARIABLES

CHAPTER I

REAL NUMBERS

1.1 Introduction. The theory of functions of real variables is based on the concept of real numbers. The system of real numbers, or the "real continuum" includes numbers of the following types:

(1) The positive integers or "natural numbers." These form a set closed under addition and multiplication, but not under subtraction and division. (A set is said to be closed under an operation if the application of the operation to any two elements of the set yields an element of the set.)

(2) The positive, negative integers, and the integer zero. This set is closed under addition, multiplication and subtraction. It is called a "domain of integrity."

(3) The rational numbers, that is, numbers of the form p/q where p and q are integers ($q \neq 0$). This set is closed under addition, multiplication, subtraction, and division (except by zero), but not under the extraction of roots.

(4) The real algebraic numbers, that is, real numbers which can be expressed as roots of polynomial equations in one unknown, the coefficients of the equations being rational numbers. (Such a polynomial equation is a statement of the form

$$a_n x^n + a_{n-1} x^{n-1} + \ldots + a_1 x + a_0 = 0$$

where n is a positive integer, $a_0, a_1, a_2, \ldots, a_n$ are rational numbers, and $a_n \neq 0$.)

(5) The real transcendental numbers, that is, real numbers which are not algebraic.

At the basis of the theory of all these numbers are the positive integers. For a detailed rigorous development of this system of numbers the reader is advised to consult E. Landau's *Grundlagen der Analysis*. We shall here give just the fundamental postulates on which the number system is based and derive some of its fundamental properties.

1

1.2 Positive integers. The word "set" can hardly be defined in terms of any simpler words. For this reason we shall not try to define it, but we give some synonyms for it. Such synonyms are "aggregate" or "collection" of definite, distinct objects associated in thought. These objects will be called the "elements of the set." When we say of elements a, b, that $a = b$, we mean a and b are the same element. We now state the postulates on which a definition of the positive integers can be based.

Peano's postulates

(1) Let S be a set such that for each element x of S there exists a unique element x' of S.

(2) There is an element in S, we shall call it 1, such that for every element x of S $1 \neq x'$.

(3) If x and y are elements of S such that $x' = y'$, then $x = y$.

(4) Let M be a subset of S such that 1 is an element of M, and for every element x of M, the element x' is also an element of M. Then $M \equiv S$, that is, M contains every element of S.

Definition 1.2.1. Every set which satisfies the above postulates will be called the *set of positive integers*, or the *set of natural numbers*. Every element of such a set will be called a *positive integer* or a *natural number*. These integers will be denoted by 1, 2, 3, 4, 5, 6, ... , where

$$2 = 1', \quad 3 = 2', \quad 4 = 3', \quad 5 = 4', \quad 6 = 5', \quad \dots .$$

Definition 1.2.2. *Addition* of positive integers is defined by the equations

$$x + 1 = x', \tag{1.2.1}$$

$$x + y' = (x + y)'. \tag{1.2.2}$$

The element $x + y$ is called the sum of x and y.

THEOREM 1.2.1. *The sum of every pair x, y of positive integers is uniquely defined.*

Proof. In the equations of Def. 1.2.2 let x be fixed, and let M be the set of y's for which $x + y$ is defined. The positive integer 1 belongs to M by eq. (1.2.1). Let y be an element of M. Then $x + y$ is defined. Therefore $x + y'$ is defined by eq. (1.2.2). Hence y' is an element of M, and $M \equiv S$ by postulate (4). Next we prove that the sum of x and y is uniquely defined. Suppose $x + y$, and $x \oplus y$

are two sums. Let x be fixed and let N be the set of elements y for which $x + y = x \oplus y$. By eq. (1.2.1),

$$x + 1 = x', \qquad x \oplus 1 = x'.$$

But by postulate (1), x' is unique. Therefore $x + 1 = x \oplus 1$, and 1 is an element of N. Let y be an element of N, i.e., $x + y = x \oplus y$. Then

$$(x + y)' = (x \oplus y)'$$

by postulate (1). But by eq. (1.2.2) the last equation can be written

$$x + y' = x \oplus y',$$

and y' belongs to N. Hence $N \equiv S$ by postulate (4).

P.[1] 1.2.1. Prove that $2 + 2 = 4$.

P. 1.2.2. Prove that $x + 1 = 1 + x$.

P. 1.2.3. Prove that $x + y = y + x$.

P. 1.2.4. Prove that $(x + y) + z = x + (y + z)$.

The last two problems establish the following theorem.

THEOREM 1.2.2. *Addition is commutative, that is,*

$$x + y = y + x,$$

and associative, that is,

$$(x + y) + z = x + (y + z).$$

Definition 1.2.3. Multiplication of positive integers is defined by the equations

$$x \cdot 1 = x, \tag{1.2.3}$$

$$x \cdot y' = x \cdot y + x. \tag{1.2.4}$$

The element $x \cdot y$ is called the product of x and y. It will also be denoted by xy.

P. 1.2.5. Prove that the product is uniquely defined for every x and y.

P. 1.2.6. Prove that $2 \cdot 3 = 6$.

THEOREM 1.2.3. *Multiplication is*

(1) *Associative*, i.e., $(xy)z = x(yz)$.

---

[1] The abbreviation P. stands for "Problem."

(2) *Commutative*, i.e., $xy = yx$.

(3) *Distributive with respect to addition*, i.e., $x(y + z) = xy + xz$.

P. 1.2.7. Prove this theorem.

P. 1.2.8. Show by examples that the Peano postulates in the order stated are independent. Give an example of a set for which postulate (1) is satisfied but no other postulate. Next give an example of a set for which postulates (1) and (2) are satisfied but not postulates (3) and (4), and so on.

1.3 Order

Definition 1.3.1. A set S is said to be linearly ordered according to a rule "$<$" (rule of precedence) if

(1) For every two elements a and b of S one and only one of the following relations holds: $a < b$, $a = b$, $b < a$.

(2) Transitivity holds, i.e., $a < b$, $b < c$, implies $a < c$.

If $a < b < c$, b is said to be *between a and c.*

We shall next define an order for the positive integers. To this end we state and prove the following theorem for positive integers.

THEOREM 1.3.1. If $x + m = x + n$, *then* $m = n$.

Proof. Let M be the set of x's for which the theorem is true. The element 1 is in M, for if $1 + m = 1 + n$, then by P. 1.2.2,[2] and Def. 1.2.2, $m' = n'$. Therefore, $m = n$ by postulate (3). Next suppose x belongs to M; then we must show that x' belongs to M. Let $x' + m = x' + n$. Then by postulate (3) and Def. 1.2.2, $m + x = n + x$. By P. 1.2.3, $x + m = x + n$, and $m = n$, since the theorem was assumed to be true for x. Thus $M \equiv S$ by postulate (4).

It can be shown that for every two positive integers x and y one, and only one, of the following equations holds.

$$x = y, \tag{1.3.1}$$

$$x + m = y, \tag{1.3.2}$$

$$y + n = x, \tag{1.3.3}$$

where m and n are positive integers.

Definition 1.3.2. For two positive integers $x \neq y$ we say x is *less than* y, and write $x < y$ if eq. (1.3.2) holds, $y < x$ if eq. (1.3.3) holds.

---

[2] When we say "by problem P." we mean "on the basis of the solution of the problem P."

(The statement $x < y$, and $y > x$ shall mean the same thing. The symbol $x \leqslant y$ is read x is less than or equal to y.)

1.4 Rational positive numbers. The equation $a = b$, as we have used it, states that a and b are the same element. It is often convenient to consider two different elements a and b equivalent with respect to a certain property. We give, therefore, a definition which generalizes the concept of our equality relation.

Definition 1.4.1. A relation among the elements a, b, c of a set is said to be an *equivalence relation*, indicated by the use of the symbol $\sim$ (tilde), if it is

(1) *reflexive*, that is, $a \sim a$,

(2) *symmetric*, that is, if $a \sim b$, then $b \sim a$,

(3) *transitive*, which means that $a \sim b$, $b \sim c$, implies $a \sim c$.

The equality relation is a particular case of an equivalence relation, for it obviously satisfies the above definition.

Definition 1.4.2. Let S be a set for whose elements an equivalence relation is given. We say two elements a and b of S belong to the same *class under the given equivalence relation* if, and only if $a \sim b$.

According to this definition all elements of a class are equivalent to each other, and each class consists of all elements equivalent to one of its elements. It follows from the transitivity relation that if two classes C_1 and C_2 have one element in common, then $C_1 = C_2$, i.e., every element of C_1 is an element of C_2 and every element of C_2 is an element of C_1.

An equivalence relation for the elements of a given set permits us to divide the given set into classes no two having a common element. On the other hand, if a given set is divided into subsets no two of which have an element in common, we can define two elements to be equivalent if they belong to the same subset. This is an equivalence relation, as is easily verified. If, however, the subsets have elements in common, the property of belonging to the same subset need not be an equivalence relation, for transitivity might not be satisfied.

P. 1.4.1. Demonstrate the truth of the last statement by means of an example.

When we speak of an *ordered pair* (a,b) of elements, we consider the pair $(a,b) \neq (b,a)$ if $b \neq a$. The word "ordered" refers only to the order in which the elements appear in the parentheses.

Let us consider the set of all ordered pairs (x_1,x_2) of positive integers x_1 and x_2. We first define equivalence for the elements of this set.

Definition 1.4.3. Two ordered pairs (x_1,x_2), (y_1,y_2) of positive integers are said to be equivalent if $x_1y_2 = y_1x_2$. Restating this in symbols,

$$(x_1,x_2) \sim (y_1,y_2) \quad \text{means} \quad x_1y_2 = y_1x_2.$$

P. 1.4.2. Prove that this is an equivalence relation.

There are various ways of establishing the theory of rational positive numbers. One widely favored way is by the use of the following definition.

Definition 1.4.4. The set of *rational positive numbers* is the set of all classes of equivalent ordered pairs of positive integers. Each *class* is called a *rational positive number* and is designated by (x_1,x_2), where (x_1,x_2) is an element of the class. Equivalence of ordered pairs now becomes equality of classes. The symbol $\sim$ can thus be replaced by the equality sign.

For rational positive numbers *addition* is defined by the equation

$$(x_1,x_2) + (y_1,y_2) = (x_1y_2 + y_1x_2, x_2y_2). \tag{1.4.1}$$

Multiplication is defined by the equation

$$(x_1,x_2)(y_1,y_2) = (x_1y_1, x_2y_2). \tag{1.4.2}$$

P. 1.4.3. Define division for rational positive numbers.

P. 1.4.4. Prove that addition and multiplication of rational positive numbers are each associative and commutative, and that multiplication is distributive with respect to addition.

Definition 1.4.5. We order the rational positive numbers by the rule of precedence,

$$(x_1,x_2) < (y_1,y_2) \quad \text{if} \quad x_1y_2 < y_1x_2,$$

and say then that (x_1,x_2) is less than (y_1,y_2).

P. 1.4.5. Prove that the rational positive numbers are linearly ordered by Def. 1.4.5.

P. 1.4.6. Show that if a rational positive number p is greater than q, then $p = q + p_1$, where p_1 is a rational positive number.

It follows that if an inequality (or equality) holds for a given set of ordered pairs of natural numbers, it holds if one or more pairs are replaced by other ordered pairs of their respective classes. On the basis of the above definitions and P. 1.4.3, it can be shown that the rational positive numbers are linearly ordered and are closed under addition, multiplication, and division.

Definition 1.4.6. Let S be a set of elements s, and T be a set of elements t. If there exists a set f of ordered pairs (s,t) such that each element s of S occurs as a first element in the set f of ordered pairs exactly once, and each element t of T occurs as the second element in the set f of ordered pairs exactly once, then f is said to define a *one-to-one correspondence from S to T*. In a given ordered pair (s,t) of f, the second element, t, is said to be the *image of s under f*, and the first element s is said to be the *source or counter image of t under f*. The set of ordered pairs, which is obtained from the given set f by interchanging in each ordered pair (s,t) the places of s and t so as to form the ordered pair (t,s), is called the inverse correspondence of f, and is indicated by f^{-1}. Then f^{-1} is a one-to-one correspondence from T to S. A one-to-one correspondence from S to T, together with its inverse is called a *one-to-one correspondence between* the sets S and T or T and S. A one-to-one correspondence f between two sets S and T is frequently designated by $f{:}S \leftrightarrow T$, and if the image of s under f is t, we indicate this by the symbol $s \leftrightarrow t$, or by the equations $t = f(s)$, or $s = f^{-1}(t)$.

If a one-to-one correspondence exists between two sets S and T, we say that their elements are in a one-to-one correspondence.

A one-to-one correspondence between S and T is also called a *simple mapping* of S onto T or of T onto S.

Definition 1.4.7. Consider two sets S_1 and S_2 whose elements are in a one-to-one correspondence. Let O_1 be an operation (defined in S_1) which associates with every pair a_1, b_1 of S_1 a unique element $a_1 O_1 b_1$ of S_1, and let O_2 be an operation (defined in S_2) which associates with every pair a_2, b_2 of S_2 a unique element $a_2 O_2 b_2$ of S_2. If the correspondence between S_1 and S_2 is such that whenever $a_1 \leftrightarrow a_2$ and $b_1 \leftrightarrow b_2$, then $a_1 O_1 b_1 \leftrightarrow a_2 O_2 b_2$, where a_1, b_1 are elements of S_1 and a_2, b_2 are elements of S_2, the one-to-one correspondence is called an *isomorphism* between S_1 and S_2 under the operations O_1 and O_2.

We can set up a one-to-one correspondence between the set of positive integers and the subset $\{(n,1)\}$ of the set of rational positive numbers. Let the positive integer n correspond to the rational positive number $(n,1)$. It is easily seen that $n \leftrightarrow (n,1)$ is an isomorphism under addition in each set, and also under the operations of multiplication in each set. The order is also preserved under the correspondence.

Definition 1.4.8. If there exists an isomorphism between the elements of S_1 and S_2 under certain operations, and if S_2 is a subset of a set S, we say that S_1 has been *imbedded* in the set S.

We have found among the rational positive numbers a subset which is isomorphic to the positive integers under the operations of addition, multiplication, and ordering. We have thus imbedded the positive numbers in the set of rational positive numbers.

1.5 Rational numbers. Similarly to the way in which rational positive numbers were defined in terms of positive integers, we now define the set of rational numbers (which will include negative numbers and the number zero) in terms of rational positive numbers. Consider the set of all ordered pairs of rational positive numbers. We first define equivalence for the elements of this set.

Definition 1.5.1. Two ordered pairs (p_1,p_2) and (q_1,q_2) of rational positive numbers are said to be *equivalent* if $p_1 + q_2 = q_1 + p_2$. Restating this in symbols,

$$(p_1,p_2) \sim (q_1,q_2) \quad \text{means} \quad p_1 + q_2 = q_1 + p_2.$$

Definition 1.5.2. The set of all rational numbers is the set of all *classes* of equivalent ordered pairs of rational positive numbers. Each *class* is called a rational number and is designated by (p_1,p_2) where (p_1,p_2) is an element of the class. If $p_1 = p_2$ we call the rational number (p_1,p_1) *zero*, and write $(p,p) = 0$; if $p_1 < p_2$ we say (p_1,p_2) is a *negative rational* number; if $p_1 > p_2$ we say (p_1,p_2) is a *positive rational* number.

Definition 1.5.3. Addition of rational numbers is defined by the equation

$$(p_1,p_2) + (q_1,q_2) = (p_1 + q_1, p_2 + q_2);$$

multiplication by

$$(p_1,p_2)(q_1,q_2) = (p_1q_1 + p_2q_2, p_1q_2 + q_1p_2).$$

P. 1.5.1. Prove that the product of two negative rational numbers is a positive rational number.

P. 1.5.2. Prove that the product of two rational numbers is zero if and only if at least one of the factors is zero.

P. 1.5.3. Define subtraction and division for rational numbers.

P. 1.5.4. Prove that addition and multiplication of rational numbers are associative, commutative, and that multiplication is distributive with respect to addition.

P. 1.5.5. Set up an isomorphism between the rational positive numbers and the positive rational numbers, and thus show that the set of rational positive numbers can be imbedded in the set of rational numbers. [Hint: For a positive rational number (p_1, p_2), $p_1 = p + p_2$, where p_1, p_2, and p are rational positive numbers. Let $(p + p_2, p_2) \leftrightarrow p$.]

The solution of these problems show that the definitions of addition and multiplication given here are consistent with previous definitions of these operations, and that the rational positive numbers can be imbedded in the set of rational numbers.

Definition 1.5.4. A set S is said to be densely ordered if the set is linearly ordered and if between every two elements of S there is an element of S.

P. 1.5.6. Prove that the set of rational numbers is densely ordered.

P. 1.5.7. Prove that there is no rational number whose square is 2.

1.6 Introduction of irrational numbers. We shall from here on assume that the rational number system and its properties are known. In a way similar to the one in which the rational numbers were defined in terms of positive integers, we shall define irrational numbers constructively in terms of rational numbers. To say that an irrational number is a number which cannot be expressed in the form p/q, where p and q are integers ($q \neq 0$), is equivalent to saying what an irrational number is *not*, and it does not tell us what an irrational number *is* in a constructive way. A constructive definition of irrational numbers was given by Dedekind. We shall here give his method of the introduction of irrational numbers.

Definition 1.6.1. A Dedekind cut in the set of rational numbers is a partition (or separation) of these numbers into two classes A and B such that

(1) every rational number belongs to A or to B, but none to both,

(2) every element of A is less than every element of B,

(3) A is not empty, B is not empty.

Under this definition there can occur the following three types of Dedekind cuts (A,B).

(i) The class A has a largest element, the class B has no smallest element.

(ii) The class A has no largest element, the class B has a smallest element.

(iii) The class A has no largest element, the class B has no smallest element.

The case where A has a largest and B has a smallest element cannot occur. For suppose the largest element of A were a, and the smallest element of B were b. Then a would be less than b. But the rational number $(a + b)/2$, which would be greater than a, and less than b, would not belong to either A or B. Hence the classes A and B would not define a Dedekind cut.

As an example of a Dedekind cut of the type (i), we have the cut (A,B), where A consists of all rational numbers less than or equal to a given rational number r, while B contains all other rational numbers. In this case the largest number of A is r, while B has no smallest element.

An example of a cut of type (ii) is the cut (A,B) where A consists of all rational numbers less than a given rational number r, and B consists of the rest of the rational numbers. Here A has no largest, B has a smallest element, which is r.

A Dedekind cut of the types (i) and (ii) is said to be *localized* at the rational number r, and is called a *rational cut*. To each rational number there correspond two cuts, one of type (i), the other of type (ii). In order to have a one-to-one correspondence between the rational Dedekind cuts and the rational numbers we shall consider of the rational cuts only those of the type (ii). We thus establish the convention; *every rational cut (A,B) which corresponds to the rational number r is such that r is the smallest number of B, and A has no largest number.* We shall also speak of the smallest number of B as the *first* element of B, and when we say the largest element of A we may also say the *last* element of A.

We next give an example of a Dedekind cut of type (iii). Let A consist of all negative rational numbers, zero, and those positive rational numbers whose squares are less than 2. Let B consist of the rest of the rational numbers. Then (A,B) is a Dedekind cut, for the three conditions of Def. 1.6.1 are satisfied by it, as can be easily verified. Since there is no rational number whose square is equal to 2 (P. 1.5.7), B has no first element, A has no last element. We have here a cut of the type (iii). This cut is therefore not localized at any rational number.

P. 1.6.1. Prove that if a positive rational number a is such that $a^2 < 2$, then $a_1 = 4a/(a^2 + 2)$ is greater than a, and a_1^2 is less than 2. Show that if the rational number $b > 0$, and $b^2 > 2$, then $b_1 = (2 + b^2)/2b$ is less than b and $b_1^2 > 2$.

Definition 1.6.2. The *set of all real numbers* is the set of all Dedekind cuts in the set of rational numbers. Every element of this set is called a *real number*.

A real number is thus defined as a Dedekind cut in the set of rational numbers.

Definition 1.6.3. An *irrational real number* is a Dedekind cut (A,B) in the set of rational numbers such that A has no last element, B has no first element.

P. 1.6.2. Define addition for Dedekind cuts, i.e., for real numbers.

P. 1.6.3. Define multiplication for Dedekind cuts.

We next establish a linear order for the set of real numbers.

Definition 1.6.4. Let (A,B) and (A',B') be two real numbers. We define a rule of precedence $<$ as follows:

$$(A,B) < (A',B')$$

if A is a proper subset of A', i.e., if every element of A is an element of A' and if there is at least one element in A' which is not in A.

If every element of A is an element of A', and every element of A' is an element of A, we say (A,B) *is equal to* (A',B') and write $(A,B) = (A',B')$.

P. 1.6.4. Prove that transitivity follows under the rule of precedence given in Def. 1.6.4.

The definition and problem just stated establish a linear order for the real numbers.

P. 1.6.5. Prove that between every two distinct real numbers there is a real number.

P. 1.6.6. Prove that if $\gamma = (A,B)$, every element of A is less than γ, every element of B is greater than or equal to γ.

Problems P. 1.6.4 and P. 1.6.5 establish the following theorem.

THEOREM 1.6.1. *The set of real numbers is densely ordered.*

We now have the set of real numbers. These were obtained by making Dedekind cuts in the set of rational numbers. The question that naturally arises is this: Can the set of real numbers be extended by means of Dedekind cuts among the real numbers? The answer to this question is no, as we now proceed to show.

We consider Dedekind cuts among the *real numbers*. Let all real numbers be divided into two classes A and B such that

(1) every real number is in A or in B, but none is in both,

(2) every real number of A is less than every real number of B,

(3) A is not empty, B is not empty.

Such a partition of the real numbers will be called a *Dedekind cut among the real numbers* and will be denoted by (A,B). We shall show that every such cut is localized at a real number, i.e., for every such cut, either A has a last element or B has a first element. This fact is known as the *fundamental theorem on Dedekind cuts* which we now state and prove.

THEOREM 1.6.2. *Let (A,B) be a Dedekind cut in the set of real numbers. Then either A has a last, or B has a first element.*

Proof. Let R_1 be the set of rational numbers in A, and let R_2 be the set of rational numbers in B. Then (R_1,R_2) is a Dedekind cut in the set of *rational numbers*, and thus a real number, say γ. Now γ is greater than every rational number of R_1 (by P. 1.6.6) and therefore of A. Furthermore, if $c(c \neq \gamma)$ is any real number of A, then $\gamma > c$. For if γ were less than a number c of A, there would exist a rational number r such that $\gamma < r < c$, and r would belong to A, which is impossible. Hence $\gamma > c$, where c is any real number of A different from γ. In the very same way we can prove that if $b(b \neq \gamma)$ is any element of B, then $\gamma < b$. We first show that γ is less than any $r(r \neq \gamma)$, where r is a rational number of B, and then we show that γ is less than any other number of B. But γ is a real number. Hence it must be either in A or in B. Therefore, γ is either the largest number of A or the smallest number of B, i.e., γ is either the last element of A or the first element of B.

This theorem establishes what is appropriately called the continuity of the set of real numbers. We call the set of real numbers the *real continuum*. Intuitively we think of a straight line as having the property that if the whole line is separated into two segments, either one segment has a last point, or the other segment has a first point. We can use this intuitive notion of a line to picture the set of real numbers geometrically as is done in analytic geometry. We lay off an arbitrary segment PQ and let the point P correspond to the number zero and the point Q correspond to the number one. Of course, we cannot prove that for every point on a line there is one real number nor that for every real number there is a point on a line. It is, however, often desirable to have such a correspondence. In order to effect such a one-to-one correspondence between the set of real numbers and the points of a straight line it is necessary to assume a postulate which is known as the *Cantor-Dedekind axiom:* To each point on a line there corresponds one and only one real number, and to each real number there corresponds one and only one point on the line. It is because of this axiom that the introduction of irrational numbers is sometimes called the *arithmetization of the continuum,* where the word *continuum* refers to the line. When we say "real continuum" we shall mean either the set of real numbers, or the points on a straight line. We shall also use the words "point on a line," and "real number" interchangeably.

The Dedekind cut is a very useful tool in proving existence theorems. To prove the existence of a real number having a given property, we need only to show that the given property determines a Dedekind cut (A,B) in the set of real numbers. This cut defines a real number γ which is either the last of A or the first of B. Next we try to show that γ has the given property. We shall use this method to prove the next theorem. Before we can state this theorem we have to give definitions of the terms involved in the statement of the theorem.

Definition 1.6.5. Let S be a set of real numbers. A number M is said to be an *upper bound* of S if every element of S is less than or equal to M. A number N is said to be a *lower bound* of S if every element of S is greater than or equal to N. The set S is said to be *bounded from above* if it has an upper bound; it is said to be *bounded from below* if it has a lower bound. The set S is said to be *bounded* if it has an upper bound and a lower bound.

Definition 1.6.6. A real number M is said to be a *least upper bound* or a *supremum* of a given set S of real numbers if

(1) M is an upper bound of S, i.e., every element of S is less than or equal to M,

(2) for every N less than M there exists at least one s of S such that $s > N$.

The least upper bound of S is sometimes called the *upper boundary* of S, but more universally it is called the *supremum* of S. For this reason we shall use the abbreviation *sup S* for the least upper bound of S.

A real number L is said to be the *greatest lower* bound, or the *infimum* of a set S of real numbers if

(1) L is a lower bound of S, i.e., every element of S is greater than or equal to L,

(2) for every number $N > L$ there exists at least one s of S such that $s < N$.

The greatest lower bound, or the infimum of a set S is sometimes called the *lower boundary* of S. When we use the abbreviated notation we shall write *inf S* for the greatest lower bound of S.

THEOREM 1.6.3. *Every bounded set of real numbers, which has at least one element, has a least upper bound and a greatest lower bound.*

Proof of the existence of sup S. Let M be an upper bound of S. We construct a Dedekind cut (A,B) in the set of real numbers as follows: A consists of all real numbers a which are less than at least one element of S; B consists of the rest of the real numbers. We now show that (A,B) is a Dedekind cut in the set of real numbers.

(1) Classes A and B contain all real numbers. This follows from the definition of the class B.

(2) Every a of A is less than every b of B. For suppose a b_1 of B were less than an a_1 of A. Thus $b_1 < a_1$. But there exists an s of S which is greater than a_1. Hence by the transitivity property of the linear order of the real numbers $b_1 < a_1 < s$, and b_1 must belong to A. This contradicts the hypothesis that b_1 is an element of B.

(3) Class A is not empty. For S has at least one element s. Hence $s - 1$ belongs to A; B is not empty for it contains M.

Therefore (A,B) is a Dedekind cut in the set of real numbers, and defines a real number γ which is either the last of A or the first of B. We now show that $\gamma = sup\ S$. We prove, first, that condition (1) of Def. 1.6.6 is satisfied by γ, i.e., that every $s \leqslant \gamma$. Suppose there were an element s of S, say s_1, such that $s_1 > \gamma$. Then between γ and s_1 there would be a real number β which would be less than s_1

of S. Hence β would belong to A, which is impossible, since every real number greater than γ belongs to B. We must also prove that condition (2) of Def. 1.6.6 is satisfied by γ. That is, we must show that if N is any real number less than γ, there exists an s of S such that $s > N$. Let N be any real number less than γ. Then N belongs to A, for γ is either the last of A or the first number of B. Hence, by the definition of the class A, there exists an s of S such that $s > N$. Therefore $\gamma = sup\ S$.

The proof of the existence of $inf\ S$ is similar.

P. 1.6.7. Prove the second part of the last theorem, i.e., prove that $inf\ S$ exists.

1.7 Properties of real numbers. The positive integers were characterized by means of postulates, and the real numbers were then obtained by extending the original set of numbers. The question arises, whether by using different methods for the extension of the natural numbers, we might have obtained a different set of real numbers. Before we can answer this question we must state the characteristic properties of our set of real numbers. After these properties have been stated, one could use them as the defining postulates for the system of real numbers and study this system on the basis of these postulates just as the natural numbers are studied on the basis of Peano's postulates.

In order to simplify the statement of the characteristic properties of the set of real numbers we give some preliminary definitions.

Definition 1.7.1. A *mathematical system* consists of at least one set of elements, an equivalence relation and at least one operation, or correspondence, between these elements.

An example of a mathematical system is the set of natural numbers, together with the equality relation and addition, or multiplication. The next several definitions give examples of various other mathematical systems.

Definition 1.7.2. A mathematical system is said to constitute a *group under an operation O* if the following properties are satisfied.

(1) The system is closed under the operation O. That is, if a and b are elements of S, then aOb is an element of S.

(2) The operation O is associative. That is, $(aOb)Oc = aO(bOc)$, where a, b, c are elements of S.

(3) There exists an identity element i in S such that for every a of S, $aOi = a$.

(4) For every element a of S there exists an element a^{-1} of S such that $aOa^{-1} = i$. This element is called the inverse of a.

Definition 1.7.3. A group is said to be an *Abelian group* if the following postulate holds.

The operation O is commutative. That is, $aOb = bOa$.

We note that the real numbers form an Abelian group under addition, and excluding zero, also under multiplication.

Definition 1.7.4. A mathematical system is said to constitute a *field* if the following postulates are satisfied.

(1) The system is an Abelian group under an operation. We call this operation *addition* and indicate it by the symbol $+$.

(2) The system is closed under an operation, which is called *multiplication* and is indicated by the symbol $\cdot$. Thus if a and b are two elements of the system, $a \cdot b$ is an element of the system. The system, excluding the identity under addition, constitutes an Abelian group under multiplication.

(3) *Multiplication is distributive with respect to addition.* That is,

$$a \cdot (b + c) = a \cdot b + a \cdot c.$$

We can now state the *defining properties* of the system of real numbers.

I. *The real numbers form a field.*

II. *The field is totally ordered.* That is, it is linearly ordered and the following additional properties hold.

(1) If $\alpha < \beta$, then for any γ, $\alpha + \gamma < \beta + \gamma$.

(2) If $\alpha < \beta$, and $\gamma > 0$, then $\alpha\gamma < \beta\gamma$. Here 0 is the identity under addition.

III. *The field is continuous.* That is, every nonempty bounded set has a least upper bound.

The properties just listed characterize the system of real numbers. They can be used as the defining postulates for the set of real numbers, for it can be shown that any two sets possessing them are isomorphic to each other under the operations implicitly defined by the properties I, II, and III. We shall indicate how such an isomorphism might be established.

Let R be our set of real numbers. Let E be any set which has the

properties I, II, III. By property I, there exists in E an identity
under addition in E. We denote this identity by e_0, and let it correspond to 0 (zero) in R. By property I, there also exists in E an identity under multiplication in E. We denote this identity by e_1. We
would like to let e_1 correspond to 1 in R. Before we can do this we
must show that the order relation between the elements corresponding
to 0 and 1 would be preserved. We show, therefore, that $e_1 > e_0$.
There exists in E an inverse of e_1 under addition. We denote it by
e_{-1}. Thus, $e_{-1} + e_1 = e_0$. Suppose $e_1 < e_0$. Let us add e_{-1} to both
sides of the last inequality. Then, by II (1), we get $e_1 + e_{-1} = e_0 < e_{-1}$.
Thus if e_1 is less than e_0, then $e_{-1} > e_0$. But by II (2), with $\alpha = e_1$,
$\beta = e_0$, and $\gamma = e_{-1}$, we have $e_1 e_{-1} = e_{-1} < e_0$, which contradicts the
statement in the preceding sentence. Thus $e_1 > e_0$. We now let $0 \leftrightarrow e_0$,
$1 \leftrightarrow e_1$. Next, by I, there exists in E the element $e_1 + e_1$. By II (1),
$e_1 + e_1 > e_1$. We designate $e_1 + e_1$ by e_2. In general, $e_{n+1} = e_n + e_1 > e_n$.
Let n of R correspond to e_n of E. This establishes an isomorphism
between the positive integers n of R and the elements e_n of E. Next
this correspondence is extended to rational numbers by letting the
rational number r of R correspond to e_r, where the elements e_r are
defined by the properties I and II. Then, by property III, a meaning
is given to e_γ where γ is any real number of R, and we let $\gamma \leftrightarrow e_\gamma$.
Thus the isomorphism can be completely established.

The result just stated is much stronger than Theorem 1.6.2. That
theorem proved that the real number system could not be enlarged
by the method of Dedekind cuts. We now have the result which
shows that the real number system cannot be extended by any
method. If one wants to introduce new numbers, then at least one
of the properties I, II, or III must be sacrificed at least in part.
Thus if the order property is given up, one might consider pairs of
real numbers and introduce complex numbers. If we do not insist
on the field property I, new elements can be introduced. This is
frequently done by the introduction of "ideal" elements $+\infty$, and
$-\infty$, such that for every other number γ, $-\infty < \gamma < +\infty$. These
elements could have been introduced by a method similar to that of
Dedekind cuts by considering also cuts (A,B) in which A might be
empty, or B might be empty. Of course, sums and products would
not be uniquely defined, for $\alpha + \infty = \beta + \infty$ even if $\alpha > \beta$, which
contradicts II (1). If we are not interested in the field properties,
it is sometimes convenient to consider a set R', which consists of the

elements of the real field R plus these ideal elements. In such a set we have a stronger theorem than Theorem 1.6.3. We can say that *every* nonempty subset of R' has a least upper bound and a greatest lower bound in R'.

The property III is sometimes called the *Dedekind property*. We shall list a few more properties of the real number field which are deducible from those listed above.

The real number field R has the following property. If α and β are two elements of R such that $\alpha > 0$, $\beta > 0$, there exists a γ in R such that $\gamma \cdot \alpha > \beta$. This is known as the *Archimedean property*.

P. 1.7.1. Prove that the real number field has the Archimedean property.

Definition 1.7.5. The *absolute value* of a real number γ will be denoted by $|\gamma|$, and is defined as follows.

(1) If $\gamma \geqslant 0$, $|\gamma| = \gamma$.

(2) If $\gamma < 0$, $|\gamma| = -\gamma$.

P. 1.7.2. Prove that $|\alpha + \beta| \leqslant |\alpha| + |\beta|$.

Definition 1.7.6. Let a and b $(b > a)$ be two real numbers. The set of numbers x such that $a \leqslant x \leqslant b$ will be called a *closed interval* and will be denoted by $[a,b]$. The numbers a and b will be called the *end points* of the interval. Each number x of the interval will also be called a point of the interval. The set of numbers x such that $a < x < b$ will be called an open interval and will be denoted by (a,b). The set of numbers x such that $a \leqslant x < b$ will be called a *semiopen interval open on the right* and will be denoted by $[a,b)$. The set of numbers x such that $a < x \leqslant b$ will be called a *semiopen interval open on the left* and will be designated by $(a,b]$. Every number x which belongs to an interval but is not an end point of this interval will be called an *interior point* of the interval. The number $b - a$ will be called the *length* of the interval.

1.8 Expansion of real numbers in radix fractions. Even though we aim to make the development of the general theory in this course independent of the previous mathematical experience of the student, we shall not hesitate to make use of that experience for the construction of examples illustrating the theory. The object of this section is to supplement this mathematical background of the student, and the results derived here will be used only in connection with illustrative examples. For this reason we take the liberty of making use of certain concepts which will be defined later. In particular, we shall assume the theory of infinite series in order to simplify the derivation of the results of this section.

The student is familiar with the decimal scale of notation of real numbers. In this notation real numbers are represented as finite sums or infinite series whose terms are multiples of powers of 10. In place of 10 it is often desirable to use some other integer r, greater than one, for the representation of numbers. The number r is then called the *radix* or *base* of the representation. We shall find it convenient at times to use 2 or 3 as bases of representations. For this reason we prove the next theorem.

THEOREM 1.8.1. *Every number* x, $0 < x < 1$, *can be represented as the sum of an infinite series*

$$\sum_{n=1}^{\infty} \frac{a_n}{r^n},$$

where r *is an integer greater than one, and the* a_n *are among the integers* $0, 1, 2, \ldots, r - 1$. *This representation is unique, unless* x *is an integer divided by a power of* r, *in which case there exist exactly two representations, one in which the* a_n *are all zero for every* n *greater than some integer* k, *and another one in which every* a_n *with* $n > k$ *is the integer* $r - 1$.

Proof. We determine the integer a_1, $0 \leqslant a_1 < r$, so that

$$\frac{a_1}{r} < x \leqslant \frac{a_1 + 1}{r}.$$

Next the integer a_2 is determined so that $0 \leqslant a_2 < r$, and

$$\frac{a_1}{r} + \frac{a_2}{r^2} < x \leqslant \frac{a_1}{r} + \frac{a_2 + 1}{r^2}.$$

By continuing this process we obtain a set of integers $a_1, a_2, a_3, \ldots, a_n, \ldots$, where each a_n is a positive or zero integer less than r. Let us consider the infinite series

$$\sum_{n=1}^{\infty} \frac{a_n}{r^n}. \tag{1.8.1}$$

Each term of this series is less than or equal to the corresponding term of the series

$$\sum_{n=1}^{\infty} \frac{r - 1}{r^n}$$

which converges. The partial sum

$$\sum_{k=1}^{n} \frac{a_k}{r^k}$$

is less than x but greater than $x - 1/r^n$. The sum of the series (1.8.1) is thus equal to x.

Next we prove the second part of the theorem. Suppose there were two representations. Let

$$\sum_{n=1}^{\infty} \frac{a_n}{r^n} = \sum_{n=1}^{\infty} \frac{b_n}{r^n},$$

and let $a_k < b_k$ be the first numerators which are different. Then the next statement is true.

$$\frac{a_k}{r^k} + \sum_{n=k+1}^{\infty} \frac{a_n}{r^n} \leqslant \frac{a_k}{r^k} + (r-1) \sum_{n=k+1}^{\infty} \frac{1}{r^n}$$

$$= \frac{a_k}{r^k} + \frac{1}{r^k} \leqslant \frac{b_k}{r^k} \leqslant \sum_{n=k}^{\infty} \frac{b_n}{r^n}.$$

But by hypothesis the last sum is equal to the first sum in this expression. Hence the equality sign must hold throughout that expression, and therefore, $a_n = r - 1$, and $b_n = 0$ for all $n > k$, which is the precise statement of the theorem.

P. 1.8.1. Show that any positive integer N can be expressed in form

$$\sum_{n=0}^{m} a_n r^n,$$

where each a_n is zero or a positive integer less than r, and m is an integer.

Definition 1.8.1. Let r be a positive integer greater than one. When we write $N = a_{-m}a_{-m+1} \ldots a_{-1}a_0 \cdot a_1 a_2 a_3 \ldots$, radix r, where each $a_i (i = -m, -m + 1, \ldots)$ is zero or a positive integer less than r, we mean

$$N = \sum_{n=-m}^{\infty} \frac{a_n}{r^n},$$

and say that N has been expressed in the *scale of notation radix r*. When no radix is mentioned it will be understood that the radix is 10.

P. 1.8.2. (a) Express 19/8 in the scale of notation radix 2,
(b) Also radix 3.

P. 1.8.3. Express 10.777... in the scale of notation radix 3.

1.9 Algebraic numbers

Definition 1.9.1. A number ξ is said to be an algebraic number if there exists a positive integer n, and a set of rational numbers $a_0, a_1, \ldots, a_n, (a_n \neq 0)$ such that

$$a_n \xi^n + a_{n-1} \xi^{n-1} + \ldots + a_1 \xi + a_0 = 0.$$

Let n be the smallest such positive integer; then ξ is said to be an algebraic number of *degree n*.

We note that every rational number is an algebraic number of degree one, and every algebraic number of degree one is a rational number. Hence, if an irrational number is algebraic it must be of degree greater than one. The number $\sqrt{2}$ is an algebraic number of degree 2.

P. 1.9.1. Show that $\sqrt[3]{4} + \sqrt[3]{2}$ is an algebraic number and find its degree.

1.10 Transcendental numbers. Proof of existence

Definition 1.10.1. A number which is not algebraic is said to be a *transcendental number.*

This definition is not a constructive definition of transcendental numbers. It does not even guarantee the existence of a transcendental number. The mathematician Liouville was the first to show the existence of such numbers (1851). He not only proved their existence but also gave a method of constructing certain real transcendental numbers. We shall here give such a method. For this purpose we prove the following theorem.

THEOREM 1.10.1. *If ξ is an irrational algebraic number of degree n, there exists a positive number c such that for every pair of integers $p, q, (q > 0)$.*

$$\left| \xi - \frac{p}{q} \right| > \frac{c}{q^n}.$$

Proof. We are given that ξ satisfies the equation

$$a_n \xi^n + a_{n-1} \xi^{n-1} + \ldots + a_1 \xi + a_0 = 0,$$

where $a_n \neq 0$, and the $a_i (i = 0, 1, \ldots, n)$ may be assumed to be integers. Let us write

$$f(x) = a_n x^n + a_{n-1} x^{n-1} + \ldots + a_1 x + a_0.$$

Then $f(\xi) = 0$. Therefore

$$-f\left(\frac{p}{q}\right) = f(\xi) - f\left(\frac{p}{q}\right) = a_n\left[\xi^n - \left(\frac{p}{q}\right)^n\right] + a_{n-1}\left[\xi^{n-1} - \left(\frac{p}{q}\right)^{n-1}\right]$$

$$+ \ldots + a_1\left(\xi - \frac{p}{q}\right) \tag{1.10.1}$$

$$= \left(\xi - \frac{p}{q}\right)\left[a_n\left(\xi^{n-1} + \frac{p}{q}\xi^{n-2} + \ldots + \frac{p^{n-1}}{q^{n-1}}\right) + \ldots\right.$$

$$\left. + \ldots + a_2\left(\xi + \frac{p}{q}\right) + a_1\right].$$

This shows that $f(p/q) \neq 0$, for if it were zero, the second factor in the last expression would have to vanish. This would imply that ξ would be an algebraic number of degree less than n, which contradicts the hypothesis of the theorem. We also have

$$\left|f\left(\frac{p}{q}\right)\right| = \left|\frac{a_n p^n + a_{n-1}p^{n-1}q + \ldots + a_0 q^n}{q^n}\right| \geqslant \frac{1}{q^n}, \tag{1.10.2}$$

for the numerator of the fraction preceding the inequality sign is an integer different from zero. By eq. (1.10.1),

$$\left|\frac{f(p/q)}{\xi - p/q}\right| \leqslant |a_n|\left(|\xi|^{n-1} + \left|\frac{p}{q}\right||\xi|^{n-2} + \ldots + \left|\frac{p}{q}\right|^{n-1}\right) + \ldots$$

$$+ |a_2|\left(|\xi| + \left|\frac{p}{q}\right|\right) + |a_1|.$$

We may assume $|\xi - p/q| < 1$. Therefore, $|p/q| < |\xi| + 1$, while $|\xi|$ is surely less than $|\xi| + 1$. Substituting $|\xi| + 1$ for $|p/q|$ and for $|\xi|$ in the right-hand side of the last displayed inequality, we get

$$\left|\frac{f(p/q)}{\xi - (p/q)}\right| < n|a_n|(|\xi| + 1)^{n-1} + \ldots$$

$$+ 2|a_2|(|\xi| + 1) + |a_1| = K.$$

From this and (1.10.2) it follows that

$$\left|\xi - \frac{p}{q}\right| > \left|\frac{f(p/q)}{K}\right| \geqslant \frac{c}{q^n},$$

where $c = 1/K$.

We can now show the existence of transcendental numbers. Consider the real number γ given by

$$\gamma = \sum_{k=1}^{\infty} \frac{a_k}{r^{k!}}, \tag{1.10.3}$$

where a_k are integers such that $0 \leqslant a_k < r$, and for every N there exists an $a_k \neq 0$ with $k > N$. Let us suppose that γ is algebraic (it is obviously irrational). Then by the last theorem there would exist a real number c where $0 < c < 1$, such that

$$\left| \gamma - \frac{p}{q} \right| > \frac{c}{q^n}$$

for every p/q, where $q > 0$. Let us take for p/q the rational number

$$\sum_{k=1}^{m} \frac{a_k}{r^{k!}} = \frac{p}{r^{m!}},$$

where p is an integer. Then we should have

$$\frac{c}{r^{m!n}} < \left| \gamma - \frac{p}{q} \right| < \frac{r}{r^{(m+1)!}},$$

which is impossible for large enough m. Thus γ is transcendental.

The numbers of the form given by (1.10.3) will be called *Liouville numbers to the base r*. It is obvious that there exists an infinite number of such transcendental numbers in any subinterval of the interval from zero to one.

No general method is known by means of which it can be determined whether a given number is transcendental or not. The number e was shown to be transcendental by Hermite in 1872. Lindemann proved the transcendentality of π in 1892. He also proved the more general theorem that if $e^x = y$, then, except for the case $x = 0$, $y = 1$, x and y cannot both be algebraic. This proves that the natural logarithm of any algebraic number is transcendental, and if the natural logarithm of a number is algebraic, the number is transcendental. There are many unsolved problems in regard to the transcendentality of given numbers. Thus it is not known at the present time whether 2^π or π^π are algebraic or transcendental.

1.11 Second proof of the existence of transcendental numbers

Definition 1.11.1. A set S whose elements can be put into a one-to-one correspondence with the positive integers is said to be *denumerable*.

The existence of transcendental numbers can be established by showing that the set of all algebraic numbers is denumerable but that the set of all real numbers is not denumerable.

THEOREM 1.11.1. *Every set consisting of elements of a denumerable set of denumerable sets is denumerable.*

Proof. Let us arrange the elements of the given set in a double array as follows.

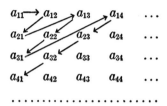

Each row is a denumerable set, and we thus have a denumerable set of rows. By following the path shown in the figure, we can reach any given term by a finite number of steps. This gives us a definite method for the enumeration of the elements in the double array. (Note that the element a_{pq} will correspond to the integer

$$p + \sum_{j=1}^{p+q-2} j \Big).$$

Thus the given set is *denumerable*.

COROLLARY 1.11.1. *The set of all rational numbers is denumerable.*

Proof. We arrange all rational numbers p/q ($q > 0$, p and q relatively prime) in a double array by putting in the first row all integers, in the second row rational numbers with $q = 2$; in the third row those with $q = 3$; in the nth row those with $q = n$. The denumerability of this set follows from Theorem 1.11.1.

P. 1.11.1. Prove that every set consisting of a finite number of denumerable sets is denumerable.

P. 1.11.2. Prove that the set of algebraic numbers is denumerable.

THEOREM 1.11.2. *The set of real numbers is not denumerable.*

Proof. We prove the theorem by proving that the set of real numbers between 0 and 1 is not denumerable. Suppose a one-to-one correspondence had been set up between these real numbers and the positive integers. Let this correspondence be given by

$$1 \leftrightarrow .c_{11} \quad c_{12} \quad c_{13} \quad \ldots$$
$$2 \leftrightarrow .c_{21} \quad c_{22} \quad c_{23} \quad \ldots$$
$$\cdots\cdots\cdots\cdots\cdots\cdots$$
$$n \leftrightarrow .c_{n1} \quad c_{n2} \quad c_{n3} \quad \ldots$$
$$\cdots\cdots\cdots\cdots\cdots ,$$

where each real number has been written in its decimal development, so that each c_{ij} is one of the integers $0, 1, 2, \ldots, 9$. We define a real number γ as $\gamma = .\gamma_1\gamma_2\gamma_3 \ldots \gamma_n \ldots$, where

$$\gamma_1 = 4 \quad \text{if} \quad c_{11} \neq 4, \qquad \text{but if} \quad c_{11} = 4, \quad \gamma_1 = 5.$$
$$\gamma_2 = 4 \quad \text{if} \quad c_{22} \neq 4, \qquad \text{but if} \quad c_{22} = 4, \quad \gamma_2 = 5.$$

In general $\gamma_n = 4$ if $c_{nn} \neq 4$, but if $c_{nn} = 4$, $\gamma_n = 5$. We see that γ is different from every number of our set, for the nth place of γ is different from the nth place of the nth number. Hence it is impossible to set up a one-to-one correspondence between the real numbers and the positive integers.

From P. 1.11.2 and Theorem 1.11.2 it follows that there exist transcendental numbers.

REFERENCES

Landau, E., *Grundlagen der Analysis*, Akademische Verlagsgesellschaft, Leipzig, 1930.

Perron, Oskar, *Irrationalzahlen*, Walter de Gruyter & Co., Berlin, 1921.

MacDuffee, C. C., *Introduction to Abstract Algebra*, John Wiley & Sons, Inc., New York, 1940.

Hobson, E. W., *The Theory of Functions of Real Variables*, Cambridge University Press, London, 1921.

Bohnenblust, H. F., *Real Variables*, Planographed by Edwards Brothers, Inc., Ann Arbor, 1938.

Chapter II

SETS AND OPERATIONS WITH SETS

2.1 Sets and subsets. A set consists of elements. These elements are definite, distinct objects. The word "definite" here means that given a set and an object, one, and only one, of the following statements is true. (a) "The given object belongs to the set," (b) "The given object does not belong to the set." We do not require that it be known which of these statements is true. For example, the set of all real algebraic numbers is a set even though we (or anyone else) may not know whether 2^π belongs to it or not. The word "distinct" means that every element of a set must be considered as a separate object, and that no two elements of a given set are identical. To indicate that a set S consists of certain elements, say a, b, and c, we write $S = \{a,b,c,\}$. If we want to indicate that certain elements, such as a and b belong to a set S, but that the set may contain other elements, we write $S = \{a,b,\ldots\}$, where the succession of dots stands for the rest of the elements of S. A set may consist of only one element, say a. We make a distinction between the set S and its element a, and write in this case $S = \text{'}a\text{'}$. If a set S of elements x is defined by a characteristic property, say P, of its elements, then this set will sometimes be designated by the symbol $\{x \mid P\}$. For example, $\{x \mid 0 < x < 1\}$ stands for the open interval $(0,1)$; the symbol $\{(x,y) \mid x^2 + y^2 < 1\}$ represents all points in the xy-plane which lie inside the circle $x^2 + y^2 = 1$.

In contradistinction to the expressions "set of elements" or "set of sets" we shall from now on use the terms "collection of elements" or "collection of sets" to indicate that the elements, or the sets (whichever the case may be) are not necessarily distinct.

Definition 2.1.1. If every element of a set S_1 is an element of a set S, we say S_1 is a *subset* of S, and we denote this relation between S_1 and S by writing $S_1 \subseteq S$. If S_1 is a subset of S, and if S contains at least one element which is not in S_1, we say that S_1 is a proper subset of S, and write $S_1 \subset S$.

26

If a *is* an element of S, we designate this by writing $a \in S$. To indicate that a is *not* an element of S, we write $a \notin S$. The symbol $\in$ is used to indicate relations between elements and sets, while the symbols $\subseteq$ or $\subset$ indicate relations between sets.

If a symbol such as a letter, say x, stands for an unspecified element of a set S, this symbol x is said to *vary* over S, and x is called a *variable over* S. If x varies over a set which consists of only one element then x is called a *constant*.

Definition 2.1.2. Two sets S_1 and S_2 are said to be *identical*, or to be the *same set*, if and only if $S_1 \subseteq S_2$, and $S_2 \subseteq S_1$. We denote this by writing $S_1 = S_2$.

2.2 Operations on sets

Definition 2.2.1. The *sum*, or *union*, $S_1 + S_2$, of two sets S_1 and S_2 is the set which consists of all elements which are either in S_1 *or in* S_2. Thus $s \in (S_1 + S_2)$ if and only if $s \in S_1$ or $s \in S_2$.

Examples. (a) Let
$$S_1 = \{a,b,c,1,2,3\},$$
$$S_2 = \{a,b,d,2,4\}.$$
Then
$$S_1 + S_2 = \{a,b,c,d,1,2,3,4\}.$$

(b) Let S_1 be the closed interval $[0,3]$, and S_2 be the open interval $(2,4)$. Then $S_1 + S_2$ is the interval $[0,4)$.

Definition 2.2.2. The *product*, or *intersection*, $S_1 S_2$, of two sets S_1 and S_2 is the set which consists of all elements which are in S_1 *and* in S_2. Thus $s \in (S_1 S_2)$ if and only if $s \in S_1$ and $s \in S_2$.

Examples. Let S_1 and S_2 be the sets given in the example (a) above. Then $S_1 S_2 = \{a,b,2\}$. If S_1 and S_2 are the sets in the example (b) given above, then $S_1 S_2$ is the interval $(2,3]$.

The *sum*, or *union*, $S_1 + S_2 + S_3 + \ldots + S_n$ *of a collection of sets* is often denoted by $S_1 \cup S_2 \cup S_3 \cup \ldots \cup S_n$, and is the set of all elements which belong to at least one of the sets $S_1, S_2, S_3, \ldots, S_n$. If $\{S_\alpha\}$ is a collection of sets, then $\sum S_\alpha$, or $\cup S_\alpha$ designates the sum or union of the sets S_α. Thus if $s \in \sum S_\alpha$, then s is an element of at least one of the sets in S_α, and if s is an element of one of the S_α, then s is an element of $\sum S_\alpha$.

The *product or intersection of a collection of sets* $\{S_\alpha\}$ is designated by ΠS_α or $\cap S_\alpha$, and is the set which consists of those elements that belong to every S_α of the $\{S_\alpha\}$. The product or intersection $S_1 S_2 \ldots S_n$ is often indicated by $S_1 \cap S_2 \cap \ldots \cap S_n$.

The product of two sets S_1 and S_2 consists of all elements common to S_1 and S_2. If S_1 and S_2 have no common elements, the product does not exist according to the concept of set as we have used it up to now. In order to have the product of sets always defined, that is, in order to have *closure* under *multiplication (the formation of products)* of sets, we extend the concept of set by admitting the existence of a set which has no element. We do this by the following definition.

Definition 2.2.3. The *null* set 0, is defined by the relations

$$0 \subseteq S, \quad S0 = 0, \quad S + 0 = 0 + S = S,$$

for every set S.

The null set is thus a subset of every set, it has no element, it is the identity under *addition (the formation of sums)* of sets. Under our definition for the equality of sets, the null set is unique. For, suppose 0 and Δ were two null sets. Then $0 \subseteq \Delta$, and $\Delta \subseteq 0$. Therefore $0 = \Delta$, by Def. 2.1.2.

It follows directly from the definitions of sum and product that *addition* and *multiplication of sets* are *commutative* and *associative operations*. That is, if A, B, and C are sets,

$$A + B = B + A, \quad AB = BA,$$
$$A + (B + C) = (A + B) + C, \quad (AB)C = A(BC).$$

We also have the relations

$$A \subseteq A + B, \quad AB \subseteq A, \quad A = A + AB, \quad AA = A.$$

THEOREM 2.2.1. *Addition and multiplication of sets satisfy the following distributive laws.*

$$A(B + C) = AB + AC, \tag{2.2.1}$$
$$A + BC = (A + B)(A + C). \tag{2.2.2}$$

The second distributive law is easily remembered if one notices that one needs only to interchange the operations of addition and multiplication in the first distributive law in order to obtain the second law.

Proof of the second distributive law. If $x \in (A + BC)$, then $x \in A$ or $x \in BC$. If $x \in A$, then $x \in (A + B)$, and $x \in (A + C)$. Therefore, $x \in (A + B)(A + C)$. Suppose $x \notin A$. Then $x \in BC$. Therefore $x \in B$, and $x \in C$. Hence $x \in (A + B)$, and $x \in (A + C)$. Thus we have proved that

$$A + BC \subseteq (A + B)(A + C). \qquad (2.2.3)$$

Next, if $x \in (A + B)(A + C)$. Then $x \in (A + B)$ and $x \in (A + C)$. Let $x \in A$, then $x \in (A + BC)$. Suppose $x \notin A$. By hypothesis $x \in (A + B)$, and $x \in (A + C)$. Therefore $x \in B$, and $x \in C$. Hence $x \in BC$, and $x \in (A + BC)$. Thus we have proved that

$$(A + B)(A + C) \subseteq A + BC. \qquad (2.2.4)$$

From the displayed expressions (2.2.3), (2.2.4), and Definition 2.1.2 it follows that

$$A + BC = (A + B)(A + C),$$

as was to be proved.

P. 2.2.1. Prove the first distributive law for sets.

2.3 Complement of a set and differences of sets

Definition 2.3.1. If all the sets in a given discussion are considered as subsets of a given set, this given set will be called the *universal set for the given discussion.*

Definition 2.3.2. The complement of a set A with respect to the universal set of a given discussion is the set which consists of those elements of the universal set which are *not elements* of A. This set is called more simply the *complement* of A and we shall designate it by cA or by $A^{\sim}$.

Definition 2.3.3. The *difference $B - A$ between the sets B and A* is the set which consists of those elements of B which are not elements of A, i.e., $x \in (B - A)$ if and only if $x \in B$ but $x \notin A$.

We note that $B - A = (AB)^{\sim}B$, and $A - B = (AB)^{\sim}A$. If $A \subseteq B$, then $B - A$ is also called the *complement of A with respect to B.*

Definition 2.3.4. The *symmetric difference* of two sets A and B is the set which consists of those elements of B which are not in A and of those elements of A which are not in B. This symmetric difference is designated by $| B - A |$, or by $| A - B |$ and is given by the equation

$$| A - B | = | B - A | = A^{\sim}B + B^{\sim}A.$$

Examples. Let the universal set S be the set of all points (x,y) in the xy-plane. Let S_1 be the set of points (x,y) such that $x^2 + y^2 \leqslant 1$, and S_2 be the set of points such that $(x - 1)^2 + y^2 < 1$. [See Figs. 1, 2, 3.] The shaded area plus the arc ADC represent $S_1 S_2$ in Fig. 2. The unshaded area within the circles plus the arcs ABC and COA represent $|S_1 - S_2|$ in Fig. 2. The shaded area plus its bounding arc represent $S_1 - S_2$ in Fig. 3. We see that $S_1 - S_2 = (cS_2)S_1$. The set cS_1 consists of all points exterior to the unit circle with center at the origin. The sum of S_1 and S_2 is represented by the shaded area and the arc ABC in Fig. 1.

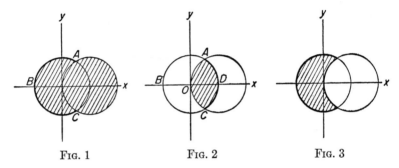

Fig. 1   Fig. 2   Fig. 3

Let the universal set S be the interval $[0,1]$ and A be the interval $[0,\frac{1}{2}]$. Then cA is the interval $(\frac{1}{2},1]$. Let B be the set of all rational points in S. Then cB is the set of all irrational points in S.

Let S be a given universal set, and A be a subset of S. Then the following relations are obvious.

$$(cA)A = 0, \quad A + cA = S, \quad c(cA) = A.$$

Theorem 2.3.1. *Let A and B be two subsets of the universal set S. Then $c(A + B) = (cA)(cB)$. That is, the complement of the sum of two sets is the product of their complements.*

Proof. If $x \in c(A + B)$, then $x \notin (A + B)$. Hence $x \notin A$, and $x \notin B$. Therefore, $x \in cA$, and $x \in cB$. Thus $x \in (cA)(cB)$, and we have shown that

$$c(A + B) \subseteq (cA)(cB). \tag{2.3.1}$$

Next, if $x \in (cA)(cB)$, then $x \in cA$, and $x \in cB$. Therefore $x \notin A$, and $x \notin B$. Thus $x \notin (A + B)$. It follows $x \in c(A + B)$, and we have shown that

$$(cA)(cB) \subseteq c(A + B). \tag{2.3.2}$$

From (2.3.1) and (2.3.2) and the Def. 2.1.2 it follows that

$$c(A + B) = (cA)(cB).$$

THEOREM 2.3.2. *The complement of the product of two sets is the sum of their complements.*

P. 2.3.1. Prove this theorem in two ways.

P. 2.3.2. Generalize theorems 2.3.1 and 2.3.2 to any number of sets.

2.4 The Cartesian product of sets and the concept of function

Definition 2.4.1. Let X and Y be two sets. *The Cartesian product of the sets X and Y is the set of all ordered pairs (x,y) where $x \in X$, and $y \in Y$.* The Cartesian product of X and Y is designated by $X \times Y$. Thus $X \times Y = \{(x,y)\}$ where $x \in X$, $y \in Y$.

Examples. (a) If X is the real continuum represented by the points (real numbers) x on the x-axis, Y the real continuum represented by the points y on the y-axis in the rectangular coordinate plane, then $X \times Y$ is represented by all points in the xy-plane whose coordinates are (x,y).

(b) If X is the same set as in example (a), and if Y is the set which consists of the number 1, then $X \times Y = \{(x,1)\}$ is the set of all points in the xy-plane whose coordinates are $(x,1)$ where x is any real number. The geometrical representation of $X \times Y$ in this case is the line $y = 1$.

The Cartesian product $X \times Y$ sets up a correspondence between the set X and the set Y by which every element y of Y corresponds to every element x of X, and every element x of X corresponds to every element y of Y.

Definition 2.4.2. Let Z be a subset of the Cartesian product $X \times Y$, and let $z = (x,y)$ be an element of Z. The element x of X is said to be the *projection* of z on the set X. The subset of X which consists of the projections of all the elements of Z on X is called the *projection of the set Z on X.* (The projections of an element of Z on Y, and of the set Z on Y are similarly defined.)

Example. The projection of the subset, $\{(x,y) \mid y = 1/x\}$, of the xy-plane on the x-axis is the x-axis minus the origin.

Definition 2.4.3. Let M be a set of ordered pairs (x,y). For a given ordered pair (x,y) of M, the second element, y, is said to be an *image* under M of the first element, x, and the first element, x, is said to be a *source* or *counter image under M* of the second element, y. Let X

be the set which consists of all the sources under M (that is, X consists of all the first elements of the set of ordered pairs in M), and let Y be the set which consists of all the images under M (that is, Y consists of all the second elements of the ordered pairs in M). Then every element x of X determines all its images under M, and we say that M is a *mapping* of X onto Y, or M is a correspondence from all of X to all of Y, under which to each element x of X there correspond all the images of x under M. The set of ordered pairs M^{-1} which is obtained from the set M by interchanging in each ordered pair (x,y) the places of y and x is called the *inverse mapping* of M, or the inverse correspondence of M. It is a mapping of Y onto X, or a correspondence from all of Y to all of X. If X and Y are subsets of some other sets, say $X \subseteq X_1$, $Y \subseteq Y_1$, the set M is said to be a mapping, or a correspondence from X_1 to Y_1.

If a mapping M is such that under it each source has only one image, then the mapping, or correspondence M is said to be *single-valued*.

We call attention to the fact that a mapping from X to Y is a subset of the Cartesian product $X \times Y$.

Definition 2.4.4. A *function* is a set of ordered pairs such that no two ordered pairs have the same first element. The set which consists of all the first elements of the ordered pairs of the given function is called the *domain of definition* of the function. The set which consists of all the second elements of the ordered pairs of the function is called the *range* of the function.

We see that a function is a particular type of mapping, namely, a single-valued mapping. Hence, the definitions of source and image given for mappings apply also to functions. (A mapping which is not single-valued is sometimes called a multiple-valued function.)

Let f be a given function, that is, f is a set of ordered pairs, say (x,y). Let X be the set which consists of all sources, and let Y be the set which consists of all images under f. Then X is the *domain of definition of f*, and Y is the *range of f*. Since x stands for an unspecified element of the set X, x is a variable (see Def. 2.1.1). We call x the *independent variable* of the function f. If y stands for an unspecified element of the range of the function f, then y is said to be the *dependent variable* of the function f. The image under f of an element x is also called the *value* of f at x, and is frequently denoted by $f(x)$, read f at x, or f of x. If f is a function whose domain of definition is X and whose range is Y, we say that f is a function on X onto Y. Such a function is frequently indicated by the symbol $f:X \Rightarrow Y$. If X is a subset of some set X_1, and Y is a subset of a set Y_1, then f is said to be a function from X_1 to Y_1. Common notations for a function are f, $f(x)$, or $y = f(x)$. These symbols may be used only when no ambiguity can arise in regard to the domain of definition and the range of the function.

Let f be a function on X onto Y. Thus f is a set of ordered pairs (x,y) where $x \in X$, and $y \in Y$. If f is such that no two of its ordered pairs have the same second element, the function obtained from the set f by interchanging in each ordered pair (x,y) the places of x and y is called the *inverse function* of f. It is indicated by f^{-1}. Its domain of definition is Y and its range is X. The symbols $f^{-1}(y)$, or $x = f^{-1}(y)$ will be used in referring to the inverse function of f only when this inverse exists and when it is clear from the context what the domain of definition and the range of this function are.

We note that a function from X to Y is a special type of subset of the Cartesian product $X \times Y$.

The definitions of mappings and functions from X to Y leave the nature of the sets X and Y unspecified. These sets may be sets of sets, sets of points, sets of real numbers or other given sets.

Definition 2.4.5. Let f be a function from a set X to a set Y. If X and Y are sets whose elements are sets, then f is said to be a *set function of sets*. If the elements of X are sets but the elements of Y are real numbers, then f is called a *real valued function of sets*, or more simply a *real set function*. If the elements of X are real numbers and the elements of Y are real numbers, f is said to be a *real valued function of a real variable*, or a *real function of a real variable*. In general, any function whose range is a subset of the real continuum is called a *real valued function*, or a *real function*.

Definition 2.4.6. Let a function f from X to Y with domain of definition X_1, and with range Y_1 be given. The *graph of the function f* is the subset

$$\{(x,y) \mid x \in X_1, y \in Y_1\}$$

of the Cartesian product $X \times Y$.

If the domain of definition X_1 of a function f is a set of n-tuplets $(x_1,x_2,\ldots,x_n)$ of elements x_1, x_2, $\ldots$, x_n, then f is said to be a function of *several variables*. If the elements x_1, x_2, $\ldots$, x_n are real numbers, we have a function of *n real variables*. If f is a function of n real variables, and if we let a single letter, say P, represent an n-tuplet of real numbers, we may designate the function by writing $f(x_1, x_2, \ldots, x_n)$ or $f(P)$. If the n-tuplet $(x_1, x_2, \ldots, x_n)$ of real numbers is interpreted as a point P in an n-dimensional space, the graph of f is a point set in an $(n + 1)$-dimensional space. A real valued function whose domain of definition is a set of functions is often called a *functional*. When the domain of definition and the range of a function are each sets of functions, the function is said to be *a functional operation*.

Examples. (a) The function f defined by the statement

$$f(g) = \int_0^1 g(x)dx,$$

where $g(x)$ is a single-valued real function, is a functional. The domain of definition is the set of real functions for which the integral is defined, the range is the real continuum.

(b) Let $g(x) = \dfrac{d}{dx} f(x)$. Here we have a functional operation. The domain of definition is the set of all differentiable functions, the range is the set which consists of all functions which can be derivatives of functions.

(c) Let

$$g(s) = \int_0^\infty e^{-st}f(t)dt, \qquad s > 0.$$

This represents a functional operation which is known as the Laplace transform of the function $f(t)$. The domain of definition is the set of all functions for which the integral on the right converges, the range is the set of all functions which can be Laplace transforms of functions.

(d) Let $f(n) = \sin n\pi/2$, where $n = 1, 2, 3, \ldots$. The domain of definition is the set of positive integers, the range is the set $\{1, 0, -1\}$. The function is a sequence given by $f(4k - 3) = 1$, $f(4k - 2) = 0$, $f(4k - 1) = -1$, $f(4k) = 0$, where $k = 1, 2, 3, \ldots$.

(e) The function given by $f(z) = |z| = |x + iy|$, where $|x + iy| = \sqrt{x^2 + y^2}$, is a real function of a complex variable if x and y are real numbers. It may also be considered a real function of two real variables x and y.

2.5 Characteristic function of a set

Definition 2.5.1. Let A be a subset of a universal set S. Then the function ϕ_A whose domain of definition is the set S and whose range is the set $\{0, 1\}$ is said to be the *characteristic function of the set A*

if $\phi_A(x) = 1$ when $x \in A$, and $\phi_A(x) = 0$ if $x \notin A$. The characteristic function ϕ_A of a set A is said to *describe the set A*.

It follows directly from this definition that if ϕ_A describes A, then the function $(1 - \phi_A)$, whose value at any point x of S is $1 - \phi_A(x)$, describes cA. If A and B are subsets of S, then $\phi_{AB}(x) = \phi_A(x)\phi_B(x)$ for every x of S.

P. 2.5.1. On the basis of Theorem 2.3.1 prove that
$$\phi_{A+B}(x) = \phi_A(x) + \phi_B(x) - \phi_{AB}(x).$$

2.6 Cardinal numbers. Let us consider the sets M and N, where

$$M = \{a,b,c,d,e\}, \qquad N = \{1,2,3,4,5\}.$$

If we disregard the nature of each element, and the order in which the elements occur in each of the sets, the sets M and N can be considered "equivalent" to each other in the sense that a one-to-one correspondence can be set up between these sets. If we let $a \leftrightarrow 1$, $b \leftrightarrow 2$, $c \leftrightarrow 3$, $d \leftrightarrow 4$, $e \leftrightarrow 5$, then to each element of M there corresponds one and only one element of N and to each element of N there corresponds one and only one element of M. Other sets, for instance, the set consisting of the fingers of the normal hand, are such that their elements can be put into a one-to-one correspondence with those of each of the given sets. The property, common to M and N, of admitting a one-to-one reciprocal correspondence between them, is ordinarily described by saying that M and N have the same number of elements or that the sets M and N have the same "cardinal number." For the particular sets given here we say each set has five elements, or the cardinal number of each set is five. In general when we speak of sets consisting of exactly five elements we can think of the class of all those sets whose elements can be put into a one-to-one correspondence with the fingers on a normal hand, or with the integers 1, 2, 3, 4, 5. We thus can say that the "cardinal number five" stands for the class of all sets "equivalent" to the given set $\{1,2,3,4,5\}$.

As another example let us consider two paper baskets. The first basket contains only white sheets of paper, the second only yellow sheets. If we can show that for every white sheet of paper in the first basket we have one and only one yellow sheet of paper in the second basket, and for every yellow sheet of paper we have only one white sheet, we say that there are just as many white sheets as there are yellow sheets, or that the cardinal number of the set of white sheets is the same as the cardinal number of the set of yellow sheets.

We now give the formal definitions which permit us to extend the concept of cardinal number to sets in general.

Definition 2.6.1. Two sets A and B are said to be *equivalent* (or *to have the same cardinal number*, or the same number of elements or the same power) if a one-to-one correspondence can be set up between them such that to every element of A there corresponds one and only one element of B, and to every element of B there corresponds one and only one element of A. We denote "A is equivalent to B" by $A \sim B$.

P. 2.6.1. Prove that the set of even positive integers is equivalent to the set of all positive integers.

Two sets which are equivalent to each other thus have the same cardinal number. The cardinal number of every set equivalent to the set of positive integers $\{1,2,3,\ldots,n\}$ is called n. The cardinal number of the null set is called *zero*.

Definition 2.6.2. A set S is said to be *infinite* if S contains a proper subset which is equivalent to S. Sets which *are not infinite* are called *finite*.

Problem P. 2.6.1 proves that the set of positive integers is infinite. It follows also from Def. 2.6.2 that every set whose cardinal number is n (where n is an integer) is finite. The null set is obviously finite for it contains no proper subset.

The cardinal number of every infinite set is called a *transfinite* cardinal number. The transfinite cardinal number of the set of positive integers is designated by $\aleph_0$ (aleph null). The cardinal number of the set of all real numbers is denoted by $\aleph$. This transfinite cardinal number can be shown to be "greater" than $\aleph_0$. The term "greater" requires an explanation which is given by the following definition.

P. 2.6.2. Prove that the cardinal number of the set of points (0,1) is $\aleph$.

P. 2.6.3. Prove that $(0,1] \sim (0,1)$ and that $[0,1] \sim (0,1)$.

Definition 2.6.3. Let a and b be the cardinal numbers of the sets A and B, respectively. We say b is *greater than* a, in symbols $b > a$, if and only if A is equivalent to a subset of B, but B is equivalent to no subset of A. The statement a is *less than* b is denoted by $a < b$, and means $b > a$.

P. 2.6.4. Prove that if a, b, and c are cardinal numbers such that $a < b < c$, then $a < c$.

P. 2.6.5. Prove that if a and b are cardinal numbers, then at most one of the relations $a < b$, $a = b$, $a > b$ holds, and hence if $a \leqslant b$, $b \leqslant a$, then $a = b$.

The last two problems do not imply that the cardinal numbers are linearly ordered, for in the comparison of the cardinal numbers of two sets A and B the following cases might possibly arise.

(1) $A \sim B_1 \subset B$, but B is equivalent to no subset of A, then $a < b$.

(2) $B \sim A_1 \subset A$, but A is equivalent to no subset of B, then $a > b$.

(3) $A \sim B_1 \subseteq B$, and $B \sim A_1 \subseteq A$, then $a = b$ (Bernstein's theorem).

(4) A is equivalent to no subset of B, and B is equivalent to no subset of A. In this case the sets might be said to be not comparable in regard to their cardinal numbers.

It is because of the possibility that the last case may exist that the cardinal numbers may possibly not form a linear order. If a certain postulate, known as Zermelo's postulate, is accepted, case (4) can be excluded. Zermelo's postulate, which is also known as the "axiom of choice" can be stated in the following form. For every nonempty set whose members are nonempty sets, it is possible to form a set which contains exactly one representative element of each of the member sets. The logical consequences of this postulate are very far reaching. On the basis of it, results have been proved which some eminent mathematicians (in particular L. E. J. Brouwer) have been reluctant to accept. A large part of the modern theory of sets does not depend on this postulate. We shall not hesitate to use it, but whenever our results depend on it we shall try to remember to state this fact.

The conclusions under cases (1) and (2) are direct consequences of Def. 2.6.3. The statement under case (3) requires a proof. We shall provide one after we have established a preliminary result.

THEOREM 2.6.1. *Let S, S_1, S_2 be given sets such that $S \sim S_2$ and $S_2 \subseteq S_1 \subseteq S$. Then $S \sim S_1$.*

Proof. If S_2 is not a *proper* subset of S, then the theorem is obvious. Let us therefore assume that S_2 is a proper subset of S. Since $S \sim S_2$, the cardinal number of S is transfinite. Let

$$S_2 = A, \quad S_1 - S_2 = B, \quad \text{and} \quad S - S_1 = C.$$

We must prove that if

$$(A + B + C) \sim A, \quad \text{then} \quad (A + B + C) \sim (A + B).$$

Since $(A + B + C) \sim A$, there exists a simple mapping, say f, of the set $A + B + C$ onto A. By this mapping A has an image A_1, B has an image B_1, and C has an image C_1. These images are disjoint sets such that $A_1 + B_1 + C_1 = A$. Since A is mapped by the very same simple mapping f onto A_1, it follows that the sets A_1, B_1, C_1 are mapped onto disjoint subsets, say A_2, B_2, C_2 of A_1, such that $A_2 + B_2 + C_2 = A_1$, and $A_1 \sim A_2$, $B_1 \sim B_2$, $C_1 \sim C_2$. Since by the same mapping f, A_1 is mapped onto A_2, it follows that the sets A_2, B_2, C_2 are mapped onto disjoint sets A_3, B_3, C_3 such that $A_3 + B_3 + C_3 = A_2$. This process of mapping does not terminate since

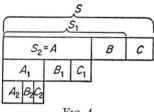

Fig. 4

$A_1 \sim A_2 \sim A_3 \sim \dots$. We call attention to the fact that $C_1 \sim C_2 \sim C_3 \sim \dots$. Let D designate the set $A_1 A_2 A_3 \dots$. This set might possibly be empty. [In order to visualize the structure of our sets we present Fig. 4, even though our argument will not depend on this geometrical representation.] We now have the equations

$$A + B + C = B + C + B_1 + C_1 + B_2 + C_2 + B_3 + C_3 + \dots + D$$

$$A + B = B + C_1 + B_1 + C_2 + B_2 + C_3 + B_3 + C_4 + \dots + D$$

Since $C_{i-1} \sim C_i$ for $i = 1, 2, 3, \dots$, it follows that

$$A + B + C \sim A + B,$$

as was to be shown.

Theorem 2.6.2 (Bernstein's theorem). *Let A and B be two given sets. If $A \sim B_1$ and $B \sim A_1$, where $B_1 \subseteq B$, and $A_1 \subseteq A$, then $A \sim B$.*

Proof. Since $B \sim A_1$, the set B is mapped (simply) onto A_1, and hence the subset B_1 of B is mapped (simply) onto a subset A_2 of A_1. Thus $A_2 \subseteq A_1 \subseteq A$ and $A \sim B_1 \sim A_2$. Hence by Theorem 2.6.1, $A \sim A_1$, and since $A_1 \sim B$, it follows that $A \sim B$.

2.7 Operations with cardinal numbers

Definition 2.7.1 (Addition). Let a be the cardinal number of a set A, let b be the cardinal number of a set B. Let A' and B' be two sets such that $A' \sim A$, $B' \sim B$, $A'B' = 0$. The *sum* $a + b$ of the cardinal numbers a and b is the cardinal number of the set $A' + B'$.

It may of course happen that $AB = 0$; then we can choose $A' = A$, $B' = B$. In general if $AB \neq 0$, we can let $A' = A \times \{1\}$, $B' = B \times \{2\}$, where the cross ($\times$) indicates the Cartesian product.

Definition 2.7.2 (Multiplication). Let a and b be the cardinal numbers of the set A and B, respectively. The *product* ab of the cardinal numbers a and b is the cardinal number of the set $A \times B$.

Examples. (a) Let $A = \{1,2,3,\ldots,n\}$,

$B = \{1,2,3,\ldots,m\}$. Then

$$
A \times B = \left\{
\begin{array}{cccc}
(1,1) & (1,2) & \ldots & (1,m) \\
(2,1) & (2,2) & \ldots & (2,m) \\
\multicolumn{4}{c}{\dotfill} \\
\multicolumn{4}{c}{\dotfill} \\
(n,1) & (n,2) & \ldots & (n,m)
\end{array}
\right\}
$$

$\sim \{1,2,3,\ldots,n \cdot m\}$.

The cardinal number of A is n, the cardinal number of B is m, and we see that the cardinal number of $A \times B$ is nm.

P. 2.7.1. Prove that if a, b, and c are cardinal numbers, then $a + b = b + a$, $ab = ba$, and $a(b + c) = ab + ac$.

P. 2.7.2. Prove that $n + \aleph_0 = \aleph_0$, and $n \cdot \aleph_0 = \aleph_0$.

P. 2.7.3. Prove that $\aleph + \aleph_0 = \aleph$.

Definition 2.7.3 (Exponentiation). Let a and b be the cardinal numbers of the sets A and B, respectively. The symbol a^b is defined as the cardinal number of the set of all functions on B to A, i.e., all functions whose domain of definition is the set B, and whose ranges lie in A.

Examples. (a) Let a be 3, the cardinal number of the set $A = \{x,y,z\}$, and let b be 2, the cardinal number of the set $B = \{1,2\}$. Here $a^b = 3^2$ is the cardinal number of the set of functions

$$\{(1,x),\ (2,x)\},\ \{(1,x),\ (2,y)\},\ \{(1,x),\ (2,z)\},$$
$$\{(1,y),\ (2,x)\},\ \{(1,y),\ (2,y)\},\ \{(1,y),\ (2,z)\},$$
$$\{(1,z),\ (2,x)\},\ \{(1,z),\ (2,y)\},\ \{(1,z),\ (2,z)\}.$$

In this case B has two elements, and A has three elements. The number of functions on B to A is the number of ways in which two places, corresponding to the elements of B, can be filled by the three elements of A, repetitions being allowed. The first place can be filled in three ways, and the second place can be filled in three ways. The total number of ways is, of course, $3 \cdot 3 = 9$.

(b) Let us consider $\aleph_0{}^2$. This is the cardinal number of the set of all functions defined on two places with range in the set of positive integers. This set of functions is equivalent to the double array.

$$
\begin{array}{llll}
a_{11} & a_{12} & a_{13} & \cdots \\
a_{21} & a_{22} & a_{23} & \cdots \\
\cdot\ \cdot\ \cdot & \cdot\ \cdot\ \cdot & & \cdots \\
\cdot\ \cdot\ \cdot & \cdot\ \cdot\ \cdot & & \cdots \\
a_{n1} & a_{n2} & a_{n3} & \cdots \\
\cdot\ \cdot\ \cdot & \cdot\ \cdot\ \cdot & &
\end{array}
$$

which was shown to be equivalent to the set of positive integers. Hence $\aleph_0{}^2 = \aleph_0$.

It can be shown that for finite cardinal numbers the definitions of the operations given in this section reduce to the usual definitions of these operations. It also follows that the same laws governing these operations for finite sets hold true in general. Thus for example

$$a^b a^c = a^{b+c}, \quad a^c b^c = (ab)^c, \quad (a^b)^c = a^{bc}.$$

P. 2.7.4. Using Def. 2.7.3, show that $2^3 = 8$.

P. 2.7.5. Prove that $\aleph^2 = \aleph$.

We shall next show that, given any cardinal number c of some set S, we can always give a set whose cardinal number is greater than c. To this end we prove the following theorem.

THEOREM 2.7.1. *Let c be the cardinal number of a set S. Let S' be the set of all subsets of S. Then the cardinal number of S' is 2^c, $> c$.*

Proof. We show first that the cardinal number of S' is 2^c. A subset of any set is described by its characteristic function. Thus to every element of S' there corresponds a unique characteristic function defined on S. But the set of all characteristic functions defined on S

has by Def. 2.7.3 the cardinal number 2^c. Hence the cardinal number of S' is 2^c.

Next we show that condition (2) of page 37 holds for the sets S' and S, that is, we show that S is equivalent to some subset of S'. Let $s \in S$. Then $'s' \in S'$. Let $s \leftrightarrow 's'$. This establishes a one-to-one correspondence between S and a subset of S'.

Next we show that no one-to-one correspondence can exist between S' and S. Here S' is equivalent to the set of characteristic functions defined on S. Let us assume that a one-to-one correspondence had been set up between S' and S. Then we would have a one-to-one correspondence between the characteristic functions defined on S and the elements of S. Let s of S correspond to $\phi_s(x)$. We define the function $f(x) = 1 - \phi_x(x)$, where x is any element of S. This function takes on the values 0 and 1 only. Hence it is a characteristic function, but it differs from every $\phi_s(x)$ when $s = x$. Hence it was left out by the given correspondence.

P. 2.7.6. Let $S = \{a,b,c\}$. Let S' be the set of all subsets of S. List all the elements of S' and all characteristic functions on S. Illustrate the last theorem.

P. 2.7.7. Show that 2 raised to the power $\aleph_0$ is $\aleph$.

2.8 Order types. In the last two sections, where we considered the cardinal numbers of sets, we disregarded the nature of each element and the order in which the elements might occur in a given set. We shall now continue to disregard the nature of each element but shall consider the order of the elements within a set.

The concept of "linear order" was defined in Def. 1.3.1. In the sequel when we say *ordered set* we shall mean a *linearly ordered set*.

Let S be an ordered set. If a and b are elements of S, and if $a < b$, we shall designate this by writing a to the left of b, that is

$$S = \{\ldots,a,\ldots,b,\ldots\}.$$

If a set is ordered by means of a certain rule of precedence, every subset of the given set can be considered as having been ordered by the same rule of precedence. Unless the contrary is stated we shall assume in this section that when we consider subsets of a given ordered set the order among the elements of the subsets has not been changed.

Definition 2.8.1. Let a be an element of an ordered set S. If there is no element b of S such that $b < a$, then a is called the *first* element of S. If there is no element b of S such that $a < b$, then a is called the *last* element of S.

All sets which in this section are denoted by A, B, C, or by these letters with subscripts, such as A_n, B_n, C_n, will be ordered sets. The equation $A = B$, states not only that $A \subseteq B$, $B \subseteq A$, but also that the elements in either set are in the same order as they are in the other set. To indicate that a, b, c are elements of A in the order $a < b < c$, we write

$$A = \{\ldots,a,\ldots,b,\ldots,c,\ldots\}.$$

The dots indicate the possibility of the existence of elements less than a, between a and b, and between b and c, and greater than c. When we write

$$A = \{a,\ldots,b,\ldots\},$$

we indicate that a is the first element of A. To indicate that c is the last element of A we write

$$A = \{\ldots,b,\ldots,c\}.$$

The absence of dots between two letters, as between a and b in

$$A = \{\ldots,a,b,\ldots\}$$

indicates that $a < b$ and that there is no element c in A such that $a < c < b$. In this case we say that a and b are *adjacent* elements, and that a is an *immediate predecessor of b*, while b is an *immediate successor of a*.

Definition 2.8.2. If in a given ordered set A the rule of precedence is reversed, that is, if the symbols $<$ and $>$ are interchanged, there results a new ordered set which is called the *inverse* set of A, and is designated by A^*. Thus if

$$A = \{\ldots,a,\ldots,b,\ldots,c,\ldots\}, \quad \text{then}$$
$$A^* = \{\ldots,c,\ldots,b,\ldots,a,\ldots\}.$$

Definition 2.8.3. Two ordered sets A and B are said to be *similar* if there exists a one-to-one order preserving correspondence between the elements of A and of B. We denote "A is similar to B" by writing $A \simeq B$.

We note that the relation of similarity is *reflexive*, *symmetric*, and *transitive*.

Definition 2.8.4. Two *similar sets* are said to be of the same *order type*. The order types of A, B, and C will be designated α, β, and γ, respectively. If $A \simeq B$ we write $\alpha = \beta$. If α is the order type of A, then α^* denotes the order type of A^*.

It follows directly from the definitions, that if $A \simeq B$, then $A \sim B$. This means that if two sets have the same order type, then they have the same cardinal number.

The order type of every set similar to the set of integers $\{1,2,\ldots,n\}$ is denoted by n. The order type of the null set is denoted by 0 (zero). The order type of the set of all positive integers, in their natural order, is designated by ω, that of the negative integers, in their natural order, by ω^*. The order type of the set of all rational numbers in the real continuum is denoted by η, that of the set of all real numbers by λ. These last two order types are *dense* order types because they belong to densely ordered sets (see Def. 1.5.4).

2.9. Operations with ordered sets

Definition 2.9.1. Let A and B be subsets of an ordered set. We say $A < B$, or A *is to the left of* B, or A *is less than* B, if for every a of A, and every element b of B, $a < b$.

Definition 2.9.2 (Addition of ordered sets). Let A and B be two ordered sets with no common elements, that is $A \cdot B = 0$. The *order-preserving sum* $A \overset{\circ}{+} B$ of A and B is the ordered set which consists of all elements which are either in A or in B, the order of the elements of A is preserved, the order of the elements of B is preserved and A is to the left of B in $A \overset{\circ}{+} B$.

If two sets A and B have no elements in common they will be said to be *disjoint sets*. The concepts of order-preserving sum of ordered sets can be extended to any number of disjoint ordered sets.

Let X be an ordered set, say

$$X = \{\ldots,x_i,\ldots,x_j,\ldots,x_k,\ldots\}. \tag{2.9.1}$$

Let A_x be a set of disjoint ordered sets such that to each element, say x_i of X, there corresponds one and only one A_{x_i}. The *order-preserving sum*

$$\sum{}_X A_x = \{\ldots,A_{x_i},\ldots,A_{x_j},\ldots,A_{x_k},\ldots\} \tag{2.9.2}$$

is the *ordered set* in which the order of the elements in each A_{x_i} is preserved, and if $x_i < x_j$ in X, then $A_{x_i} < A_{x_j}$ in the set given by eq. (2.9.2).

Definition 2.9.3 (Addition of order types). Let α and β be the order types of two ordered sets A and B, respectively. Let A' and B' be two disjoint sets such that $A' \simeq A$, $B' \simeq B$. The *sum* $\alpha + \beta$ of the order types α and β is the *order type* of $A' \overset{\circ}{+} B'$.

From this definition it follows that *addition of order types* is associative, that is $(\alpha + \beta) + \gamma = \alpha + (\beta + \gamma)$, but it is *not commutative*, that is $\alpha + \beta \neq \beta + \alpha$.

We can extend the definition of the addition of order types to any number of order types.

Let X be the set given by eq. (2.9.1). Let $\{\alpha_x\}$ be a set of order types such that to each element x_i of X there corresponds a unique order type α_{x_i} of a set A_{x_i}. Let every two sets A_{x_i} and $A_{x_j}(x_i \neq x_j)$ be disjoint sets. Then the *sum*

$$\sum_X \alpha_x = \ldots + \alpha_{x_i} + \ldots + \alpha_{x_j} + \ldots + \alpha_{x_k} + \ldots$$

is *defined as the order type of the set given by eq. (2.9.2).*

Examples. (a) Consider the two sets

$$A = \{1,2,\ldots,n\},$$
$$B = \{n+1, n+2, n+3,\ldots\}.$$

The order types of these two sets are n and ω, respectively. Since A and B are disjoint sets, $A \overset{\circ}{+} B$ is defined, and we have, $A \overset{\circ}{+} B = 1, 2, \ldots, n,$ $n+1, n+2, \ldots$. The order type of this set is ω. Thus we have proved that $n + \omega = \omega$.

(b) We notice, however, that $\omega + n$ is the order type of the set $n+1,$ $n+2, \ldots; 1, 2, \ldots, n$. This set has a last element, while any set of order type ω does not have a last element. Hence $\omega + n \neq \omega = n + \omega$.

(c) The sets

$$\{1,2,3,\ldots;-1\},$$
$$\{1,2,3,\ldots;-1,-2\},$$
$$\{1,2,3,\ldots;-1,-2,-3,\ldots\},$$
$$\{1,2,3,\ldots;\ldots,-3,-2,-1\},$$
$$\{\ldots3,2,1,-1,-2,-3,\ldots\},$$
$$\{\ldots,-3,-2,-1;\ldots,3,2,1\}$$

have the respective order types $\omega + 1$, $\omega + 2$, $\omega + \omega$, $\omega + \omega^*$, $\omega^* + \omega$, $\omega^* + \omega^*$.

THEOREM 2.9.1. *Let α and β be two order types. Then*

$$(\alpha + \beta)^* = \beta^* + \alpha^*,$$

that is, the inverse of the sum of two given order types is the sum of their inverses in reverse order.

Proof. Let α and β be the order types of the disjoint sets A and B, respectively. Let

$$A = \{\ldots,a_1,\ldots,a_2,\ldots,a_3,\ldots\},$$
$$B = \{\ldots,b_1,\ldots,b_2,\ldots,b_3,\ldots\}.$$

Then $\alpha + \beta$ is the order type of the set

$$A \overset{\circ}{+} B = \{\ldots,a_1,\ldots,a_2,\ldots,a_3,\ldots,$$
$$\ldots,b_1,\ldots,b_2,\ldots,b_3,\ldots\},$$

and $(\alpha + \beta)^*$ is the order type of

$$(A \overset{\circ}{+} B)^* = \{\ldots,b_3,\ldots,b_2,\ldots,b_1,\ldots,$$
$$\ldots,a_3,\ldots,a_2,\ldots,a_1,\ldots\}.$$

which by Defs. 2.8.2, 2.9.2, is $B^* \overset{\circ}{+} A^*$. But by Def. 2.9.3 this last set has the order type $\beta^* + \alpha^*$.

P. 2.9.1. Prove the associative law for the addition of order types, that is, prove that if α, β, γ are order types, then $\alpha + (\beta + \gamma) = (\alpha + \beta) + \gamma$.

Definition 2.9.4. Let A be a set of sets each of order type n, that is,

$$A = \{\ldots,a',\ldots,a'',\ldots,a''',\ldots\}$$

where
$$a' = \{x_1',x_2',\ldots,x_n'\},$$
$$a'' = \{x_1'',x_2'',\ldots,x_n''\},$$
$$a''' = \{x_1''',x_2''',\ldots,x_n'''\}.$$

The set A is said to be *lexicographically* ordered if for any two elements a and a' of A, where

$$a = \{x_1,x_2,\ldots,x_n\}, \quad a' = \{x_1',x_2',\ldots,x_n'\}$$

$a < a'$ if $x_1 < x_1'$, or in case $x_i = x_i'$ for $i < j$, if $x_j < x_j'$.

Definition 2.9.5. Let A and B be two ordered sets. The *ordered Cartesian product* $A \overset{\circ}{\times} B$ is the lexicographically ordered set $A \times B$. Thus if (a,b) and (a',b') are two elements of $A \overset{\circ}{\times} B$, $(a,b) < (a',b')$ if $a < a'$, or if $a = a'$, if $b < b'$.

Definition 2.9.6. Let α and β be the order types of A and B, respectively. The *product $\alpha\beta$ of the order types α and β* is the order type of the set $B \overset{\circ}{\times} A$.

Examples. (a) Consider the order types 2 and ω. To find $\omega 2$ we construct the Cartesian product

$$\{1,2\} \times \{1,2,3,\ldots\}$$

and order it thus:

$$\{(1,1),(1,2),(1,3),\ldots;(2,1),(2,2),(2,3),\ldots\},$$

which is similar to the set

$$\{1,2,3,\ldots;-1,-2,-3,\ldots\} = \omega + \omega.$$

Hence $\omega 2 = \omega + \omega$. In general $\omega + \omega + \ldots + \omega$ (n terms) is denoted by ωn, and is the order type of the set

$$\{1,2,\ldots n\} \overset{\circ}{\times} \{1,2,3,\ldots\}.$$

(b) We note that $n\omega \neq \omega n$. For $n\omega$ is the order type of the set

$$\{1,2,3,\ldots\} \overset{\circ}{\times} \{1,2,\ldots,n\} = \{(1,1),(1,2),\ldots,(1,n),$$
$$(2,1),(2,2),\ldots,(2,n),$$
$$\cdots\cdots\cdots\cdots\cdots$$
$$(k,1),(k,2),\ldots,(k,n),$$
$$\cdots\cdots\cdots\cdots\cdots\}.$$

This set is seen to be similar to the set $\{1,2,3,\ldots\}$ by letting (k,j) of the first set correspond to the element $(k-1)n + j$, $1 \leqslant j \leqslant n$. We have thus proved that $n\omega = \omega$.

(c) It also follows that $\alpha(\beta + \gamma) = \alpha\beta + \alpha\gamma$, but $(\alpha + \beta)\gamma \neq \alpha\gamma + \beta\gamma$. For instance, $2(\omega + 1)$ is the order type of

$$\{1,2,\ldots,I\} \overset{\circ}{\times} \{a,b\} = \{(1,a),(1,b),(2,a),(2,b),\ldots,(I,a),(I,b)\}.$$

This set is of order type $\omega + 2$, which is equal to $2\omega + 2$. Thus $2(\omega + 1) = 2\omega + 2$. On the basis of Def. 2.9.6 it is easily seen that $(\omega + 1)2$ is of order type

$$\omega + \omega + 1 = \omega 2 + 1 \neq \omega 2 + 2.$$

Thus $(\omega + 1)2 \neq \omega 2 + 2$.

THEOREM 2.9.2. *The product of inverse order types is the inverse of their product, that is,* $\alpha^*\beta^* = (\alpha\beta)^*$. (We note that the order of the order types is not reversed as is the case under the addition of inverse order types, as is shown by Theorem 2.9.1.)

Proof. Let α be the order type of the set

$$A = \{\ldots,a_1,\ldots,a_2,\ldots,a_3,\ldots\},$$

let β be the order type of the set

$$B = \{\ldots,b_1,\ldots,b_2,\ldots,b_3,\ldots\}.$$

Then $\alpha^*\beta^*$ is the order type of the set

$$B^* \overset{\circ}{\times} A^* = \{\ldots,b_3,\ldots,b_2,\ldots,b_1,\ldots\} \overset{\circ}{\times} \{\ldots,a_3,\ldots,a_2,\ldots,a_1,\ldots\}$$

$$= \{\ldots,(b_3,a_3),\ldots,(b_3,a_2),\ldots,(b_3,a_1),\ldots,(b_2,a_3),$$

$$\ldots,(b_2,a_2),\ldots,(b_2,a_1),\ldots,(b_1,a_3),\ldots,(b_1,a_2),$$

$$\ldots,(b_1,a_1),\ldots\},$$

while $\alpha\beta$ is the order type of

$$B \overset{\circ}{\times} A = \{\ldots,b_1,\ldots,b_2,\ldots,b_3,\ldots\} \overset{\circ}{\times} \{\ldots,a_1,\ldots,a_2,\ldots,a_3,\ldots\}$$

$$= \{\ldots,(b_1,a_1),\ldots,(b_1,a_2),\ldots,(b_1,a_3),\ldots,(b_2,a_1),$$

$$\ldots,(b_2,a_2),\ldots,(b_2,a_3),\ldots,(b_3,a_1),\ldots,(b_3,a_2),$$

$$\ldots,(b_3,a_3),\ldots\}.$$

The order type of $(\alpha\beta)^*$ is given by $(B \overset{\circ}{\times} A)^*$, which from the last displayed equation is seen to be the same as that of $B^* \overset{\circ}{\times} A^*$ given above. This completes the proof of the theorem.

The generalization of the product of order types to more than two factors can be indicated in the following way: $(\alpha\beta)\gamma$ is the order type of $C \overset{\circ}{\times} (B \overset{\circ}{\times} A)$ where α, β, γ are the order types of the ordered sets A, B, and C, respectively.

Example.
Let $A = \{\ldots,a_1,\ldots,a_2,\ldots,a_3,\ldots,\}$,
     $B = \{\ldots,b_1,\ldots,b_2,\ldots,b_3,\ldots,\}$,
     $C = \{\ldots,c_1,\ldots,c_2,\ldots,c_3,\ldots,\}$.

Then

$$B \overset{\circ}{\times} A = \{\ldots,(b_1,a_1),\ldots,(b_1,a_2),\ldots,(b_1,a_3),$$
$$\ldots,(b_2,a_1),\ldots,(b_2,a_2),\ldots,(b_2,a_3),$$
$$\ldots,(b_3,a_1),\ldots,(b_3,a_2),\ldots,(b_3,a_3),\ldots\}.$$

Hence,

$$C \overset{\circ}{\times} (B \overset{\circ}{\times} A) = \{\ldots,c_1,\ldots,c_2,\ldots,c_3,\ldots\} \overset{\circ}{\times} \{\ldots,(b_1,a_1),$$
$$\ldots,(b_1,a_2),\ldots,(b_1,a_3),\ldots,(b_2,a_1),\ldots,(b_2,a_2),$$
$$\ldots,(b_2,a_3),\ldots,(b_3,a_1),\ldots,(b_3,a_2),\ldots,(b_3,a_3),\ldots\}.$$

In writing out this expression we shall write in place of $(c,(b,a))$ the simpler expression (c,b,a). Thus we get

$$C \overset{\circ}{\times} (B \overset{\circ}{\times} A) = \{\ldots,(c_1,b_1,a_1),\ldots,(c_1,b_1,a_2),\ldots,(c_1,b_1,a_3),$$
$$\ldots,(c_1,b_2,a_1),\ldots,(c_1,b_2,a_2),\ldots,(c_1,b_2,a_3),$$
$$\ldots,(c_1,b_3,a_1),\ldots,(c_1,b_3,a_2),\ldots,(c_1,b_3,a_3),$$
$$\ldots,(c_2,b_1,a_1),\ldots,\ldots,(c_3,b_3,a_3).$$

2.10 Ordinal numbers

Definition 2.10.1. An ordered set A is said to be *well-ordered if every nonempty subset of A has a first element.*

Definition 2.10.2. The *order type* of a *well-ordered set* is called the *ordinal number* of the set.

Every ordered finite set is well-ordered, every set similar to the set of all positive integers in their natural order is well ordered. The set

$$\{1,2,3,\ldots;-1,-2,-3,\ldots\}$$

which has the order type $\omega + \omega$ is well-ordered. It follows that n, ω, $\omega 2$, are ordinal numbers. The order types ω^*, η, and λ are not ordinal numbers. The null set is well ordered because Def. 2.10.1 is vacuously satisfied.

Let A be a well-ordered infinite set. We designate its first element a_0. The subset $A - a_0$ has a first element; we designate it a_1. The first element of $A - \{a_0,a_1\}$ we designate by a_2, and so on. If the set a_0, a_1, a_2, $\ldots$ does not exhaust the elements of A, we designate the first element of the nonempty subset of A given by

$$A - \{a_0,a_1,a_2,\ldots\},$$

by a_ω. Next we define $a_{\omega+1}$ as the first element of

$$A - \{a_0,a_1,a_2,\ldots,a_\omega\},$$

if this set is not the null set. It follows that A can be represented as

$$A = \{a_0, a_1, a_2, \ldots, a_\omega, a_{\omega+1}, \ldots, a_{\omega 2}, a_{\omega 2+1}, \ldots\}.$$

In this manner each element is given the subscript which represents the order type of the set consisting of all the elements preceding the given element, that is, a_0 has the subscripts 0, which is the order type of the null set; a_1 has the subscript 1, which is the order type of the set $\{a_0\}$ consisting of one element, and so on.

We shall not go into any greater detail into the theory of the transfinite ordinal numbers than just to introduce its fundamental concepts. From the two formal definitions given in this section the following results follow. We state them in the form of problems to be worked by the reader.

P. 2.10.1. Every subset of a well-ordered set is well ordered.

P. 2.10.2. If a is an element of a well-ordered set A, and if a is not the last element of A, then a has an immediate successor.

Definition 2.10.3. Let A be a well-ordered set, and a be an element of A. The subset $A(a)$ of A which consists of all elements x of A such that $x < a$, is called an *initial segment of A.* (The initial segment of a_0 where a_0 is the first element of A, is the null set.)

THEOREM 2.10.1. *Let A be a well-ordered set, and let a be an element of A, then A is not similar to the initial segment $A(a)$.*

Proof. If $A \simeq A(a)$, there exists a one-to-one correspondence between the elements of A and of $A(a)$. Under this correspondence the element a of A would have to correspond to an element a' of $A(a)$. But every element x of $A(a)$ is less than a. Thus under the given similarity relationship a would correspond to an a', and $a' < a$. We show that this is impossible.

Let A_1 be the subset of elements x of A which correspond to an x' in $A(a)$ such that $x' < x$. The subset A_1 is not empty, for it contains a. Hence A_1 has a first element, say a_1. Then the element a_1' of $A(a)$ which is the mate (image) of a_1 in A, is such that $a_1' < a_1$. But a_1' is an element of A and as such has to have a mate, say a_1'', in $A(a)$. And because $A \simeq A(a)$, $a_1'' < a_1'$ in $A(a)$ since $a_1' < a_1$ in A. Thus a_1' corresponds to an element a_1'' which is less than a_1'. This implies that $a_1' \in A_1$. This contradicts the definition of a_1 as the first element of A_1.

As a direct consequence of this theorem we have the following result.

Theorem 2.10.2. *If $A(a)$ and $A(a')$ are two distinct initial segments of a well-ordered set A, then $A(a)$ is not similar to $A(a')$.*

Proof. Since $A(a)$ and $A(a')$ are two distinct initial segments of A, $a \neq a'$. Suppose $a' < a$. Then $A(a')$ is an initial segment of $A(a)$, and by the last theorem $A(a') \not\simeq A(a)$.

Theorem 2.10.3. *Let A and B be two well-ordered sets. If to every initial segment $A(a)$ of A, there corresponds an initial segment $B(b)$ of B such that $A(a) \simeq B(b)$, and conversely to every $B(b)$, there corresponds an $A(a)$ of A such that $B(b) \simeq A(a)$, then $A \simeq B$.*

P. 2.10.3. Prove this theorem. Hint: First show that to every $A(a)$ there corresponds only one $B(b)$ such that $A(a) \simeq B(b)$, and conversely. Next let $a \leftrightarrow b$ if $A(a) \leftrightarrow B(b)$, and show that this correspondence between the elements of the sets A and B is order preserving.

Theorem 2.10.4. *Let A and B be well-ordered sets. If there exists an initial segment $A(a)$ such that for every b of B, $A(a) \not\simeq B(b)$, then B is similar to an initial segment of A.*

P. 2.10.4. Prove this theorem. Hint: Let A' be the subset of A which consists of all elements a' of A such that for every b of B, $A(a') \not\simeq B(b)$. The set A' has a first element, say a_0'. Show that $B \simeq A(a_0')$.

These last two theorems can be restated in the following form.

Theorem 2.10.5. *(Fundamental theorem on well-ordered sets.) Let A and B be two well-ordered sets. Then one and only one of the following relations can hold.*

$$\text{(i) } A \simeq B, \quad \text{(ii) } A \simeq B(b), \quad \text{(iii) } B \simeq A(a),$$

where $A(a)$ and $B(b)$ indicate initial segments of A and B, respectively.

This theorem permits us to give the following definitions.

Definition 2.10.4 (Order of ordinal numbers). Let α and β be the ordinal numbers of the well-ordered sets A and B, respectively. We say $\alpha = \beta$ if $A \simeq B$, $\alpha < \beta$, if $A \simeq B(b)$, $\beta < \alpha$ if $B \simeq A(a)$, where $A(a)$ and $B(b)$ are initial segments of A and B, respectively. [$\alpha < \beta$ is read "α is less than β," and shall mean the same thing as $\beta > \alpha$, which is read "β is greater than α."] Any set of ordinal numbers which has been ordered according to this definition is said to be *ordered according to the magnitudes of the elements.*

It can be shown that any set of ordinal numbers which has been ordered according to the magnitudes of its elements is a well-ordered set. Thus if α is an ordinal number, and $W(\alpha)$ is the set of all ordinal numbers less than α which have been ordered according to their magnitude, $W(\alpha)$ is well-ordered. Furthermore, the ordinal number of $W(\alpha)$ is α. It also follows that if α is an ordinal number there exists an ordinal number β such that $\alpha < \beta$, and α and β are adjacent elements, that is, there exists no ordinal γ such that $\alpha < \gamma < \beta$. This β will be denoted by $\alpha + 1$. Thus for every ordinal number α there is a next. For the derivations of these results and their implications the reader is referred to more extensive treatises. [*Reelle Funktionen*, Hans Hahn.] The method of transfinite induction and the theorem that every set can be well ordered are further important results of the theory indicated in this section.

REFERENCES

Hausdorff, F., *Mengenlehre*, Walter de Gruyter & Company, Berlin, 1927.

Fraenkel, A., *Einleitung in die Mengenlehre*, Julius Springer, Leipzig, 1928.

Hahn, Hans, *Reelle Funktionen*, Akademische Verlagsgesellschaft m.b.H., Leipzig, 1932.

Carathéodory, Constantine, *Vorlesungen über reelle Funktionen*, B. G. Teubner, Leipzig and Berlin, 1939.

Chapter III

SPACES

3.1 Hausdorff space

Definition 3.1.1. A set of elements is called a *Hausdorff space* if with each element of the set there is associated a class of subsets (of the given set) known as *neighborhoods*, which satisfy the following postulates.

(1) Every element x has at least one neighborhood N_x and is an element of each of its neighborhoods.

(2) If there exist two neighborhoods of x, then there exists a neighborhood of x which is contained in each of these.

(3) If y is an element of an N_x, there exists a neighborhood N_y of y which is contained in N_x.

(4) If x and y are distinct, there exist an N_x and an N_y with no common elements.

Examples. (a) The set of real numbers constitutes a Hausdorff space if the neighborhoods of a point are defined as the set of open intervals containing the point.

(b) The same set is a Hausdorff space if the set of neighborhoods of each point is the set consisting of the given point only.

Definition 3.1.2. Let a set S of elements x be given. Let two sets of neighborhoods $\{N_x\}$ and $\{N_x'\}$ for the elements of the set S be defined. The sets of neighborhoods $\{N_x\}$ and $\{N_x'\}$ are said to be equivalent if for every given x of the set S the following two statements are true.

(1) For every given N_x of x there exists an N_x' such that $N_x' \subseteq N_x$.

(2) For every given N_x' of x there exists an N_x of x such that $N_x \subseteq N_x'$.

We note that this is a true equivalence relation according to Def. 1.4.1, for it is reflexive, symmetric, and transitive. The two sets of neighborhoods defined in examples (a) and (b) above obviously are not equivalent. The Hausdorff spaces defined in those examples are considered to be different Hausdorff spaces. Two Hausdorff spaces defined for the same set of elements, but with different sets of neighborhoods are said to be the same space, if the sets of neighborhoods are equivalent.

P. 3.1.1. Define equivalent sets of neighborhoods for the points in a plane. Show that your sets of neighborhoods are equivalent. Also define for the plane two sets of neighborhoods which are not equivalent. Show that they are not equivalent.

Definition 3.1.3. A subset S of a given Hausdorff space is said to be *open with respect to a set of neighborhoods* N_x, if for every element x of S there exists an N_x of x such that $N_x \subseteq S$. A point x of a set S is an interior point of S if there exists an $N_x \subseteq S$.

THEOREM 3.1.1. *Every neighborhood N_x of a point x is open.*

Proof. Postulate 3 of Def. 3.1.1.

P. 3.1.2. Prove that if a set is open with respect to one set of neighborhoods, it is open with respect to every equivalent set of neighborhoods.

P. 3.1.3. For the real continuum define two sets of neighborhoods which are not equivalent. Give examples of sets which are open with respect to one of these sets of neighborhoods but not with respect to the other set of neighborhoods.

THEOREM 3.1.2. *Let S be a Hausdorff space with neighborhoods N_x. With each element x of S let us associate all subsets G_x (containing x) of S which are open with respect to the set of neighborhoods N_x. The set (for all x of S) of all G_x constitutes a set of neighborhoods equivalent to the set of the neighborhoods N_x.*

Proof. We first show that the set of the G_x constitutes a set of neighborhoods. To this end we show that the set of the G_x satisfies the four postulates of Def. 3.1.1.

(1) Every element x has a G_x, and is an element of each of its G_x. For, every x has an N_x. By Theorem 3.1.1, N_x is open. Hence N_x is a G_x. From the definition of the G_x in the statement of the theorem it follows that x is an element of each G_x associated with it.

(2) If there exist two open sets, say G_x', G_x'', for a given x, then there exists a G_x contained in both. For, since G_x' and G_x'' are open, we can find an N_x' and an N_x'', the first lying in G_x', the second in G_x''. Then $N_x' \cdot N_x'' \subseteq G_x' \cdot G_x''$. By postulate (2) of Def. 3.1.1 there

exists an $N_x \subseteq N_x' \cdot N_x''$. This N_x is also a G_x and is contained in $G_x' \cdot G_x''$, and hence in each of the sets G_x' and G_x''.

(3) If y lies in G_x, then there exists a G_y contained in G_x. Since G_x is open, there exists for y an N_y which is contained in G_x (see Def. 3.1.3). This N_y will serve as a G_y.

(4) If x and y are distinct, there exist a G_x and a G_y with no common elements. By postulate (4) of Def. 3.1.1 there exist N_x and N_y with no common elements. These neighborhoods N_x and N_y are G_x and G_y, respectively.

Next we show that the sets of neighborhoods G_x and N_x are equivalent. By the definition of the open sets G_x, we can find in each G_x an N_x, and for every given N_x we can find a G_x, namely N_x, contained in N_x. This completes the proof of the theorem.

THEOREM 3.1.3. *The sum,* $\sum G_\alpha$, *of the sets of any collection of open sets is open.*

Proof. Let $x \in \sum G_\alpha$. Then x is an element of at least one of the G_x, say G_{α_1}. But G_{α_1} is open. Hence there exists an N_x such that $x \in N_x \subseteq G_{\alpha_1}$. But $G_{\alpha_1} \subseteq \sum G_\alpha$, and hence $N_x \subseteq \sum G_\alpha$. This proves the theorem.

THEOREM 3.1.4. *The product* $G_1 \cdot G_2$ *of two open sets* G_1 *and* G_2 *is open.*

Proof. We must show that for every x, such that $x \in G_1 \cdot G_2$, there exists an N_x such that $N_x \subseteq G_1 \cdot G_2$. Let us assume that $x \in G_1 \cdot G_2$. Since $x \in G_1$, there exists an N_x' such that $x \in N_x' \subseteq G_1$. Similarly, since $x \in G_2$, there exists an N_x'' such that $x \in N_x'' \subseteq G_2$. By postulate (2) of Def. 3.1.1, there exists an $N_x \subseteq N_x' \cdot N_x''$. Hence $N_x \subseteq G_1 \cdot G_2$. If $G_1 \cdot G_2$ is the null set, it is open because the definition of an open set is vacuously fulfilled for a null set.

P. 3.1.4. Prove that the product of finitely many open sets is open.

When we deal with subsets of a Hausdorff space S we shall consider this space as the universal set. The complements which may occur shall always be taken with respect to the whole space. We note that the null set 0 is open, and its complement $c0$, which is S, is also open.

Definition 3.1.4. A subset of a Hausdorff space is said to be *closed* if its complement is open.

THEOREM 3.1.5. *The sum $F_1 + F_2$ of two closed sets F_1 and F_2 is closed.*

Proof. Given cF_1 is open, cF_2 is open. To prove $c(F_1 + F_2)$ is open. By Theorem 2.3.1, $c(F_1 + F_2) = cF_1 \cdot cF_2$. By Theorem 3.1.4 the last product is open. Therefore $c(F_1 + F_2)$ is open, as was to be proved.

P. 3.1.5. Prove that the sum of finitely many closed sets is closed.

THEOREM 3.1.6. *The product, πF_α, of the sets of any collection of closed sets F_α is closed.*

Proof. We are given that cF_α is open for every α. We must prove that πF_α is closed, i.e., that $c(\pi F_\alpha)$ is open. But $c(\pi F_\alpha) = \sum cF_\alpha$, by P. 2.3.2. By Theorem 3.1.3 the last sum is open; hence πF_α is closed as was to be proved.

P. 3.1.6. Show by example that the *product* of *infinitely many open sets need not be open.*

P. 3.1.7. Show by example that the *sum* of *infinitely many closed sets need not be closed.*

Definition 3.1.5. A space is said to be *connected* if every subset of it which is *both open* and *closed* is either the null set or the whole space.

Example. Let the whole Hausdorff space under consideration be the points of the intervals (0,1) and (2,3) on the real x-axis. Let N_x be any open interval, with x as center, lying in the space. The subsets (0,1) and (2,3) are both open. But each is the complement of the other, and is thus a closed set. The given space is therefore not connected.

3.2 Homeomorphisms and topological spaces

Definition 3.2.1. Let S and T be two Hausdorff spaces. Let a function f on a subset S_1 of S to a subset T_1 of T be given. Let x_1 be a point of S_1, and let $y_1 = f(x_1)$. The function f is said to be *continuous at* x_1 if for every neighborhood N_{y_1} of y_1 there exists a neighborhood N_{x_1} of x_1 such that if $x_2 \in N_{x_1} \cdot S_1$, then $f(x_2) \in N_{y_1}$.

Definition 3.2.2. A function which is continuous at every point of its domain of definition is called a continuous function.

P. 3.2.1. Prove that if f is a continuous function on S onto T, the inverse correspondence (see Def. 2.4.3) maps every open set in T into an open set of S.

Definition 3.2.3. A simple function f on S onto T which is continuous and whose inverse is a continuous function on T onto S is called a *homeomorphism* or a *topological map* of S onto T or of T onto S. The sets S and T are said to be *homeomorphic to each other* or to be *topologically equivalent,* or *topological images* of each other.

We have here defined continuity and homeomorphism in Hausdorff spaces. Hausdorff spaces belong to a more general class known as neighborhood spaces, which in turn are particular types of still more general spaces known as topological spaces. The term *space* is usually applied to any set for whose elements a scheme is provided to specify "how near" they are one to another. The three most common schemes make use of the concepts of *limit, neighborhood,* and *metric.* Corresponding to each of these we have *limit spaces, neighborhood spaces,* and *metric spaces,* all of which are topological spaces which we shall now define.

Definition 3.2.4. Let S be a set. If with each subset M of S there is associated a subset M^- of S, we say a *topological correspondence* has been set up in S. Here M^- is called the *closure of M under this topological correspondence.*

Definition 3.2.5. A set S with a topological correspondence is called a *general topological space.* It is called a *topological space* if the following postulates are satisfied.

$$(1) \qquad (A + B)^- = A^- + B^-,$$
$$(2) \qquad A \subseteq A^-,$$
$$(3) \qquad (A^-)^- = A^-,$$
$$(4) \qquad 0^- = 0,$$

where 0 is the null set. (These postulates are known as the Kuratowski postulates for a topological space.)

Example. Let S be a set which consists of an office staff whose members are the president p, four secretaries s_1, s_2, s_3, s_4, and four office boys b_1, b_2, b_3, b_4. These members occupy nine rooms arranged as indicated in Fig. 5. The following rules prevail in the office. The president can give orders to every-

body; each secretary can give orders to two office boys only, namely those
whose rooms are adjacent to his; no office boy is permitted to give orders to
any other member of the staff; it is assumed that each member can give orders
to himself. We make the definition: if b can give orders
to a, then a is a *servant* of b.

Let a general topological correspondence be defined in
S as follows. If M is a subset of S, then M^- consists of
*those elements of S which are servants of at least one element
of M.*

b_2	s_2	b_1
s_3	p	s_1
b_3	s_4	b_4

FIG. 5

P. 3.2.2. Is S of this example a topological space under
the given general topological correspondence? If an open
set in S is defined as the complement in S of the closure
of a set, list all open sets in S. If the neighborhoods of every element x of
S are defined to be the open sets containing x, is the resulting neighborhood
space a Hausdorff space?

3.3 Metric spaces

Definition 3.3.1. A *metric* or *distance function* for a set of elements S
is a function, say $\rho(x,y)$, on the set of all pairs x, y of elements of S
to the real continuum which satisfies the following postulates.

(1) $\rho(x,x) = 0$, $\rho(x,y) > 0$ if $x \neq y$.

(2) $\rho(x,y) = \rho(y,x)$.

(3) $\rho(x,z) \leqslant \rho(x,y) + \rho(y,z)$.

The last postulate is known as the triangle axiom, and corresponds
to the triangle inequality, which states that any side of a triangle is
less than or equal to the sum of the other two sides.

P. 3.3.1. Prove that the three postulates just given can be derived from
the postulate (1), and the postulate $\rho(z,x) \leqslant \rho(x,y) + \rho(y,z)$.

Definition 3.3.2. A set with a metric is called a *metric space*.

Definition 3.3.3. Let x_0 be an element of a metric space S, and let
r be a positive number. The subset $K(x_0,r)$ of S which consists of
all those elements x of S for which $\rho(x_0,x) < r$ is called the *open sphere*
with center x_0, and of radius r.

THEOREM 3.3.1. *Every metric space can be made into a Hausdorff
space in which the open spheres constitute the set of neighborhoods for
the respective centers.*

Proof. We must show that in every metric space there exists a class of subsets N_x which satisfy the postulates of the Def. 3.1.1 for a Hausdorff space. Let x_0 be an element of the given metric space. We define a neighborhood of x_0 as any open sphere with center at x_0. Next, we show that the set of all open spheres satisfies the postulates for neighborhoods.

(1) Every element x has an open sphere and is an element of it. This follows from Def. 3.3.3.

(2) If there are two open spheres of x_0, say $K(x_0,r_1)$, and $K(x_0,r_2)$ and if $r_1 \leqslant r_2$, then $K(x_0,r_1)$ is in both spheres; if $r_2 \leqslant r_1$, then $K(x_0,r_2)$ is in both.

(3) If y lies in $K(x_0,r_0)$, let $r = r_0 - \rho(x_0,y)$. Let x be any point in $K(y,r)$. Then by the triangle property

$$\rho(x_0,x) \leqslant \rho(x_0,y) + \rho(y,x) < \rho(x_0,y) + r_0 - \rho(x_0,y) = r_0.$$

Hence any element in $K(y,r)$ is contained in $K(x_0,r_0)$, and

$$K(y,r) \subseteq K(x_0,r_0).$$

(4) If $x_0 \neq y_0$, $\rho(x_0,y_0) = r > 0$.
The two open spheres $K(x_0,r/3)$, and $K(y_0,r/3)$ have no points in common. For suppose x were an element of both spheres. Then $\rho(x_0,x) < r/3$, and $\rho(y_0,x) < r/3$. But

$$\rho(x_0,y_0) = r \leqslant \rho(x_0,x) + \rho(x,y_0) < \frac{r}{3} + \frac{r}{3} = \frac{2r}{3}$$

which is impossible. This completes the proof of the theorem.

The question naturally arises whether the converse of the last theorem is true, that is, whether every Hausdorff space can be made into a metric space. For any given point set, it is of course possible to define a metric. One way is the following. If x, y is a given pair of elements of a set S, we define $\rho(x,y) = 0$ if $x = y$, and $\rho(x,y) = 1$ if $x \neq y$. It is obvious that this function $\rho(x,y)$ is a metric. The term *metrization* as applied to a Hausdorff space (or to any topological space) has a more restrictive meaning. A metric in a set induces a system of neighborhoods given by the open spheres defined by the metric. A Hausdorff space is *metrizable* if it is possible to define such a metric $\rho(x,y)$ for the given space, that the system of neighborhoods of the Hausdorff space is equivalent to the system of open spheres determined by the metric $\rho(x,y)$. For a definition of the metrization of a topological space the reader is referred to *Topologie* by Paul Alexandroff and Heinz Hopf, Vol. 1, p. 28. In order to characterize the metrizable Hausdorff spaces, we give the following definitions.

Definition 3.3.4. A Hausdorff space is said to be *regular* if for every element s_0 of S and every closed set F which does not contain s_0, there exist two open sets G_1 and G_2, such that $G_1 \cdot G_2 = 0$, and $s_0 \subset G_1$, $F \subseteq G_2$.

Examples. (a) Let S be the xy-plane. Let a neighborhood of $s_0, = (x_0, y_0)$, be given by $K(s_0, r)$, the set of points x, y such that $(x - x_0)^2 + (y - y_0)^2 < r^2$. Let F be a given closed set not containing s_0. Since F is closed, cF is open, and since $s_0 \subset cF$, there exists a neighborhood $K(s_0, r_0)$ such that $K(s_0, r_0) \cdot F = 0$. Let G_1 be the neighborhood $K(s_0, r_0/2)$, let G_2 be the open set consisting of all points x, y such that $(x - x_0)^2 + (y - y_0)^2 > r_0/2$. Then G_1 is open and contains s_0, and G_2 is open and contains F. Also $G_1 \cdot G_2 = 0$. Hence S is a regular Hausdorff space.

(b) Let S again be the xy-plane. Let a neighborhood of each point $s_0 = (x_0, y_0)$, except the origin, be $K(s_0, r)$ as defined above. Let a neighborhood of the point $(0,0)$ be the circle $x^2 + y^2 < r^2$ except those points on the x-axis, for which $x > 0$. This set of neighborhoods defines a Hausdorff space in the plane. But this space is not regular because of the point $(0,0)$.

Definition 3.3.5. A Hausdorff space is said to satisfy the *first axiom of countability* if its neighborhood system is equivalent to one in which each point has at most denumerably many neighborhoods.

Definition 3.3.6. A Hausdorff space is said to satisfy the *second axiom of countability* if its neighborhood system is equivalent to a set of neighborhoods which is denumerable.

We state now without proof a result due to P. Urysohn and A. Tychonoff, *Math. Ann.*, **94**, 309 (1925); **95**, 139 (1925).

THEOREM 3.3.2. *Every regular Hausdorff space which satisfies the second axiom of countability is metrizable.*

P. 3.3.2. Give an example of a Hausdorff space which does not satisfy the first axiom of countability. Give an example of a Hausdorff space which does not satisfy the second axiom of countability.

3.4 Linear, normed spaces

Definition 3.4.1. A set of elements is called a *linear* space if it satisfies the following postulates. Here x, y, z are elements of the space; 1, 0, α, β, γ are real (or complex) numbers; n is a positive integer.

(1) An *operation* $+$ (called addition) is defined for the elements of the space, and the elements of the space form a commutative group under this addition. The identity of the group is denoted by O, and is called the *origin*.

(2) *Multiplication* of the elements of the space by real (or complex) numbers is defined: $\alpha x = y$. This multiplication satisfies the *associative law* $\alpha(\beta x) = (\alpha\beta)x$, and the two distributive laws $(\alpha + \beta)x = \alpha x + \beta x$, and $\alpha(x + y) = \alpha x + \alpha y$. It is also assumed that $1 \cdot x = x$.

THEOREM 3.4.1. $0 \cdot x = O$.

Proof. $0x + 1 \cdot x = (0 + 1)x$ by the first distributive law.

$$(0 + 1) \cdot x = 1 \cdot x = x$$

by addition of numbers and postulate (2). Hence, for every x of the space $0 \cdot x + x = x$, and $0 \cdot x = O$, by definition and uniqueness of the unit of addition of a group.

THEOREM 3.4.2. $\underset{n \text{ terms}}{x + x + \ldots + x} = nx$.

Proof. $x = 1 \cdot x$, by postulate (2). Substituting equals for equals,

$$x + x + \ldots + x = 1 \cdot x + 1 \cdot x + \ldots + 1 \cdot x$$
$$= (1 + 1 + \ldots + 1)x = nx$$

by the distributive law and addition of numbers.

If the *same element a* of a linear space is *added* to *each element of the linear space*, we say the space has been *translated* by the amount a. Under such a translation the elements x and y become the elements $x + a$, and $y + a$. If *each element of a linear space* is *multiplied* by the same real (or complex) number α, we say the space has been *dilated by the factor* α. Two elements x and y become αx, and αy under such a dilation.

We next consider a linear metric space, that is, a linear space which has associated with it a metric $\rho(x,y)$. The number $\rho(x,y)$ is called the distance from x to y or from y to x.

Definition 3.4.2. A metric $\rho(x,y)$ of a linear metric space is said to be *invariant under translation* if for every pair of elements x, y of the space and every given element a of the space, $\rho(x + a, y + a) = \rho(x,y)$. The metric is said to be *linear homogeneous under dilation* if for every given real (or complex) number λ,

$$\rho(\lambda x, \lambda y) = |\lambda| \, \rho(x,y).$$

THEOREM 3.4.3. *If the metric $\rho(x,y)$ of a linear metric space is invariant under translation,*

$$\rho(x,y) = \rho(0, y - x),$$

that is, the distance between two elements can be computed as the distance between the origin and the difference between the elements.

Proof. By hypothesis and Def. 3.4.2,

$$\rho(x,y) = \rho(x + a, y + a).$$

Let $a = -x$; then

$$\rho(x,y) = \rho(0, y - x).$$

Definition 3.4.3. Let x be an element of a linear metric space. The distance from the origin to x is called the *norm* of x and is denoted by $\| x \|$, that is $\rho(0,x) = \| x \|$.

THEOREM 3.4.4. *The norm satisfies the following conditions.*

(1) $\| x \| \geqslant 0$, $\| x \| = 0$ if and only if $x = 0$.

(2) $\| x + y \| \leqslant \| x \| + \| y \|$.

(3) $\| \alpha x \| = | \alpha | \cdot \| x \|$, where α is any real (or complex) number.

P. 3.4.1. Prove Theorem 3.4.4.

We have defined a norm for a metric linear space. Conversely, a linear space in which the notion of norm is defined (i.e., in which a function $\| x \|$ is given satisfying the conditions of the last theorem) becomes a metric space with the metric $\rho(x,y) = \| y - x \|$.

P. 3.4.2. Let $\rho(x,y) = \| y - x \|$ where x and y are elements of a linear space, and $\| x \|$ satisfy the conditions of Theorem 3.4.4. Prove that $\rho(x,y)$ is a metric which is invariant under translation and linear homogeneous under dilation.

Definition 3.4.4. A linear space with a norm is called a *normed linear* space.

Definition 3.4.5. If in the same linear space two norms $\| x \|$, and $\| x \|'$ are defined and related by the inequalities

$$\alpha \| \, x \, \| \leqslant \| \, x \, \|' \leqslant \beta \| \, x \, \|,$$

where α and β are two positive numbers (constants), then $\| \, x \, \|$ and $\| \, x \, \|'$ are called *equivalent norms*.

P. 3.4.3. Show that the relation between equivalent norms is a true equivalence relation, that is, show that it is reflexive, symmetric, and transitive.

P. 3.4.4. In the xy-plane define the sum of two elements (points),

$$P_1 = (x_1, y_1), \quad P_2 = (x_2, y_2),$$

as $$P_1 + P_2 = (x_1 + x_2, y_1 + y_2),$$

multiplication by real numbers as $\alpha P_1 = (\alpha x_1, \alpha y_1)$, thus making a linear space out of the set of points in the plane. Let $\| \, P \, \| = \sqrt{x^2 + y^2}$, $\| \, P \, \|' = | \, x \, | + | \, y \, |$. Show that $\| \, P \, \|$ and $\| \, P \, \|'$ are equivalent norms, i.e., find α and β of Def. 3.4.5.

Examples. (a) The set of real numbers is a linear normed space if $\| \, x \, \| = | \, x \, |$, and addition and multiplication are the ordinary addition and multiplication.

(b) The set of all complex numbers is a normed linear space if

$$\| \, x + iy \, \| = | \, x + iy \, | = \sqrt{x^2 + y^2},$$

and addition and multiplication by real (or complex) numbers are the usual operations.

(c) Consider the n-dimensional Cartesian space, R_n, where any element $P = (x_1, x_2, \ldots, x_n)$. We define addition as

$$P + Q = (x_1, \ldots, x_n) + (y_1, \ldots, y_n)$$
$$= (x_1 + y_1, x_2 + y_2, \ldots, x_n + y_n),$$

multiplication by real (or complex) numbers as

$$\alpha P = (\alpha x_1, \alpha x_2, \ldots, \alpha x_n),$$

and $$\| \, P \, \| = \sqrt{x_1^2 + x_2^2, \ldots, x_n^2}.$$

This is a normed linear space. We could have defined the norm in various other ways. For example, as

$$\| \, P \, \|' = \max | \, x_i \, | \quad \text{or} \quad \| \, P \, \|'' = \sum_{i=1}^{n} | \, x_i \, |.$$

(d) The space C of all continuous real functions defined over the interval $[a, b]$, where

$$\| \, x \, \| = \max | \, x(t) \, |,$$
$$a \leqslant t \leqslant b$$

is a linear normed space if addition and multiplication have the usual meaning.

(e) The space L^2 of all real functions whose square is integrable over the interval $[a,b]$, with

$$\| x \| = \left[\int_a^b x^2(t)dt \right]^{1/2}$$

is another example.

(f) As another example of a normed linear space we have the space H of all real sequences $x = (x_1,x_2,\ldots,x_n,\ldots)$ such that $\sum x_i^2$ converges. Here we define

$$\| x \| = [\sum x_i^2]^{1/2}.$$

REFERENCES

Hausdorff, F., *Mengenlehre*, Walter de Gruyter & Company, Berlin, 1927.

Hahn, Hans, *Reelle Funktionen*, Akademische Verlagsgesellschaft, m.b.H., Leipzig, 1932.

CHAPTER IV

POINT SETS

4.1 Fundamental definitions and theorems. In this chapter we shall consider subsets of Hausdorff spaces. Examples of such spaces are the real continuum E_1, with the neighborhood system defined as the set of open intervals, or the points in an xy-plane, with neighborhoods defined as the interior of circles or squares. Because the material on sets treated here admits a quite natural geometrical interpretation we shall refer to the elements of the sets as points, and to the sets themselves as point sets.

The reader should recall the definitions of open set, closed set, interior point, and that of a connected space.

Definition 4.1.1. A point x, which may or may not belong to a given set S, *is a limit point of* S if every neighborhood of x contains an infinite number of points of S.

P. 4.1.1. Prove that if a set S is closed, every limit point of S is an element of S, and conversely, if every limit point of S belongs to S, then S is closed.

P. 4.1.2. Prove that if a point x is such that every neighborhood of x contains at least one point of s of S, $s \neq x$, then x is a limit point of S.

Definition 4.1.2. The set which consists of all the limit points of a set S is called the *derived set of* S, and is denoted by S'.

THEOREM 4.1.1. *For each set S, the derived set S' is closed.*

Proof. Let S be the given set, and S' the derived set of S. We denote the set of limit points of S' by $(S')'$. We must show that if $x \in (S')'$, then $x \in S'$. Let $x \in (S')'$. Then by Def. 4.1.1 every neighborhood N_x of x contains at least one point x' of S'. By postulate (3) of Def. 3.1.1, there exists a neighborhood of x', say $N_{x'}$, which is contained in N_x. Thus $N_{x'} \subseteq N_x$. But since x' is by hypothesis a limit point of S, every neighborhood of x', and in particular $N_{x'}$, contains an infinite number of elements of S. Therefore N_x contains

64

an infinite number of elements of S, and x is a limit point of S by Def. 4.1.1. Thus $x \in S'$ as was to be proved.

Definition 4.1.3. The set $S + S'$ is called the *closure of S*, and is denoted by S^-.

THEOREM 4.1.2. *The closure of a set is a closed set.*

P. 4.1.3. Prove this theorem.

Definition 4.1.4. If $S = S'$, the set S is said to be *perfect*, i.e., S is perfect if every limit point of S belongs to S, and if every point of S is a limit point of S.

Definition 4.1.5. A set S is said to be *dense in itself* if every point of S is a limit point of S, i.e., if $S \subseteq S'$.

We see that a perfect set could have been defined as a set which is closed and dense in itself.

Definition 4.1.6. A point x is a *condensation* point of S if every neighborhood of x contains nondenumerably many points of S.

It follows that every condensation point of a set S is a limit point of S, but not every limit point of S needs to be a condensation point of S.

Examples. (a) Consider the set of points

$$S = \left\{ 1, \frac{1}{2}, \ldots, \frac{1}{n}, \ldots \right\}$$

as a subset of the Hausdorff space E_1. The point $x = 0$ is the only limit point of this set. This set is not closed because the limit point does not belong to it. The set cannot have a condensation point because it consists of denumerably many elements.

(b) Let the set S be the set of all rational numbers in $(0,1)$ considered as a subset of E_1. Here $S \subseteq S'$, for S' is the set of all points in $[0,1]$. This set S is dense in itself, but it is not a closed set, and hence not a perfect set. It has no condensation points because it is denumerable.

(c) The set of all points in the closed interval $[0,1]$ considered as a subset of the space E_1, is closed, dense in itself, and hence perfect. Every point of this set is a condensation point.

It is obvious that if a set S is non-null and finite, S cannot be perfect. For the null set the definition of a set being perfect (Def. 4.1.4) is fulfilled. Thus the null set, in addition to being open and closed is also dense in itself and perfect.

P. 4.1.4. Let S_1 and S_2 be subsets of the same Hausdorff space. Prove that $(S_1 S_2)^- \subseteq (S_1^-)(S_2^-)$.

P. 4.1.5. Let the set S and the open set G be subsets of the same Hausdorff space. Prove that

(1) $S'G \subseteq (SG)'$;

(2) $(S^-)G \subseteq (SG)^-$;

(3) if $SG = 0$ (null set), then $(S^-)G = 0$.

Definition 4.1.7. The subset of S which consists of all interior points of S is called the *interior of S*, and is denoted by $I(S)$.

THEOREM 4.1.3. *Let S be a given set. The interior of S is the sum of all open sets contained in S.*

P. 4.1.6. Prove Theorem 4.1.3.

Definition 4.1.8. The point x is a *boundary point* of a set S if every neighborhood of x contains points of S and points of cS (the complement of S).

Definition 4.1.9. The set which consists of all the boundary points of S is called the *boundary of S* and is denoted by $B(S)$.

P. 4.1.7. Prove that if G is open, then $B(G) \subseteq G'$, and $B(G) = G'(cG)$.

P. 4.1.8. Prove that if G_1 and G_2 are two open sets in a Hausdorff space, and if $B(G_1) \cdot B(G_2) = 0$, then

$$B(G_1 G_2) = G_1 B(G_2) + G_2 B(G_1).$$

Definition 4.1.10. A point x of S is an *isolated* point of S if there exists a neighborhood N_x of x which contains no other point of S.

The set of integers, also the set $\left\{\dfrac{1}{n}\right\}$, $n = 1, 2, 3, \ldots$, considered as subsets of E_1, are sets which consist of isolated points only.

Definition 4.1.11. A subset A of S is said to be *everywhere dense* in S if every neighborhood of every point of S contains at least one point of A.

P. 4.1.9. Show that if A lies in a space S and A is everywhere dense in S, then $A^- = S$.

Definition 4.1.12. A subset A of S is said to be *nowhere dense* in S if every neighborhood of every point of S contains a neighborhood which contains no point of A.

P. 4.1.10. Prove that if A is nowhere dense in S, then $S - A^-$ is everywhere dense in S, and conversely, if $S - A^-$ is everywhere dense in S, then A is nowhere dense in S.

4.2 Separable and compact spaces

Definition 4.2.1. A space S is said to be *separable* if it contains a denumerable set A which is *everywhere dense* in S.

Example. The real continuum E_1 is a separable space because it contains the set of all rational numbers as a subset. The set of rational numbers is denumerable, and it is everywhere dense in E_1.

Definition 4.2.2. A space S is said to be compact if every infinite subset of S has at least one limit point in S. A set K is compact if every infinite subset of K has at least one limit point in K.

Definition 4.2.3. A space S is *locally compact* if every x of S has an N_x whose closure is compact.

The real continuum is not compact, for the infinite set which consists of all positive integers does not have a limit point in the real continuum. We have, however, the following result.

THEOREM 4.2.1 (BOLZANO-WEIERSTRASS). *The real continuum E_1 is locally compact, that is, every infinite set S of points which lies in the closed interval $[a,b]$ has at least one limit point in $[a,b]$.*

P. 4.2.1. Prove this theorem by the use of the Dedekind cut.

THEOREM 4.2.2. *If S_1, S_2, S_3, ... is a denumerable set of compact, closed non-null sets such that*

$$S_1 \supseteq S_2 \supseteq S_3 \supseteq \ldots ,$$

they have at least one point in common.

Proof. Using the axiom of choice, we select a p_n out of each S_n. We form the set $\{p_{n_i}\}$ which consists of all the different p_n. If $\{p_{n_i}\}$ is a finite set, at least one of its elements must be in infinitely many of the S_n, and hence in every S_n. If the set $\{p_{n_i}\}$ is an infinite set, it has a limit point p. Since the set $\{p_{n_i}\}$ is infinite, there exists for every n an n_i greater than n, and all p_{n_i} with n_i greater than n are in S_n. Hence p is a limit point of S_n. But S_n is closed; hence p is in every S_n, and thus common to all the S_n.

P. 4.2.2. Prove the Bolzano-Weierstrass theorem on the basis of Theorem 4.2.2.

THEOREM 4.2.3. *Every separable metric space, whose set of neighborhoods is equivalent to the set of open spheres, satisfies the second axiom of countability* (see Def. 3.3.6).

Proof. By hypothesis there exists a set, say $\{p_n\}$, of denumerably many points (see Def. 4.2.1), which is everywhere dense in the space S. Let x be a point of S with neighborhood N_x. There exists an open sphere $K^1(x,r) \subseteq N_x$, where $K^1(x,r)$ has its center at x, and is of radius r. Let $K^2(x,r/3)$ be another open sphere with center at x and of radius $r/3$. This second sphere will contain at least one element of the set $\{p_n\}$, say p_m. With p_m as center we construct an open sphere $K(p_m,\rho)$ with a rational radius ρ such as $r/3 < \rho < 2r/3$. From the properties of a metric (Def. 3.3.1) it follows that $x \in K(p_m,\rho) \subseteq N_x$. The set of all such open spheres with rational radii and center at the points of the set $\{p_n\}$ is denumerable. That it constitutes a set of neighborhoods equivalent to the original ones is a direct consequence of its construction.

4.3 Covering theorems

Definition 4.3.1. A point x is said to be *covered* by a set S if x is an interior point of S. If every point x of a set E is covered by at least one set G_{α_x} of a collection of sets G_α, then E *is* said to be covered by the sets G_α.

Example. Consider in E_1 the set $S = \{1/n\}$ where $n = 1, 2, 3, \ldots$. Let us cover each point $1/n$ by means of the interval

$$I_n = \left(\frac{2n+1}{2n(n+1)}, \frac{2n+3}{2n(n+1)} \right).$$

The set $\{I_n\}$, $n = 1, 2, 3, \ldots$, constitutes a covering of the set S.

THEOREM 4.3.1 (LINDELÖF). *If a nondenumerable set $\{G_\alpha\}$ of open sets G_α covers a set E in a space in which the second axiom of countability holds, there exists a denumerable subset of $\{G_\alpha\}$ which covers E.*

Proof. Let M be the denumerable set of neighborhoods which is equivalent to the set of all neighborhoods of the space in which E lies. Let all the elements of M be ordered in the order of the natural numbers. Let N_1^* be the first element (set) of M which is contained in at least one G_α, and call the latter G_1'. The existence of N_1^* follows from the fact that the sets G_α cover the set E. Let N_2^* be the next element of M which is contained in at least one G_α, which we call G_2', where G_2' may be the same as G_1'. We continue in this manner. It must be shown that the set $\{N_1^*, N_2^*, N_3^*, \ldots\}$ covers the set E. Let x be an element of E. By hypothesis there exists an open set G_α which covers x. Hence there exists an N_x such that $N_x \subseteq G_\alpha$. This N_x is therefore one of the N_i^*. Thus for every x of E there exists an N_i^* which covers x. But the G_i' cover the N_i^*, and thus the set $\{G_i'\}$, which consists of at most a denumerable number of G_α, covers the set E.

THEOREM 4.3.2. *If a denumerable set $\{G_i\}$ of open sets $G_1, G_2, G_3, \ldots$ covers a compact space E, there exists a finite subset of $\{G_i\}$ which covers E.*

Proof. Suppose the set E is not coverable by a finite number of G_i. Take $S_n = c(G_1 + G_2 + \ldots + G_n)$. Each S_n is closed, non-null, compact, and contains S_{n+1}. Therefore, by Theorem 4.2.2, the S_n have at least one point p in common. Since p belongs to every S_n it belongs to no G_i. This is a contradiction, for the set $\{G_i\}$ covers E.

THEOREM 4.3.3 (HEINE-BOREL). *If a nondenumerable set $\{G_\alpha\}$ of open sets covers a compact space E, in which the second axiom of countability holds, there exist a finite number of the sets G_α which cover E.*

P. 4.3.1. Prove the Heine-Borel theorem for the space E_1 where it takes the following form. If every point of a closed and bounded set is covered by an open interval, the set can be covered by finitely many of these open intervals.

That this theorem does not hold for sets which are not closed is illustrated by the example which was given above in this section.

4.4 Structure of perfect sets in E_1. It is quite easy to see that in E_1 the set of open intervals with rational end points constitutes a denumerable set of neighborhoods which is equivalent to the set of all open intervals. Thus E_1 satisfies the second axiom of countability. This fact follows also from Theorem 4.2.3 because E_1 is separable.

THEOREM 4.4.1. *A necessary and sufficient condition for a set S in E_1 to have at least one condensation point is that S be nondenumerable.*

Proof. That it is necessary is obvious. To prove sufficiency, let us suppose that a nondenumerable set S has no condensation point. Then for every x in the space there exists an N_x which has at most a denumerable number of points of S. Thus the space is covered by such N_x. By Lindelöf's theorem (Theorem 4.3.1) a denumerable number of these neighborhoods covers the space. Hence the set S is denumerable, since $\aleph_0{}^2 = \aleph_0$. This contradicts our hypothesis.

P. 4.4.1. Prove this theorem by means of a Dedekind cut. Hint: First show that if S is a nondenumerable set of points (real numbers) on the real axis, there exists an interval $[a,b]$ which contains a nondenumerable number of elements of S. Next show the existence of a left most condensation point of S in $[a,b]$.

THEOREM 4.4.2. *Let S be a set in E_1, and let P be the set of all condensation points of S. Then P is dense in itself.* [This theorem states that every element of P is a limit point of P, or that no element of P is an isolated point of P.]

Proof. Let us suppose that some element x of P were not a limit point of P. Then there would exist a neighborhood N_x of x which would contain no other point of P than x. Let N_x be the open interval (a,b). Then each of the intervals

$$\left[\frac{a + (2^n - 1)x}{2^n}, \frac{a + (2^{n+1} - 1)x}{2^{n+1}}\right],$$

and

$$\left[\frac{(2^{n+1} - 1)x + b}{2^{n+1}}, \frac{(2^n - 1)x + b}{2^n}\right],$$

(where $n = 0,1,2,3,\ldots$) would contain at most a denumerable number of elements of S. But then the sum of all these intervals would contain at most a denumerable number of points S. This contradicts the hypothesis that x is a point of condensation of S.

THEOREM 4.4.3. *The set P of points of condensation of a set S in E_1 is perfect.*

Proof. By the preceding theorem P is dense in itself, that is $P \subseteq P'$. We now show that P is closed. Let us assume that $x \in P'$. Then every N_x contains at least one point, say y, which is an element of P. By postulate (3), Def. 3.1.1, there exists an $N_y, \subseteq N_x$. But each N_y contains nondenumerably many points of S. Hence $x \in P$, and $P' \subseteq P$. We have shown that $P = P'$, which states that P is perfect.

THEOREM 4.4.4. *If S is any set in E_1, the points of S which are not condensation points of S constitute a denumerable or finite set.*

Proof. For each element x of S, with x not a condensation point of S, there exists an interval I_x with rational endpoints which contains at most $\aleph_0$ points of S. The totality of such I_x with rational end points is at most $\aleph_0$. Hence the points of S, which are not condensation points of S, constitute a set whose cardinal number is at most $\aleph_0{}^2$ which is equal to $\aleph_0$.

As a consequence of Theorem 4.4.1 and Theorem 4.4.4, we have the following important result.

Theorem 4.4.5. *Every nondenumerable set S in E_1 has nondenumerably many condensation points of S belonging to S.*

The theorems in this section throw light on the structure of every closed set in E_1.

Theorem 4.4.6. *Every closed set of points in E_1 is the sum of a perfect set and a set whose cardinal number is at most denumerable.*

Proof. Let F be any given closed set in E_1. Let P be the set of condensation points of F. By Theorem 4.4.3 P is perfect, and since F is closed, $P \subseteq F$. Let D be the set which consists of those elements of F which are not condensation points of F. By Theorem 4.4.4 this set D is either denumerable or finite.

P. 4.4.2. Prove that the sum of the sets of any collection of sets, each dense in itself, is dense in itself.

P. 4.4.3. (a) Prove that the sum of finitely many perfect sets is perfect.

(b) Show by example that the sum of infinitely many perfect sets needs not to be a perfect set.

P. 4.4.4. Show by means of an example that the projection (see Def. 2.4.2) of a perfect set needs not to be a perfect set.

4.5 The Cantor discontinuum or ternary set. We have seen that a closed interval $[a,b]$ is a perfect set. By P. 4.4.3 (a) the sum of finitely many closed intervals is also a perfect set in E_1. But not every perfect set in E_1 is the sum of a finite number of closed intervals. We shall now give a procedure due to Cantor for the construction of nowhere dense bounded perfect sets in E_1. [Cantor, G., *Math. Ann.*, **21**, 590 (1883).]

We start with the closed interval $[0,1]$ and blacken the middle third of this interval, keeping its end points white (see Fig. 6). Next we blacken the middle third of each of the two white intervals thus formed, again keeping the end points white. Then we blacken the middle third of each of the four new white intervals, keeping the end points of the black intervals white, and so on. The *Cantor ternary set consists of the points of* [0,1] *that remain white.*

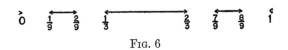

FIG. 6

The Cantor ternary set has the following properties.

(a) *It is nowhere dense.* For if (α,β) is any subinterval of [0,1], there is in (α,β) a portion of a black interval of the nth stage for n large enough. If this were not so, there would be a white interval in [0,1] of fixed length, no part of which would ever be blackened. This is impossible since the lengths of the white intervals go to zero.

(b) *It is perfect.* It is *closed* because the complementary set, consisting as it does of the sum of open intervals, is open. It is *dense in itself* because it cannot have an isolated point. For if x were an isolated white point, x would be the end point of two black intervals. But according to the definition of the black intervals, there are no abutting black intervals.

P. 4.5.1. Find the sum of the lengths of the black intervals at the nth stage in the construction of the Cantor ternary set. What does this sum approach as n goes to infinity?

P. 4.5.2. Show that a point of the interval [0,1] is in the Cantor ternary set if and only if its ternary development can be written without using the digit 1.

4.6 General structure of open and closed sets in E_1

THEOREM 4.6.1. *Every non-null open set in E_1 is the sum of finitely or denumerably many nonoverlapping open intervals.* [It is here understood that we permit, if necessary, an interval to extend from $-\infty$ to $+\infty$. Thus in addition to the open intervals (a,b), where a and b are real numbers, we may have the open intervals $(-\infty,a)$, $(a,+\infty)$, $(-\infty,+\infty)$.]

Proof. Let G be an open set, and let x be a point of G. If there exists in cG an element u such that $u > x$, let r_x be the greatest lower bound of all elements of cG which lie to the right of x. If no element of cG lies to the right of x let r_x be $+\infty$. This greatest lower bound r_x,

if it is a real number, cannot belong to G, for if it did, a neighborhood
of r_x would exist, containing only points of G contrary to the definition of r_x as the greatest lower bound of the part of cG to the right
of x.

Likewise there exists an l_x which is either $-\infty$ or the least upper
bound of cG to the left of x. Obviously $l_x \neq r_x$, otherwise G would
not be open. The open interval (l_x,r_x) is the largest open interval
all of whose points belong to G and which contains x.

Every point of G thus lies in a uniquely defined maximum interval
(l_x,r_x). Two distinct intervals of this type cannot overlap. Let J
be the totality of these maximum nonoverlapping intervals. Since of
mutually nonoverlapping intervals there are at most $\aleph_0$ in E_1, there
are at most $\aleph_0$ such intervals in J. Every point of G is in but one of
these elements of J, and every point in any element of J belongs to G.
Therefore G is the sum of at most $\aleph_0$ nonoverlapping open intervals.

THEOREM 4.6.2. *Every closed set in E_1 is the complement of a set of
at most $\aleph_0$ nonoverlapping open intervals.*

Proof. Definition 3.1.4, and Theorem 4.6.1.

Other results on the structure of sets in E_1 are the following.

Every *closed, nowhere dense* set is the *complement* of an *everywhere
dense* set of at most $\aleph_0$ *nonoverlapping open* intervals.

Every *perfect nowhere dense* set is the *complement* of a set of at most
$\aleph_0$ *nonoverlapping, nonabutting, everywhere dense open* intervals.

4.7 Exhaustible and residual sets in E_1. For a more complete
understanding of the structure of the continuum E_1, and of the type
of discontinuous real functions that can exist in it, the concepts given
in the following two definitions are of importance.

Definition 4.7.1. A set S in E_1 is called *exhaustible* if it is the sum
of at most denumerably many nowhere dense sets in E_1.

We shall designate exhaustible sets by the letter X, and nowhere dense sets by N. Thus in symbols, X is exhaustible if
$X = N_1 + N_2 + N_3 + \ldots$ where each N_i is a nowhere dense set.
Since a single point in E_1 is a nowhere dense set in E_1, every finite
or denumerable set of points is exhaustible. The converse is, of course,
not true, since the Cantor ternary set is a nowhere dense set; hence
an exhaustible set which is nondenumerable.

Definition 4.7.2. A *residual* set in E_1 is the complement of an exhaustible set.

We shall designate a residual set by R. Thus $R = E_1 - X$, where X is exhaustible.

THEOREM 4.7.1. *A residual set in E_1 is everywhere dense in E_1.*

Proof. Let R be a residual set. Then $cR = E_1 - R = X$, an exhaustible set. Thus $X = N_1 + N_2 + N_3 + \ldots$ where each N_i is nowhere dense in E_1.

Let $[\alpha,\beta]$ be a given closed interval. We must show that there exists at least one point of R in this interval. Since N_1 is nowhere dense in $[\alpha,\beta]$, there exists a closed subinterval $[\alpha_1,\beta_1]$ of $[\alpha,\beta]$ containing no point of N_1. Since N_2 is nowhere dense, there exists in $[\alpha_1,\beta_1]$ a closed subinterval $[\alpha_2,\beta_2]$ containing no points of N_2. Continuing in this manner, we define a closed interval $[\alpha_n,\beta_n]$ as lying in $[\alpha_{n-1},\beta_{n-1}]$ and containing no point of $N_1, N_2, N_3, \ldots, N_n$. The sequence of closed intervals

$$[\alpha,\beta] \supseteq [\alpha_1,\beta_1] \supseteq [\alpha_3,\beta_3] \supseteq \ldots$$

constitutes a set of compact sets. By Theorem 4.2.2, there is at least one point, say γ, which lies in each $[\alpha_n,\beta_n]$. This point γ is therefore in none of the N_i. Hence γ is in R. Since $[\alpha,\beta]$ was an arbitrary closed interval, R is everywhere dense in E_1.

THEOREM 4.7.2. *The continuum E_1 is not exhaustible.*

Proof. If E_1 were exhaustible, the null set, being the complement of E_1, would be a residual set. But this is impossible, since the null set is not everywhere dense in E_1.

THEOREM 4.7.3. *A residual set is not exhaustible.*

Proof. If a residual set were exhaustible, the continuum E_1 would be the sum of two exhaustible sets, and hence would be exhaustible. But by Theorem 4.7.2 this is not possible.

4.8 Functions whose points of continuity and points of discontinuity constitute everywhere dense sets

Definition 4.8.1. The *saltus* or *jump* or *oscillation* of a real function $f(x)$ in an interval is defined as the least upper bound of $f(x)$ in the interval minus the greatest lower bound of $f(x)$ in the interval if these bounds exist. If at least one of these bounds does not exist, the saltus of $f(x)$ in the interval is said to be plus infinity $(+\infty)$.

Definition 4.8.2. The *saltus of a real function* $f(x)$ *at a point* x_0 is the greatest lower bound, if it exists, of the salti of $f(x)$ for all intervals (a,b) containing x_0. If this bound does not exist, the saltus of $f(x)$ at x_0 is said to be plus infinity.

It follows from these definitions that the saltus of $f(x)$ at a point of continuity of $f(x)$ is zero, and if the saltus of $f(x)$ at x_0 is zero, and if $f(x)$ is defined at x_0, then $f(x)$ is continuous at x_0.

Example. (a) Let a real function be defined on $[0,1]$ as

$$f(0) = f(1) = 1, \qquad f(p/q) = 1/q,$$

where p and q are relatively prime positive integers, $f(x) = 0$ if x is an irrational number. This function has the saltus 1 at $x = 0$ and $x = 1$. At $x = p/q$ the saltus is $1/q$. At all irrational points in $[0,1]$ the saltus is zero. The function is thus seen to be discontinuous at every rational point in $[0,1]$, but continuous at every irrational point. The points of discontinuity constitute an everywhere dense set which is exhaustible. The points of continuity form also an everywhere dense set, but this set is not exhaustible.

P. 4.8.1. Prove that if a real function is continuous on an everywhere dense set in $[0,1]$, the set of points where the saltus of $f(x)$ is greater than $k(k>0)$ is nowhere dense in $[0,1]$.

P. 4.8.2. Making use of the preceding problem, prove that there cannot exist a real function, defined for all points in $[0,1]$, which is continuous at every rational point and discontinuous at every irrational point.

4.9 Borel sets. Sometimes it is convenient to single out certain subsets of a given space for special consideration. These subsets may be considered as being equivalent to each other with respect to a certain property that they may have in common. In this sense they are said to form a class. For example, we may speak of the class of open sets. The whole space belongs to this class. The sum of the members of any collection of elements of this class is an element of the class. The complement of an element of this class, however, is not in general an element of the class, for the complement of an open set need not be open. We shall now give the defining properties of an important class of sets.

Definition 4.9.1. A class C of subsets of a space S is called an *additive class* if it satisfies the following properties.

(1) The whole space belongs to C.

(2) If each set of a finite or denumerable collection of sets S_1, S_2, S_3, ... belongs to C, then the sum $S_1 + S_2 + S_3 + ...$ belongs to C.

(3) If S belongs to C, then the complement of S, cS, belongs to C.

P. 4.9.1. Prove that if each set S_i of a sequence $\{S_i\}$ belongs to an additive class C, then the intersection πS_i also belongs to C.

The set of open sets of a space is not an additive class, since the condition (3) is not satisfied for this class. The class of all subsets of a given space is obviously an additive class. In the real continuum the class of all intervals, open, closed, half-open, or degenerate is not an additive class, for the sum of two nonabutting intervals is not an interval.

Definition 4.9.2. The class of sets which consists of all sets which can be reached by starting from intervals in E_1 and performing the operations of addition, multiplication, and taking complements a finite or denumerably infinite number of times is called the *class B_1*, of *Borel* sets in E_1.

As a direct consequence of the last two definitions we have the following result.

THEOREM 4.9.1. *The class B_1 of Borel sets in E_1 is an additive class.* Thus the sum or product of any finite or denumerable collection of Borel sets is a Borel set. The complement of any Borel set is also a Borel set.

THEOREM 4.9.2. *Every additive class of sets in E_1 which contains all intervals, contains B_1. In other words, the class B_1 of Borel sets is the smallest additive class in E_1 which contains all intervals.*

Proof. Let C be an additive class of sets in E_1 which contains all intervals. By Def. 4.9.1 of an additive class, C must contain every set that can be obtained from intervals by finitely or denumerably many operations such as addition, multiplication, and the taking of complements. Therefore C must contain the whole class B_1.

We have restricted our discussions in some of the sections in this chapter to subsets of E_1. Most of the results can be extended to the n-dimensional Euclidean space E_n, which consists of all n-tuplets $X = (x_1, x_2, \ldots, x_n)$ of real numbers. In order to carry out these extensions it is of course necessary to generalize some of the concepts by making new definitions. Thus, for instance, an *interval*

$$(a_i, b_i)(i = 1, 2, \ldots, n)$$

in E_n is defined as the set of all

$$X, = (x_1, x_2, \ldots, x_n),$$

such that $a_i < x_i < b_i$.

We call attention to the fact that the projection of a Borel set needs not to be a Borel set. For a proof of this fact the student is referred to F. Hausdorff, *Mengenlehre* (1927), p. 212, or to Hans Hahn, *Reelle Funktionen* (1932), p. 351.

4.10 Continuous curves. It seems appropriate at this point to introduce the concept of curve, since it is based on the concept of continuous function which was considered in this chapter.

Definition 4.10.1. A *continuous curve* in the xy-plane is a set of points x, y for which

$$x = f(t), \qquad y = g(t), \qquad (a \leqslant t \leqslant b)$$

where $f(t)$ and $g(t)$ are continuous in the closed interval $[a,b]$. In other words, a continuous curve is a continuous image of an interval.

Even though this definition has been generally accepted as a natural one from the analytic (nongeometric) point of view, it is open to objections from the geometric viewpoint. It was pointed out by the mathematician G. Peano (1890) that a curve as just defined can fill a square. A simpler construction shows that a curve may fill a closed triangle. We give here an example, due to Polya, which shows that the continuous image of the closed unit interval can be a closed triangle.

Example. Let the unit interval $0 \leqslant t \leqslant 1$, and the right triangle ABC, with $AC \neq BC$ be given (Fig. 7). We represent each point t of the unit interval as a radix fraction with radix 2.
Let t_0 be a given point of the closed interval $[0,1]$. Then

$t_0 = 0 \cdot a_1 a_2 a_3 \ldots$, where a_i $(i = 1,2,3,\ldots)$

is either 0 or 1. We drop a perpendicular CD_0 from C upon the hypotenuse AB. Then we drop a perpendicular $D_0 D_1{}'$ upon the smaller leg of the given tri-

FIG. 7

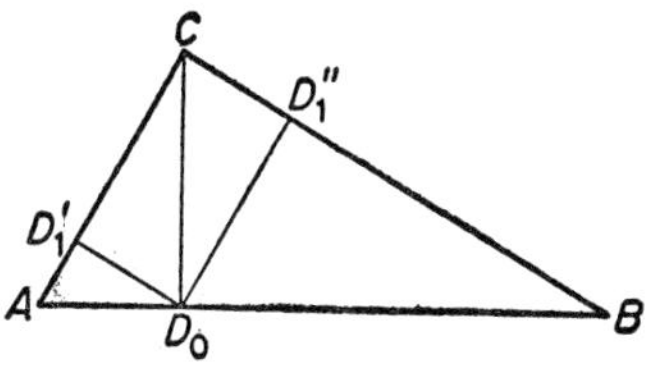

angle if $a_1 = 0$; if $a_1 = 1$ we drop a perpendicular $D_0 D_1{}''$ upon the longer leg of the given triangle. We repeat this process dropping perpendiculars from D_1' or D_1'' as the case may be, with the right triangle ABC replaced by ACD_0 in the first case, by CBD_0 in the second case. We denote the successive feet of the perpendiculars by D_1, D_2, D_3, ... , where D_i is either D_i' or D_i''. This sequence $\{D_i\}$ of points has a limit point p_0 in the closed triangle ABC. We define $f(t_0)$ to be p_0. It is easily seen that this construction defines a continuous function f on $[0,1]$ onto the closed triangle ABC. Thus it is shown that a continuous curve can pass through every point of a two-dimensional interval.

The objection raised to the above definition of a continuous curve from the geometric viewpoint is that it makes a curve of a triangle or of a square, while it rejects certain point sets which a geometer would like to have fall under the definition of curve. One such planar point set is the set which consists of the points $E(x,y)$ where $y = \sin(1/x)$ if $x \neq 0$, and $-1 \leqslant y \leqslant 1$ if $x = 0$. On the basis of a dimension theory, which goes beyond the bounds of this book, a definition of the concept "curve" has been given which seems more natural, than the one given here, from the geometric viewpoint. In dimension theory a curve is a metric space which is "one-dimensional at each of its points." Under this definition a planar point set such as a square or a triangle cannot be a curve, but the set of points $E(x,y)$ mentioned above is a curve under this definition. For more information on this topic the reader is referred to *Introduction to Topology*, by S. Lefschetz, and the literature cited there.

REFERENCES

Hahn, Hans, *Reelle Funktionen*, Akademische Verlagsgesellschaft, m.b.H., Leipzig, 1932.

Hahn, Hans, and Rosenthal, Arthur, *Set Functions*, The University of New Mexico Press, Albuquerque, New Mexico, 1942.

Hausdorff, F., *Mengenlehre*. Walter de Gruyter & Company, Berlin and Leipzig, 1927.

Lefschetz, Solomon, *Introduction to Topology*, Princeton University Press, Princeton, 1949.

CHAPTER V

SEQUENCES

5.1 Functions defined on ordered sets. According to our earlier definition (Def. 2.4.4 and sequel) a function on a set S_1 onto a set S_2 sets up a correspondence by which to each element of S_1 there corresponds a unique element of S_2. The set S_1 is called the domain of definition of the function, the set S_2 is the range of the function. Functions may be classified with regard to the nature of their domains of definition, their ranges, or with respect to some of their properties. Certain functions, whose domains of definition are ordered sets, are of special importance in analysis.

Definition 5.1.1. A function whose domain of definition is an ordered set similar (see Def. 2.8.3) to the set of positive integers in their natural order, is called a *sequence.*

A sequence is thus a function whose values can be written in the form $f(1), f(2), f(3), \ldots$, or $f_1, f_2, f_3, \ldots$. Each value $f(n)$, or f_n is called an *entry* of the sequence.

If the range of a sequence is a subset of the set of real numbers, we have a sequence of real numbers. If the range is a set of sets we have a sequence of sets. We shall usually represent a sequence $x_1, x_2, x_3, \ldots$ by $\{x_n\}$. We must, however, make a distinction between the entries of the sequence and the elements of the range of the sequence. Every sequence has infinitely many entries, but the range may be a finite set. Thus, for example, the sequence $\{x_n\}$ where $x_n = 2$ if n is an even positive integer, and $x_n = 3$ if n is an odd positive integer has infinitely many entries, namely, 3, 2, 3, 2, 3, 2, $\ldots$, but its range consists of only two elements, 2 and 3.

Definition 5.1.2. If from the sequence $\{x_n\}$ we select an infinite set of entries, say $x_{n_1}, x_{n_2}, x_{n_3}, \ldots$, and do not change their order, the sequence $x_{n_1}, x_{n_2}, x_{n_3}, \ldots = \{x_{n_i}\}$ is called a *subsequence* of the *original sequence.*

5.2 Convergent sequences. We shall consider sequences whose entries are points in a Hausdorff space R. If we choose for this Hausdorff space the space E_1 we have the theory of sequences of real numbers; if this space is E_2, it can be interpreted as the theory of sequences of complex numbers.

Definition 5.2.1. An element b of R is *the limit* of a sequence $\{x_n\}$ if for every given neighborhood N_b of b there exists a positive integer n_0 such that for every $n, > n_0$, $x_n \in N_b$. If b is the limit of $\{x_n\}$ we say that the sequence $\{x_n\}$ *is convergent*, and *converges to b*. We indicate this by writing

$$\lim_{n \to \infty} x_n = b, \quad \text{or} \quad x_n \to b \quad \text{as} \quad n \to \infty.$$

A sequence which is not convergent is said to be *divergent*.

This definition can also be restated in the following way. An element b of R is the limit of the sequence $\{x_n\}$ if every neighborhood N_b of b contains *all but* a finite number of entries of $\{x_n\}$.

THEOREM 5.2.1. *If a sequence has a limit, it has only one limit. Otherwise stated, a sequence can converge to at most one limit.*

Proof. Let us assume that b and b' are limits of $\{x_n\}$, and $b \neq b'$. Then there exist by postulate (4), Def. 3.1.1, two neighborhoods N_b, and N_b' such that their intersection is the null set. But by the hypotheses that b and b' are limits of $\{x_n\}$ there exist two positive integers n_0 and n_0' such that for every $n, > n_0$, $x_n \in N_b$ and for every $n, > n_0'$, $x_n \in N_b'$. Hence for every $n, >$ maximum of n_0 and n_0', x_n would be in N_b and in N_b'. This contradicts the definition of N_b and N_b' as two neighborhoods whose intersection is the null set.

P. 5.2.1. Prove that every subsequence of a convergent sequence converges.

Definition 5.2.2. A point p is a *limit point of a sequence* $\{x_n\}$ if every neighborhood of p contains infinitely many entries of the sequence.

THEOREM 5.2.2. *A convergent sequence has one and only one limit point.*

P. 5.2.2. Prove this theorem.

The converse of the last theorem is not true, as is illustrated by the following counter example. The sequence $\{x_n\}$, where $x_n = 1/n$, when n is an odd positive integer, and $x_n = n$ for n an even positive integer, has only one limit point in E_1, but the sequence does not have a limit and hence is not convergent. The reason that this sequence does not converge, even though it has only one limit point, is that the space E_1 is not compact. For compact spaces the converse of Theorem 5.2.2 does hold, and can be stated as follows.

THEOREM 5.2.3. *In a compact space, a sequence which has only one limit point converges to that limit point.*

Proof. Let x be the only limit point of a given sequence $\{x_n\}$ whose entries lie in a compact space R. If every neighborhood N_x of x contains all but a finite number of entries of the sequence $\{x_n\}$, then x is the limit of the sequence, and the theorem is proved. Let us assume therefore that there exists an N_x such that an infinite number of entries of the sequence lie outside this N_x, that is, in the compact complement $c(N_x)$ of N_x. This infinite set of entries may represent a finite or an infinite number of points of $c(N_x)$. In the first case at least one of the points of this finite set must correspond to an infinite number of entries of the sequence, and hence it must be a limit point (of the sequence) distinct from x. This contradicts our hypothesis. In the second case, an infinite number of points of $c(N_x)$ correspond to entries of the sequence. This infinite set of points has a limit point, say y, in $c(N_x)$ since $c(N_x)$ is compact. But $y \neq x$, and y is also a limit point of the sequence $\{x_n\}$. This contradicts the hypothesis that x is the only limit point of $\{x_n\}$.

5.3 Cauchy sequences. In order that the concept of Cauchy sequence may be defined, the space R, in which the range of the sequence lies, must be assumed to be a metric Hausdorff space with open spheres as neighborhoods. The metric of the space will be denoted by $\rho(x,y)$.

Definition 5.3.1. A sequence $\{x_n\}$ is a *Cauchy sequence* if for every positive number ϵ there exists a positive number $n(\epsilon)$ such that for every pair of positive integers n and m each of which is greater than $n(\epsilon)$, it is true that $\rho(x_n,x_m) < \epsilon$.

Example. The sequence $\{x_n\}$, where

$$x_n = 1 - \frac{1}{2} + \frac{1}{3} + \ldots + \frac{(-1)^{n+1}}{n},$$

is a Cauchy sequence in E_1, since if a positive number ϵ is given we can choose the positive $n(\epsilon)$ as $1/\epsilon$. Then for every pair of integers n, and m which are such that $n > n(\epsilon)$, $m > n(\epsilon)$, we can state that

$$\rho(x_n,x_m) = |\, x_m - x_n \,| < \left| \frac{(-1)^{n+2}}{n+1} + \frac{(-1)^{n+3}}{n+2} + \ldots + \frac{(-1)^{m+1}}{m} \right|$$

$$< \frac{1}{n+1} < \epsilon.$$

Theorem 5.3.1. *In a metric space every convergent sequence is a Cauchy sequence.*

Proof. We are given a convergent sequence $\{x_n\}$, and we must show that for every positive number ϵ there exists a positive number $n(\epsilon)$ such that for every pair of positive integers n and m, which are such that $n > n(\epsilon)$, $m > n(\epsilon)$, it is true that $\rho(x_n,x_m) < \epsilon$. Let the positive number ϵ be given. Since the sequence $\{x_n\}$ is convergent, there exists a point x such that for the positive number $\epsilon/2$ there exists a positive integer n_0 such that for every pair of integers n and m each of which is greater than n_0 we have the inequalities

$$\rho(x_n,x) < \epsilon/2, \qquad \rho(x_m,x) < \epsilon/2.$$

By the triangle axiom (see Def. 3.3.1),

$$\rho(x_n,x_m) \leqslant \rho(x_n,x) + \rho(x,x_m) < \epsilon/2 + \epsilon/2 = \epsilon,$$

for $n > n_0$, and $m > m_0$. This shows that $n(\epsilon)$ can be chosen equal to n_0.

The converse of this theorem need not be true if the space R lacks certain points. For example, in the space which consists of all rational numbers the sequence $\{x_n\}$, where $x_n = (1 + 1/n)^n$, can be shown to be a Cauchy sequence, but this sequence does not have a limit and hence is not convergent in the space of rational numbers. It converges however in E_1.

5.4 Complete spaces

Definition 5.4.1. A space is said to be *complete* if every Cauchy sequence in it is convergent, that is, has a limit.

Theorem 5.4.1. *Every Cauchy sequence $\{x_n\}$ has at most one limit point.*

Proof. Let x and y be two limit points of a Cauchy sequence $\{x_n\}$. We shall show that the distance $\rho(x,y) = 0$. By the triangle axiom (Def. 3.3.1),

$$\rho(x,y) < \rho(x,x_n) + \rho(x_n,x_m) + \rho(x_m,y).$$

Let a positive number ϵ be given. Then there exists a positive integer $n(\epsilon)$ such that for all integers n and m, each greater than $n(\epsilon)$, $\rho(x_n,x_m) < \epsilon/3$. This follows from the hypothesis that $\{x_n\}$ is a Cauchy sequence. Since x and y are limit points of $\{x_n\}$, there exists an integer n greater than $n(\epsilon)$ and there exists also an integer m greater than $n(\epsilon)$ such that $\rho(x_n,x) < \epsilon/3$, and $\rho(x_m,y) < \epsilon/3$. Thus the fixed number $\rho(x,y)$ is less than every given positive number ϵ. Hence $\rho(x,y) = 0$ and $x = y$.

THEOREM 5.4.2. *Every compact metric space is complete.*

Proof. Because the space is compact every sequence in it will have at least one limit point. By the preceding theorem a Cauchy sequence can have at most one limit point. The result now follows from Theorem 5.2.3.

Definition 5.4.2. A sequence whose limit is zero is called a *null sequence.*

P. 5.4.1. (a) Prove that if the sequence of real numbers $\{x_n\}$ is a null sequence, the sequence of arithmetic means $\{x_n'\}$ where

$$x_n' = \frac{\sum_{i=1}^{n} x_i}{n}$$

is also a null sequence.

(b) Prove that if the sequence of real numbers $\{x_n\}$ converges to a number a, the sequence of arithmetic means converges to the same number a.

P. 5.4.2. Prove that if the sequence $\{y_n\}$ of positive numbers y_n converges to a positive number p then the sequence of geometric means $\{y_n'\}$, where

$$y_n' = \sqrt[n]{y_1 y_2 \ldots y_n},$$

converges to p.

P. 5.4.3. Making use of the fact that

$$\lim_{n \to \infty} \left(1 + \frac{1}{n}\right)^n = e,$$

prove on the basis of the last problem that

$$\lim_{n\to\infty} \frac{\sqrt[n]{n!}}{n} = \frac{1}{e}.$$

5.5 Completing a space. The metric space R_1 which consists of all rational numbers with the usual metric, $\rho(x,y) = |x - y|$, is not complete, for the sequence $\{x_n\}$, with

$$x_n = \sum_0^n \frac{(-1)^k}{k!},$$

is easily seen to be a Cauchy sequence, but it converges to e^{-1}, which is not a rational number. By the construction of Dedekind cuts we enlarged the space R_1 to the space E_1 of all real numbers, which will be shown to be complete.

Definition 5.5.1. Let S be a metric space which is not complete. Any process, which by the addition of elements to S, produces a new space which is complete is called a *method of completing the space S.*

Instead of following Dedekind, we could have completed the space of rational numbers by using the concept of Cauchy sequences. This method is quite general since it is applicable to any metric space. Before we can describe it we need some preliminary definitions.

Definition 5.5.2. Let S be a metric space. Two Cauchy sequences $\{x_n\}$ and $\{y_n\}$ in S will be called equivalent if the sequence $x_1, y_1, x_2, y_2, x_3, y_3, \ldots, x_n, y_n, \ldots$ is a Cauchy sequence in S.

P. 5.5.1. Show that the notion of equivalence between sequences as given by Def. 5.5.2 is reflexive, symmetric, and transitive.

We now proceed to show how any given metric space can be made into a complete metric space.

Let S be a metric space with metric $\rho(x,y)$. We consider the set A of all classes of equivalent Cauchy sequences in S. In order to make A into a metric space we define the distance $\rho(\{x_n\},\{y_n\})$ between two Cauchy sequences $\{x_n\}$ and $\{y_n\}$ as

$$\rho(\{x_n\},\{y_n\}) = \lim_{n\to\infty} \rho(x_n,y_n).$$

P. 5.5.2. On the basis of Theorem 5.4.2 prove that the space E_1 is complete and thus show that the distance function $\rho(\{x_n\},\{y_n\})$ actually exists.

This distance function is nonnegative; it is zero if and only if $\{x_n\}$ is equivalent to $\{y_n\}$; it is symmetric, and it satisfies the triangle axiom

$$\rho(\{x_n\},\{z_n\}) \leqslant \rho(\{x_n\},\{y_n\}) + \rho(\{y_n\},\{z_n\}).$$

This last inequality is obtained by taking the limit as n goes to infinity of the triangle axiom for $\rho(x,y)$ in S, i.e.,

$$\rho(x_n,z_n) \leqslant \rho(x_n,y_n) + \rho(y_n,z_n).$$

We next show that if $\{x_n\}$ is equivalent to $\{x_n'\}$, and $\{y_n\}$ is equivalent to $\{y_n'\}$, then

$$\rho(\{x_n\},\{y_n\}) = \rho(\{x_n'\},\{y_n'\}).$$

Obviously

$$\rho(\{x_n'\},\{y_n'\}) = \rho(\{x_n'\},\{x_n\}) + \rho(\{x_n'\},\{y_n'\}) + \rho(\{y_n\},\{y_n'\}),$$

since the first and last terms of the right-hand side are zero. Rewriting the last equation, we get, because of the symmetry of a metric, and the triangle axiom,

$$\rho(\{x_n'\},\{y_n'\}) = \rho(\{x_n\},\{x_n'\}) + \rho(\{x_n'\},\{y_n'\}) + \rho(\{y_n'\},\{y_n\})$$
$$\geqslant \rho(\{x_n\},\{y_n'\}) + \rho(\{y_n'\},\{y_n\})$$
$$\geqslant \rho(\{x_n\},\{y_n\}).$$

Similarly it can be shown that

$$\rho(\{x_n\},\{y_n\}) \geqslant \rho(\{x_n'\},\{y_n'\}),$$

and thus the required equality is established. The metric $\rho(\{x_n\},\{y_n\})$ can thus be taken as the metric for our space A which consists of all classes of equivalent Cauchy sequences. The set A has thus been made into a metric space which we shall also denote by A.

In order to describe the relation which exists between the given metric space S and the space A, we need some additional concepts.

Definition 5.5.3. Let S_1 be a space with a metric $\rho_1(a_1,a_2)$, where a_1 and a_2 are elements of S_1. Let $\rho_2(b_1,b_2)$ be similarly defined as the metric of a space S_2. The spaces S_1 and S_2 are said to be *isometric with each other* if the following conditions are satisfied.

(1) There exists a one-to-one correspondence between the elements of S_1, and those of S_2.

(2) Let a of S_1 correspond to b of S. Let $\{a_n\}$ be such that

$$\lim_{n \to \infty} \rho_1(a, a_n) = 0.$$

Then if b_n corresponds to a_n, the sequence $\{b_n\}$ will converge to b, i.e.,

$$\lim_{n \to \infty} \rho_2(b, b_n) = 0.$$

Making use of our definition of isomorphism (Def. 1.4.7), we can say that if the metric spaces S_1 and S are *isometric*, they are *isomorphic* under the operation of taking *limits of convergent sequences*. In this respect isometry is a special case of isomorphism. The concept of "imbedding" (Def. 1.4.8) hence applies also to a metric space which is isometric to a subset of another metric space.

In regard to the given metric space S and the metric space A of all equivalent classes of Cauchy sequences in S we have the following results.

The space S can be imbedded in the space A. This means that there exists in A a certain subspace S' that is isometric with S. This space S' consists of all those particular elements of A which are equivalent to those sequences $\{x_n\}$ of A for which $x_n = x_m$ for all positive integers n and m. (These sequences will be called the constant sequences in A.) The isometry is easily established by letting a given element x of S correspond to the class of sequences of S' which are equivalent to the sequence $\{x_n\}$ in which each $x_n = x$, that is,

$$\{x_n\} = x, x, x, \ldots .$$

Next, we show that *the space S' is everywhere dense in A.* Let $\{x_n\}$ represent an element of A, and let ϵ be greater than zero. Then there exists a positive integer n_0 such that, for every n greater than n_0, and for every m greater than n_0, $\rho(x_n, x_m) < \epsilon$. The element of S' given by the constant sequence $\{x_n'\}$, where each $x_n' = x_{n_0+1}$ is at a distance less than ϵ from the element of A represented by $\{x_n\}$.

Finally *the space A is complete.* Let us take a Cauchy sequence whose entries are elements of A. The entries of such a sequence are Cauchy sequences in S. For the sake of simplicity we shall designate the elements of A by Greek letters. Then a given Cauchy sequence of elements of A can be written as $\{\alpha^k\} = \alpha^1, \alpha^2, \alpha^3, \ldots$, where each α^k is a Cauchy sequence $\{x_n^k\}$ of elements in S, that is, $\alpha^k = x_1^k$, $x_2^k, x_3^k, \ldots .$ We shall designate the metric in A by ρ_A and the metric in S by ρ_S. Thus, if α and β are elements of A, represented by the Cauchy sequences $\{x_n\}$ and $\{y_n\}$, respectively, then

$$\rho_A(\alpha,\beta) = \rho_A(\{x_n\},\{y_n\}) = \lim_{n\to\infty} \rho_S(x_n,y_n).$$

We must show that an arbitrarily given Cauchy sequence, say $\{\alpha^k\}$, of elements of A has a limit in A. Let β^1, β^2, β^3, ... be a sequence of elements in the subset S' of A, such that $\rho_A(\alpha^k,\beta^k) < 1/k$. Such a sequence of β^k exists because the elements of S' are everywhere dense in A, as was shown above. We must verify that these β^k form a Cauchy sequence in A. To this end we must show that for every positive ϵ there exists an n_0 such that for all p greater than n_0, and all q greater than n_0, $\rho_A(\beta^p,\beta^q) < \epsilon$. Let a positive number ϵ be given. Since α^k is a Cauchy sequence we can find n_1 so large that $\rho_A(\alpha^p,\alpha^q) < \epsilon/3$ for p, q each greater than n_1. Next we choose n_2 greater than $3/\epsilon$. Let n_0 be the larger one of n_1 and n_2. Then for all p, q each greater than n_0, we have

$$\rho_A(\beta^p,\beta^q) \leqslant \rho_A(\beta^p,\alpha^p) + \rho_A(\alpha^p,\beta^q)$$
$$\leqslant \rho_A(\beta^p,\alpha^p) + \rho_A(\alpha^p,\alpha^q) + \rho_A(\alpha^q,\beta^q)$$
$$< \frac{1}{p} + \frac{\epsilon}{3} + \frac{1}{q} < \epsilon.$$

Since the β^k are elements of S' (the subset of A which consists of constant sequences in S) it follows that each β^k corresponds to a y_k in S. The sequence $y_1,y_2,y_3,\ldots$ is a Cauchy sequence in S, and hence defines an element γ of A. We show that the Cauchy sequence $\{\alpha^k\}$ converges to γ.

$$\rho_A(\gamma,\alpha^k) \leqslant \rho_A(\gamma,\beta^k) + \rho_A(\beta^k,\alpha^k)$$
$$= \rho_A(\{y_n\},\beta^k) + \rho_A(\beta^k,\alpha^k)$$
$$= \lim_{n\to\infty} \rho_S(y_n,y_k) + \rho_A(\beta^k,\alpha^k)$$
$$< \lim_{n\to\infty} \rho_S(y_n,y_k) + \frac{1}{k}.$$

Thus if a positive number ϵ is given we can choose K greater than $2/\epsilon$, and so large that for all n and k larger than K $\rho_S(y_n,y_k) < \epsilon/2$. This proves that γ is the limit of the Cauchy sequence $\{\alpha^k\}$, as was to be proved.

We have thus shown how every metric space can be made complete.

5.6 Sequences of real numbers. We now consider sequences whose entries lie in the space E_1 of real numbers.

THEOREM 5.6.1. *The space E_1 of real numbers is complete.*

Proof. We must show that every Cauchy sequence in E_1 has a limit in E_1. We first show that every Cauchy sequence in E_1 is bounded. Let $\{x_n\}$ be a Cauchy sequence in E_1. In the definition of a Cauchy sequence (Def. 5.3.1) let $\epsilon = 1$. Then there exists a positive integer n_1 such that for all integers n greater than n_1,

$$\rho(x_{n_1}, x_n) = |x_{n_1} - x_n| < 1.$$

Hence for every positive integer n, $|x_n|$ is less than or equal to the maximum number, say M, of the finite set of numbers $|x_1|$, $|x_2|$, $\ldots$, $|x_{n_1}|$ and $|x_{n_1}| + 1$. Thus the entries of $\{x_n\}$ lie in the closed interval $[-M, M]$, which is a compact metric subspace of E_1. By Theorem 5.4.2, $\{x_n\}$ has a limit in this interval, and hence in E_1.

The theory of sequences as developed in the preceding sections of this chapter applies of course to the special case considered in this section. The space E_1, however, in addition to being a metric Hausdorff space, is totally ordered. This fact permits us to generalize the concept of limit for the case of real sequences. Before we introduce the new concepts we find it convenient to add to the space E_1 two more elements designated $+\infty$, and $-\infty$, called *plus infinity* and *minus infinity*. In order to preserve the character of a Hausdorff space for the new set of elements, we define the neighborhoods $N_{+\infty}$ of $+\infty$, and $N_{-\infty}$ of $-\infty$ as follows.

$N_{+\infty}$ consists of $+\infty$ and all real numbers x such that $x > M$, where M is some real number.

$N_{-\infty}$ consists of $-\infty$ and all real numbers x such that $x < M$, where M is some real number.

The new space which consists of E_1 and the new elements, together with their neighborhoods, will be designated E_1'. If we define the order relation for the new elements as $-\infty < x < +\infty$, where x is any real number, E_1' is a linearly ordered space.

P. 5.6.1. Show that E_1' is a Hausdorff space.

P. 5.6.2. Define a metric in E_1'.

THEOREM 5.6.2. *The space E_1' is compact.*

Proof. If $-\infty$ and $+\infty$ are not limit points of an infinite set S, it follows from the definition of $N_{+\infty}$ and $N_{-\infty}$, that there exists a number M such that every element s of S is such that $-M < s < M$. Thus the infinite set lies in the closed interval $[-M,M]$, which is compact by Theorem 4.2.1.

5.7 Limit superior, limit inferior. In this section the entries of sequences of real numbers are considered as lying in the compact Hausdorff space E_1', but since $+\infty$ and $-\infty$ are not real numbers, these elements cannot be entries in a sequence of real numbers. In this space every non-null set has a least upper bound and a greatest lower bound, which are either real numbers or the elements $+\infty$, or $-\infty$. We also admit (in E_1') as limit points of a sequence of real numbers the elements $+\infty$, and $-\infty$. Thus $+\infty$ is a limit point of a sequence $\{x_n\}$ if every $N_{+\infty}$ contains an infinite number of entries of the sequence. A similar definition applies to $-\infty$ as a limit point of a sequence. It follows that every sequence of real numbers which is not bounded from above has $+\infty$ for a limit point, and every sequence which is not bounded from below has $-\infty$ for a limit point; and conversely, if $+\infty$ is a limit point of a sequence, the sequence is not bounded from above, and if $-\infty$ is a limit point of a sequence, the sequence is not bounded from below. The set of limit points of a sequence will be called the *derived set of the sequence*. It is easily seen that the derived set of a sequence of real numbers is closed, and that its least upper bound is its maximum and its greatest lower bound is its minimum.

P. 5.7.1. Give a formal proof of the theorem that the derived set of a sequence is closed.

P. 5.7.2. Give a formal proof of the theorem that every closed set in E_1' has a maximum and a minimum.

The derived set of a sequence is not the same as the derived set of a set of points. Thus the derived set of the *set* '1' is the null set, while the derived set of the *sequence* $\{1\} = 1, 1, 1, \ldots$ is the set which consists of the one element 1.

Since the space E_1' is often represented by a horizontal line as shown in Fig. 8, the maximum element of a subset S of E_1' will be

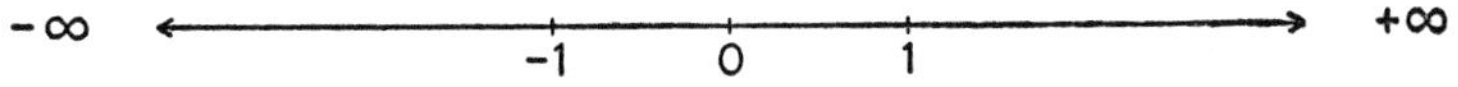

$-\infty$ ⟵————————|————|————|————⟶ $+\infty$
$\qquad\qquad\qquad\quad -1 \qquad 0 \qquad 1$

FIG. 8

called the rightmost element of S, while the minimum of S will be called the leftmost element of S. The elements of ∞ and $-\infty$ are, respectively, the rightmost and leftmost elements of E_1'.

Definition 5.7.1. The *limit superior* of a sequence $\{x_n\}$ of real numbers is the *rightmost limit point of the sequence*. It is designated $\lim \sup x_n$ or simply $\lim \sup x_n$. The *limit inferior* of a sequence $\{x_n\}$
$_{n \to \infty}$
of real numbers is the *leftmost limit point of the sequence*, and is denoted $\lim \inf x_n$ or simply $\lim \inf x_n$.
$_{n \to \infty}$
This definition can be restated as follows.

Definition 5.7.1a. The limit superior of a sequence $\{x_n\}$ of real numbers is an element a of E_1' such that

(1) For every b of E_1', $b > a$, there exist at most finitely many entries x_n which are greater than b.

(2) For every c of E_1', $c < a$, there exist infinitely many entries x_n which are greater than c.

The condition (1) insures that there exists no limit point of the sequence $\{x_n\}$ to the right of a, while conditions (2) and (1) define a as a limit point of the sequence $\{x_n\}$. Thus a is the rightmost limit point of $\{x_n\}$.

P. 5.7.3. Formulate a definition for the limit inferior similar to that of Def. 5.7.1a.

We notice that the limit superior and the limit inferior of every sequence of real numbers exist, and that they can be real numbers or the elements $+\infty$ and $-\infty$ of E_1'. We call attention to the fact that the term *limit of a sequence of real numbers* is always defined as an element of E_1 and hence it *is always a real number*. This agrees with the definition of the term limit of a sequence as given by Def. 5.2.2 if in that definition we let the space R be the space E_1.

THEOREM 5.7.1. *The greatest lower bound of the entries of a sequence $\{x_n\}$ is less than or equal to the limit inferior of $\{x_n\}$, which is less than or equal to the limit superior of $\{x_n\}$ which in turn is less than or equal to the least upper bound of the entries of $\{x_n\}$.* In symbolic notation the theorem takes the form

$$\inf \{x_n\} \leqslant \lim \inf x_n \leqslant \lim \sup x_n \leqslant \sup x_n.$$

P. 5.7.4. Prove Theorem 5.7.1.

THEOREM 5.7.2. *If $\{x_{n_k}\}$ is a subsequence of $\{x_n\}$, then*

$$\liminf x_n \leqslant \liminf x_{n_k} \leqslant \limsup x_{n_k} \leqslant \limsup x_n.$$

P. 5.7.5. Prove Theorem 5.7.2.

THEOREM 5.7.3. *A necessary and sufficient condition that limit of $\{x_n\}$ exists is that*

$$\liminf x_n = \limsup x_n = \text{real number.}$$

Proof. Since the common value of $\liminf x_n$ and $\limsup x_n$ is a real number, the sequence x_n is bounded, and since its rightmost and leftmost limit points coincide, the sequence has only one limit point. By Theorem 5.2.3, the sequence converges to the limit point given by the common value of $\liminf x_n$, and $\limsup x_n$.

If $\liminf x_n = \limsup x_n = +\infty$ we say the sequence $\{x_n\}$ *diverges to* $+\infty$;

If $\liminf x_n = \limsup x_n = -\infty$, we say the sequence $\{x_n\}$ *diverges to* $-\infty$.

P. 5.7.6. Prove that a nondecreasing sequence $\{x_n\}$ of real numbers either has a limit or it diverges to $+\infty$.

P. 5.7.7. Prove that $\liminf (-x_n) = -\limsup x_n$.

P. 5.7.8. Prove that

$$\liminf x_n + \liminf y_n \leqslant \liminf (x_n + y_n)$$

$$\leqslant \genfrac{}{}{0pt}{}{\liminf x_n + \limsup y_n}{\limsup x_n + \liminf y_n}$$

$$\leqslant \limsup (x_n + y_n) \leqslant \limsup x_n + \limsup y_n.$$

P. 5.7.9. Prove that

$$\liminf x_n \liminf y_n \leqslant \liminf (x_n y_n)$$

$$\leqslant \genfrac{}{}{0pt}{}{\liminf x_n \cdot \limsup y_n}{\limsup x_n \cdot \liminf y_n} \leqslant \limsup (x_n y_n)$$

$$\leqslant \limsup x_n \cdot \limsup y_n,$$

if every $x_n > 0$, and every $y_n > 0$.

If in the last two problems each of the sequences converges, all the inequality signs can be replaced by equality signs, and we thus obtain important theorems on limits.

THEOREM 5.7.4. *If a real number, say a, is a limit point of a sequence $\{x_n\}$, there exists a subsequence $\{x_{n_k}\}$ of $\{x_n\}$ such that $\lim x_{n_k} = a$.*

Proof. Since a is a limit point of $\{x_n\}$, every interval

$$I_k = \left[a - \frac{1}{2k}, \, a + \frac{1}{2k} \right],$$

where k is a positive integer, contains at least one entry x_n. In the sequence $x_1, x_2, x_3, \ldots$, let x_{n_k} be the entry with the smallest subscript which lies in I_k. The sequence $\{x_{n_k}\}$ has a limit point which must lie in each I_k. The only point in common to all the I_k is a. Hence the sequence $\{x_{n_k}\}$ has only one limit point, and by Theorem 5.2.3 converges to that limit point.

The following three statements are corollaries to Theorem 5.7.4.

(1) If a sequence $\{x_n\}$ is such that its limit inferior is a real number a, and its limit superior is a real number b, there exist subsequences $\{x_{n_p}\}$ and $\{x_{n_q}\}$ of $\{x_n\}$ such that

$$\lim x_{n_p} = a, \quad \lim x_{n_q} = b.$$

(2) If a sequence $\{x_n\}$ is such that $\lim \inf x_n = -\infty$, there exists a subsequence $\{x_{n_k}\}$ of $\{x_n\}$ such that $\{x_{n_k}\}$ diverges to $-\infty$.

(3) If a sequence $\{x_n\}$ is such that $\lim \sup x_n = +\infty$, there exists a subsequence $\{x_{n_r}\}$ of $\{x_n\}$ such that $\{x_{n_r}\}$ diverges to $+\infty$.

P. 5.7.10. For a given sequence $\{x_n\}$ of real numbers let

$$s_1 = x_1, \, x_2, \, x_3, \, \ldots$$

$$s_2 = x_2, \, x_3, \, x_4, \, \ldots$$

$$\ldots\ldots\ldots\ldots\ldots\ldots$$

$$s_k = x_k, \, x_{k+1}, \, x_{k+2}, \, \ldots$$

$$\ldots\ldots\ldots\ldots\ldots\ldots\ldots\ldots\ldots\ldots$$

Let S_k denote the set of points (real numbers) which correspond to the entries of the sequence s_k. Give the necessary extension of the concept of limit of a sequence of real numbers to justify the following definitions of limit superior and limit inferior.

$$\lim_{n \to \infty} \sup x_n = \lim_{k \to \infty} (\sup S_k) = \inf(\sup S_k)$$

$$\lim_{n \to \infty} \inf x_n = \lim_{k \to \infty} (\inf S_k) = \sup(\inf S_n)$$

Show the equivalence of these definitions to Def. 5.7.1 and 5.7.1a.

CHAPTER VI

FUNCTIONS

6.1 Limits of functions. The domains of definition, D, and the ranges, R, of the functions which we shall consider in this chapter will be assumed to be subsets of Hausdorff spaces, that is, $D \subseteq D_1$, and $R \subseteq R_1$, where D_1 and R_1 are Hausdorff spaces.

Definition 6.1.1. Let a function f on D onto R be given. Let a be an element of the closure of D in D_1, and let b be an element of R_1. We say b is the *limit of* the function f at a, if for every neighborhood N_b of b there exists a neighborhood N_a of a such that if $x \in N_a D$, then $f(x) \in N_b$. We express this statement symbolically as

$$\lim_{x=a} f(x) = b.$$

It is important to note that if $a \in D$, and if the limit of f at a exists, then this limit must be $f(a)$. Some authors admit in the definition of the $\lim_{x=a} f(x)$ only *deleted neighborhoods*, i.e., $N_a - \,'a'$, where we use N_a. If we want to consider the limit of the function as x goes to a with $x \neq a$, we need only to exclude the point a from the domain of definition of the function. Whenever we want to consider this type of limit we shall write $\lim_{x \to a} f$, $(x \neq a)$, or simply $\lim_{x \to a} f$, and say that we are taking the limit of f as x goes *toward* a. It is understood that since x is going toward a it cannot be equal to a. In most elementary books on the calculus the limit of a function at a point is used in this sense, and such a limit is independent of the value of the function at the point where the limit is taken. Unless it is otherwise explicitly specified, we shall mean by the limit of a function the concept defined in Def. 6.1.1.

We call attention to the fact that the general definition of the limit of a function agrees with that given earlier for the particular functions that are sequences. We need only to consider the set of positive integers as a subset of the Hausdorff space E_1', which includes the

93

element $+\infty$. Then the earlier definition (Def. 5.2.2) can be reworded in the following way. An element b of R is the limit of the sequence $\{x_n\}$ if for every neighborhood N_b of b there exists a neighborhood N_∞ of ∞ such that if $n \in N_\infty$ then $x_n \in N_b$.

P. 6.1.1. Prove that if $\lim f$ exists, it is unique, that is, prove that a function f can have at most one limit at a point a.

We shall show that the general definition of the limit of a function can be expressed in terms of the limit of sequences, which concept was considered in the preceding chapter. We shall now assume that the space D_1 is a metric space.

THEOREM 6.1.1. *Let D, a subset of the metric space D_1, be the domain of definition of a function f whose range, R, lies in a Hausdorff space R_1. A necessary and sufficient condition that for a given a, which is an element of D^-, the limit of f at a will exist, is that $\lim f(x_n)$ exists for every sequence $\{x_n\}$ in D which tends to a as $n \rightarrow \infty$.*

Proof of necessity. We assume the existence of b in R_1, such that $\lim_{x=a} f = b$. Let $\{x_n\}$ be a sequence in D which converges to a. We must show that the sequence $\{f(x_n)\}$ converges to b in R_1. Let a neighborhood N_b of b be given. By Def. 6.1.1 this determines a neighborhood N_a of a such that if $x \in N_a D$, then $f(x) \in N_b$. Since the sequence $\{x_n\}$ converges to a, there exists an integer N such that for all n greater than N, each entry $x_n \in N_a$. For this n, the functional value $f(x_n) \in N_b$ as was to be shown.

Proof of sufficiency. We assume that for every given sequence $\{x_n\}$ which lies in D and converges to a, the sequence $\{f(x_n)\}$ converges to some point in R_1. We first show that if $\{x_n\}$ and $\{x_n'\}$ are two sequences in D which converge to a, then $\{f(x_n)\}$ and $\{f(x_n')\}$ converge to the same point in R_1. For suppose $\{f(x_n)\}$ converge to b_1, and $\{f(x_n')\}$ converge to b_1'. The sequence $x_1, x_1', x_2, x_2', x_3, x_3', \ldots$ is also a sequence in D which converges to a. But the corresponding sequence $f(x_1), f(x_1'), f(x_2), f(x_2'), \ldots$ in R would not converge in R_1 if $b_1 \neq b_1'$. We have thus shown that if $\lim_{n \to \infty} f(x_n)$ exists, it is unique. We may then designate it b. Next suppose $\lim_{x=a} f \neq b$. Then there would exist an N_b of b such that for every N_a of a there would exist at least one x of N_a such that $f(x)$ is not contained in N_b. We choose the open spheres $K(1/n, a)$ with center at a, and of radius $1/n$, for neighborhoods of a, where $n = 1, 2, 3, \ldots$. In each sphere we select an x_n such that $f(x_n) \nsubseteq N_b$. We obtain thus a sequence $\{x_n\}$ which converges to a and lies in D, but is such that $\lim_{n \to \infty} f(x_n) \neq b$, since none of the $f(x_n)$ lie in N_b. This contradicts our hypothesis. Hence the theorem is proved.

The verification of the existence of the limit of a function at a given point requires the knowledge of this limit according to Def. 6.1.1. This requirement was avoided in the case of the limit of sequences in complete metric spaces by the introduction of the notion of Cauchy sequences. For the case of the limit of more general functions whose ranges lie in a complete metric space, the existence of the limit can be established without the knowledge of this limit by the following theorem.

THEOREM 6.1.2. *Let R_1 be a complete metric space, and let D_1 be a metric space. Let f be a given function whose domain of definition D is a subset of D_1, and whose range R is a subset of R_1. Let a be a given element of D^-. If for every positive number ϵ there exists a neighborhood N_a of a such that for every pair of elements x and x' of $N_a D$ the image under f of x is at a distance less than ϵ from the image of x', then there exists an element b of R_1 such that $\lim f = b$.*

Proof. Let $\{x_n\}$ be a sequence in D which converges to a. The sequence $\{f(x_n)\}$ is a Cauchy sequence, as will now be shown. Let a positive number ϵ be given. Then by hypothesis there exists an N_a such that for all x and x' in $N_a D$, the distance from the element $f(x)$ to the element $f(x')$ is less than ϵ. Since $\lim_{n \to \infty} x_n = a$, there exists an integer N such that for all n greater than N, and for all m greater than N, x_n and x_m are elements of the given N_a, and since $\{x_n\}$ lies in D by hypothesis, x_n and x_m are elements of $N_a D$. Therefore the distance between $f(x_n)$ and $f(x_m)$ is less than ϵ. This proves that $\{f(x_n)\}$ is a Cauchy sequence and as such has a limit. Hence $f(x)$ has a limit at a, by Theorem 6.1.1.

Examples. (a) The function given by $f(x) = x$ if x is an irrational number, $f(x) = -x$ if x is rational has a limit at $x = 0$ only.

(b) The function given by $y = \sin 1/x$, $0 < |x| < 1$, has a limit at every point in its domain of definition but does not have a limit at $x = 0$.

P. 6.1.2. Give examples of real functions defined at all points of the closed interval [0,1], and such that the limits of the functions exist only at the points of the given sets:

(a) S_a is the set consisting of the one point $x = 1$;

(b) S_b is the set $1, \dfrac{1}{2}, \dfrac{1}{3}, \dfrac{1}{4}, \cdots, \dfrac{1}{n}$;

(c) S_c is the infinite set $0, 1, \dfrac{1}{2}, \dfrac{1}{3}, \dfrac{1}{4}, \cdots$;

(d) S_d is the set of all irrational numbers;

(e) S_e is a nondenumerable everywhere dense set such that the complement of S_e in [0,1] is nondenumerable and nowhere dense;

(f) S_f is a nondenumerable everywhere dense set, and the complement of S_f in [0,1] is also nondenumerable and everywhere dense;

(g) S_g is everywhere dense, nondenumerable, and can be covered by a denumerable number of intervals the sum of whose lengths is less than any preassigned positive number. (In the language of Chapter 8, S_g has Lebesgue measure zero.)

6.2 Continuity of functions. We reword our earlier definition of the continuity of a function (Def. 3.2.1) at a point in terms of the concept of limit.

Definition 6.2.1. A function f is said *to be continuous at a point a* of its domain of definition *if* $\lim\limits_{x=a} f$ *exists.* This limit is then equal to $f(a)$ by Def. 6.1.1.

If instead of Def. 6.1.1 we use the definition $\lim\limits_{x \to a} f$, $x \neq a$, we define f to be continuous at the point a *if* $\lim\limits_{x \to a} f$ *exists and is equal to* $f(a)$. Every definition of the continuity of a function at a point implies that the function be defined at that point.

To prove the equivalence of Def. 3.2.1 and Def. 6.2.1, we need only express $\lim\limits_{x=a} f$, which is equal to $f(a)$, in terms of Def. 6.1.1. It follows directly from the definition of continuity that a function is continuous at every isolated point of its domain of definition.

As before we say a function is defined to be continuous on D if it is continuous at each point of D.

P. 6.2.1. Give examples of real functions defined at all points of the closed interval [0,1] and which are continuous only at the points of the sets given in each part of P. 6.1.2.

P. 6.2.2. Give (if possible) an example of a real function defined at all points of $[0,1]$ which is continuous at every rational point, and discontinuous at every irrational point. If this is impossible, prove it to be impossible.

P. 6.2.3. Prove that if two functions are continuous at the same point, their sum, product, and quotient (provided the divisor is not zero at the point) are also continuous at this point.

On the basis of P. 3.2.1 we have an alternate definition of continuity of a function over a domain of definition.

Definition 6.2.2. A function on D_1 onto R *is continuous on* D_1 if the inverse correspondence maps every open set of R_1 onto an open set of D_1.

We shall now consider functions whose domains of definitions and ranges are metric spaces. In order to simplify the statements of some of our later results we shall first give some preliminary definitions.

Definition 6.2.3. Let A be a subset of a metric space with metric $\rho(x,y)$. The nonnegative number, or $+\infty$, given by sup $\rho(x,y)$, where x and y vary over A, is called the *diameter of* A.

The diameter of a subset A of a metric space is thus the least upper bound (if it exists) of the distances between the points of the set A. If this least upper bound does not exist, the diameter of A is said to be $+\infty$. The diameter of A will be denoted by $d(A)$.

P. 6.2.4. Prove that a necessary and sufficient condition for a function (on a metric space D to a metric space R) to be continuous is that whenever the diameter of a subset of D goes to zero, the diameter of the corresponding subset of R also goes to zero.

Definition 6.2.4. Let A and B be nonempty subsets of a metric space with metric $\rho(x,y)$. The nonnegative number $\rho(A,B) = \inf \rho(a,b)$ where a runs through all the elements of A, and b runs through all the elements of B is called the *distance between the sets A and B*.

This distance $\rho(A,B)$ obviously always exists. If the set $A = {}'a'$, that is, if A consists of one element a only, then the distance $\rho(A,B)$ is written simply as $\rho(a,B)$, and it is called the distance between the element a and the set B.

P. 6.2.5. Let S be a metric space. For every non-null subset M of S we define the closure M^- of M as the set of all points p of S such that $\rho(p,M) = 0$. Show that the following postulates are satisfied.

(1) $(A + B)^- = A^- + B^-$

(2) $A \subseteq A^-$

(3) $(A^-)^- = A^-$

If we also define $0^- = 0$, where 0 is the null set, we have the four postulates known as Kuratowski's postulates for a topological space.

Let a function on a metric space D onto a metric space R be given by $y = f(x)$. We shall designate the metric of D by ρ_D, and the metric in R by ρ_R.

Definition 6.2.5. The function given by $y = f(x)$ is said to be *uniformly continuous* over D if for every positive number ϵ there exists a positive number $\delta(\epsilon)$ such that for every x, and x' for which $\rho_D(x,x') < \delta(\epsilon)$ it is true that $\rho_R(f(x),f(x')) < \epsilon$.

P. 6.2.6. Restate the last definition in terms of the diameters of subsets of D and of subsets of R.

It is easily seen that uniform continuity implies continuity, but the converse is not true.

P. 6.2.7. Show that the function $1/x$ defined on $0 < x < 1$ is continuous but is not uniformly continuous.

THEOREM 6.2.1. *If the domain of definition D of a function is compact, continuity of the function on D implies uniform continuity over D.*

Proof. Let the ϵ in the definition of uniform continuity (Def. 6.2.5) be given. We cover each point x of D with a sphere of radius $r(x)/2$, where $r(x)$ is chosen small enough to guarantee that $\rho_R(f(x),f(x')) < \epsilon/2$ for all x and x' which are at a distance less than $r(x)$ from x. By the Heine-Borel theorem a finite number of these spheres will cover the whole space D. Let $x_1, x_2, \ldots, x_n$ be their centers, and let r be the smallest one of the numbers $r(x_1), r(x_2), \ldots,$ $r(x_n)$. Let x and x' be any two points which are less than $r/2$ from each other. The distance of the point x from at least one, say x_{n_0}, of the points $x_1, x_2, \ldots, x_n$ is less than $r(x_{n_0})/2$. By the triangle axiom for a metric, the other point x' will be at a distance less than $r(x_{n_0})$ from x_{n_0}. Therefore

$$\rho_R[f(x),f(x')] \leqslant \rho_R[f(x),f(x_{n_0})] + \rho_R[f(x_{n_0}),f(x')]$$

$$< \frac{\epsilon}{2} + \frac{\epsilon}{2} = \epsilon.$$

6.3 Limit superior, limit inferior and semicontinuity. If $y = f(x)$ represents a function whose range R is a subset of the real continuum, while its domain of definition may be any Hausdorff space D, the concept of limit may be extended in a manner similar to the one by which limits superior and inferior were introduced for sequences.

Definition 6.3.1. (a) Let a real-valued function, $y = f(x)$, be defined on $D \subseteq D_1$ and let a be a point of D^-. The *limit inferior* of $f(x)$ at $x = a$, denoted by

$$\liminf_{x=a} f(x),$$

is the *greatest lower bound* of the limits inferior of $f(x_n)$ over all sequences $\{x_n\}$ which have the limit a; thus

$$\liminf_{x=a} f(x) = \frac{\text{infimum over all } \{x_n\} \text{ converging to}}{a\,\{\liminf_{n\to\infty} f(x_n)\}.}$$

(b) The limit superior of $f(x)$ at $x = a$, denoted by

$$\limsup_{x=a} f(x),$$

is the least upper bound of the $\limsup f(x_n)$ for all sequences $\{x_n\}$ converging to a; thus

$$\limsup_{x=a} f(x) = \text{supremum over all } \{x_n\} \text{ converging to}$$
$$a\,\left\{\limsup_{n\to\infty} f(x_n)\right\}.$$

It should be recalled that the limits inferior and superior of sequences always existed, since we permitted $+\infty$ and $-\infty$ as values for them. The least upper bound of any subset of E' which contains $+\infty$ as an element is $+\infty$, and the greatest lower bound of any subset of E' which contains $-\infty$ is $-\infty$. With these conventions in mind, we see that the $\liminf_{x=a} f(x)$ and $\limsup_{x=a} f(x)$ always exist if a is an element of the closure of D.

It follows at once from the definitions that if

$$\liminf_{x=a} f(x) = \limsup_{x=a} f(x) = A,$$

where A is a finite number, then $\lim_{x=a} f(x)$ exists and is equal to A.

The concepts of limit superior and limit inferior of a given function at a point have been defined in terms of similar concepts which were given for the special functions known as sequences. Here we have proceeded from the particular case to the general case. We shall now give a few alternative definitions of these concepts for functions without the notion of sequences.

Definition 6.3.2. (a) The limit inferior of $f(x)$ at $x = a(a \in D^-)$ is the least upper bound over all neighborhoods N_a of a of the greatest lower bound of the values of $f(x)$ with x contained in N_aD. Symbolically,

$$\liminf_{x=a} f(x) = \frac{\text{supremum}}{\text{over all } N_a} \left[\begin{array}{c} \text{infimum } f(x) \\ x \in N_aD \end{array} \right]$$

(b) The limit superior of $f(x)$ at $x = a(a \in D^-)$ is the greatest lower bound over all neighborhoods of the least upper bound of the values of $f(x)$ with x contained in N_aD. Symbolically,

$$\limsup_{x=a} f(x) = \frac{\text{inf over}}{\text{all } N_a} \left[\begin{array}{c} \sup f(x) \\ x \in N_aD \end{array} \right]$$

P. 6.3.1. Show the equivalence of Def. 6.3.1 and Def. 6.3.2.

P. 6.3.2. The *saltus* of a real function at a point $x = a$ was defined in Chapter 4 (Def. 4.8.2). Show that the earlier definition is equivalent to the following. The saltus of $f(x)$ at $x = a$ is

$$\limsup_{x=a} f(x) - \liminf_{x=a} f(x)$$

if each of these limits is finite. If at least one of them is infinite, the saltus is said to be plus infinity.

It is obvious that if the saltus of $f(x)$ at $x = a$ is zero, and if $f(x)$ is defined at $x = a$, then $f(x)$ is continuous at $x = a$.

Definition 6.3.3. (a) A real function $f(x)$ is said to be *upper semicontinuous at $x = a$* if $f(x)$ is defined at $x = a$, and if

$$\limsup_{x=a} f(x) = f(a);$$

$f(x)$ is *lower semicontinuous at $x = a$* if

$$\liminf_{x=a} f(x) = f(a).$$

These definitions can also be given in the following words:

$f(x)$ is upper semicontinuous at $x = a$ if for every positive number ϵ there exists an $N_a(\epsilon)$ of a such that if $x \in N_a D$, then

$$f(x) - f(a) < \epsilon;$$

$f(x)$ is lower semicontinuous at $x = a$ if for every positive number ϵ there exists an $N_a(\epsilon)$ of a such that if $x \in N_a D$, then

$$f(x) - f(a) > -\epsilon.$$

Examples. If $f(x) = 0$ for $x \neq 0$, $f(0) = c$, where $c > 0$, then $f(x)$ is upper semicontinuous at $x = 0$, but it is not continuous at $x = 0$. If $f(x)$ were defined as above for $x \neq 0$, and $f(0) = c$, where $c < 0$, this $f(x)$ would be lower semicontinuous at $x = 0$.

It should be noticed that the space D_1 in which D is assumed to be imbedded plays no rôle whatsoever in the definition of continuity and semicontinuity. Since the limit superior and limit inferior of a function at a point are unique, a function must be single-valued at each point where it is semicontinuous.

P. 6.3.3. Prove that if $\lim \sup_{x=a} f(x) = A$, a finite number, A has the following properties.

(a) For $b > A$, $a \notin S[f(x) > b]^-$;

(b) For $b' < A$, $a \in S[f(x) > b']^-$,

where $S[f(x) > c]^-$ stands for the closure of the set of all x, such that $f(x) > c$. Conversely, prove that if there exists a number A which has the properties (a) and (b), then A is the limit superior of $f(x)$. State a similar result for the limit inferior of a function.

P. 6.3.4. Prove

(a) $\lim \sup [-f(x)] = -\lim \inf f(x)$.

(b) $\lim \inf f(x) + \lim \inf g(x) \leqslant \lim \inf (f(x) + g(x))$

$\leqslant \begin{array}{l} \lim \inf f(x) + \lim \sup g(x) \\ \lim \sup f(x) + \lim \inf g(x) \end{array} \leqslant \lim \sup (f(x) + g(x))$

$\leqslant \lim \sup f(x) + \lim \sup g(x).$

P. 6.3.5. Prove that for nonnegative functions

(a) $\lim \inf \dfrac{1}{f(x)} = \dfrac{1}{\lim \sup f(x)}.$

(b) $\lim \inf f(x) \lim \inf g(x) \leqslant \lim \inf f(x)g(x)$

$\leqslant \begin{array}{l} \lim \inf f(x) \lim \sup g(x) \\ \lim \sup f(x) \lim \inf g(x) \end{array} \leqslant \lim \sup f(x)g(x)$

$\leqslant \lim \sup f(x) \lim \sup g(x).$

P. 6.3.6. Give examples of real-valued functions defined at all points of the closed interval [0,1] which are upper semicontinuous (but not continuous) at the points of the sets given in each part of problem P. 6.1.2.

THEOREM 6.3.1. *If D is a compact Hausdorff space, and $f(x)$ is a real-valued function which is upper semicontinuous on D, then $f(x)$ attains its least upper bound, that is, $f(x)$ has a maximum on D. In other words there exists an x_0 belonging to D such that $f(x) \leqslant f(x_0)$ for every x of D. This is known as the Weierstrass maximum theorem.*

Proof. We show first that $f(x)$ is bounded, and hence has a least upper bound on D. Since $f(x)$ is upper semicontinuous we have for each x of D, and for every given positive ϵ, a neighborhood $N_x(\epsilon)$ such that if $x' \in N_x(\epsilon)$, then $f(x') < f(x) + \epsilon$. The set of $N_x(\epsilon)$ constitutes a covering of the space D. Since D is compact, there exists a finite subset of the set of the $N_x(\epsilon)$ which covers D. Let n be the number of these neighborhoods. Select one point say x_k $(k = 1,2,\ldots,n)$ out of each of the neighborhoods. Then

$$f(x) < \sup_k f(x_k) + \epsilon$$

for each x in D. Thus $f(x)$ is bounded in D.

Let the sup $f(x) = M$. Then for every x of D, the function $f(x) \leqslant M$, but for every $M_n, < M$, there exists at least one x, say x_n, such that $f(x_n) > M_n$. Let us take a sequence $\{M_n\}$ which converges to M. Corresponding to each M_n we take an x_n such that $f(x_n) > M_n$. Then the sequence $\{x_n\}$ in D has at least one limit point, say x_0. We select a subsequence $\{x_{n_k}\}$ of $\{x_n\}$ which has the limit x_0. Thus

$$M = \lim_{k \to \infty} f(x_{nk}) \leqslant \lim_{k \to \infty} \sup f(x_{nk}) \leqslant \lim_{x = x_0} \sup f(x).$$

But because of upper semicontinuity,

$$\lim_{x = x_0} \sup f(x) = f(x_0) \leqslant M.$$

Thus $$M \leqslant f(x_0) \leqslant M, \quad \text{and} \quad f(x_0) = M.$$

6.4 Properties of continuous functions. We have seen that a function is defined at each point where it is continuous, or semicontinuous. We shall derive a few other important properties of continuous functions.

THEOREM 6.4.1. *A function given by* $y = f(x)$, *which is continuous on a connected set D assumes every value between its greatest lower bound and its least upper bound on D.*

(A set is connected if it, considered as the whole space, satisfies the definition of a connected space, Def. 3.1.5.)

Proof. We shall show that if we assume the theorem to be false, we are led to the contradictory conclusion that the set D is not connected. Let us assume that there exists a real value k, between $m, = \inf f(x)$, and $M, = \sup f(x)$, which $f(x)$ does not take on. The set $S_1[f(x) < k]$, namely, the set of points x of D for which $f(x) < k$ is not empty, for otherwise m could not be the greatest lower bound of $f(x)$ in D. This set is open, for it is the map in D of the open set $y < k$ of the range of the continuous function $y = f(x)$ (see P. 3.2.1). Similarly the set $S_2[f(x) > k]$, that is, the set of points x of D for which $f(x) > k$, is a nonempty open set of D. But $S_1 + S_2 = D$. Thus S_1 and S_2 are each open and closed in D. This contradicts the hypothesis that D is connected.

In order to be able to apply this theorem to functions of one real variable we state the following theorem.

THEOREM 6.4.2. *An open, semiopen, or closed interval of the one-dimensional space E_1 is connected.*

Proof. Let A be a closed and open subset of the interval I, where I may stand for the open, semiopen, or closed interval defined by $a \leqslant x \leqslant b$. Let c be a point of A. Let c_r be the greatest lower bound of that part of the complement of A in I to the right of c. Since A is closed, c_r must belong to A. If $c < c_r < b$, then, since A is open, there must exist an open interval to the right of c_r containing points of A only. This means that c_r cannot be the greatest lower bound of the complement of A to the right of c. Hence A contains all points of I to the right of c. Similarly it is easily shown that if c_l is the least upper bound of the complement of A to the left of c, then c_l cannot lie between a and c. Hence A contains all points in I to the left of c. Thus $A = I$.

As a corollary to the last two theorems we have the following result.

THEOREM 6.4.3. *If a real-valued continuous function of a single variable x takes on the value $f(a)$ at a and $f(b)$ at b, and if k is any value between $f(a)$ and $f(b)$, then $f(x) = k$ for some value c between a and b.*

P. 6.4.1. By the use of the Dedekind cut, prove that if the real function $f(x)$ is continuous in $a \leqslant x \leqslant b$, then $f(x)$ has a maximum in $[a,b]$, that is, $f(x)$ attains its least upper bound.

P. 6.4.2. By the use of the Dedekind cut, prove that if a real function $f(x)$ of a single variable x is continuous in $a \leqslant x \leqslant b$, and if $f(a) < 0$, $f(b) > 0$, then $f(x) = 0$ for some $x = c$, such that $a < c < b$. Hence give another proof of Theorem 6.4.3. Show by example that the converse of that theorem is not true, that is, construct a real function which takes on all values between $f(a)$ and $f(b)$, is defined at every point of $[a,b]$, but is not continuous on this interval.

6.5 Extension of a function. Let a function be given by $y = f(x)$ on the domain of definition $D \subset D_1$. Let another function $y = F(x)$ be such that it coincides with $y = f(x)$ on D, but let its domain of definition be D_1; then we say that the *function $F(x)$ is an extension of $f(x)$*.

THEOREM 6.5.1. *Let $f(x)$ be a uniformly continuous function on an everywhere dense set D of a metric space D_1 to a compact metric space R. There exists a uniquely determined function $F(x)$ which coincides with $f(x)$ on D, and which is continuous on D_1.*

Proof. For every element a of D_1 we define $F(a)$ as $\lim_{x=a} f(x)$, where $x \in D$. The uniqueness of $F(x)$ is assured by the uniqueness of the limit of a function at a point. We must prove that the limit occurring in the definition of $F(x)$ always exists. That it exists for each point a of D and is equal to $f(a)$ is a consequence of the continuity of $f(x)$ on D. To prove the existence of the defining limit if $a \in D_1$, we introduce the following notation: we designate the metric in D_1 by ρ, the metric in R by ρ_R. Let $\{x_n\}$ be a sequence in D converging to a in D_1. This is a Cauchy sequence, for every converging sequence in a metric space is a Cauchy sequence by Theorem 5.3.1. The sequence $\{f(x_n)\}$ in R is also a Cauchy sequence. To prove this we must show that for every ϵ greater than 0, there exists an integer $N(\epsilon)$ such that for all

$$n > N(\epsilon), \quad m > N(\epsilon) \quad \text{the distance} \quad \rho_R[f(x_n), f(x_m)] < \epsilon.$$

Let ϵ be given. Since $f(x)$ is uniformly continuous there exists a δ greater than 0 such that for every x and x' for which

$$\rho(x,x') < \delta, \quad \rho_R[f(x), f(x')] < \epsilon.$$

But since $\{x_n\}$ is a Cauchy sequence, there exists a real number $N(\delta)$ such that $\rho(x_n, x_m) < \delta$ for all $n > N(\delta)$, $m > N(\delta)$. If we let $N(\epsilon)$ be equal to $N(\delta)$, we have

$$\rho_R[f(x_n), f(x_m)] < \epsilon.$$

Hence the sequence $\{f(x_n)\}$, being a Cauchy sequence in a compact space, converges. Since $\{x_n\}$ was an arbitrary sequence converging to a, we have shown that $\lim_{x=a} f(x)$ exists.

We next prove that $F(x)$ is continuous in D_1. As a matter of fact we shall prove that $F(x)$ is uniformly continuous in D_1. Let a positive number ϵ be given. Because of the uniform continuity of $f(x)$ on D, there exists a positive number δ such that

$$\rho_R[f(x), f(x')] < \epsilon/4 \quad \text{if} \quad \rho(x, x') < \delta/2.$$

Let u and u' be two points of D_1 such that $\rho(u, u') < \delta/2$. We shall show that

$$\rho_R[F(u), F(u')] < \epsilon.$$

We construct two spheres of radius $\delta/4$ with centers at u and u' (see Fig. 9). Since the set D is everywhere dense in D_1, we can find a point x of D in the sphere whose center is at u, and a point x' of D in the sphere whose center is at u'. Then

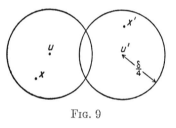

FIG. 9

$$\rho_R[F(u), F(u')] \leqslant \rho_R[F(u), f(x)] +$$
$$\rho_R[f(x), f(x')] + \rho_R[f(x'), F(u')] < 3\epsilon/4.$$

This completes the proof of the theorem.

This theorem has wide applications. As a direct consequence of it we have the result that a continuous function over an interval has all its values determined by the values it assumes at the rational points only. This fact is used in defining the exponential function for irrational exponents, and it is also used in proofs for the uniqueness of the continuous solutions of important functional equations.

P. 6.5.1. Prove that all real continuous solutions of the functional equation $f(x + y) = f(x) + f(y)$, which are defined for all x, are of the form $f(x) = Ax$ where A is an arbitrary real constant.

THEOREM 6.5.2. *For every $a > 0$, there exists a real continuous function a^x, defined for all real values of x, which has the following properties.*

(1) $a^1 = a$.

(2) $a^x a^y = a^{x+y}$.

(3) a^x *is uniformly continuous on every bounded interval.*

Proof. The proof of this theorem consists of the construction of the required function and the verification of the listed properties for the function. We shall define the required function first for integers and for rational values. After we have shown then that the function is uniformly continuous on the set of rational numbers lying in any given bounded interval, we extend the definition to irrational values by the last theorem. Since the proof is rather long, we shall give it in the form of a succession of lemmas.

Let a be a positive number, n a positive integer. We define a^n to mean the product of n factors each equal to a. Then a^0 is defined to be 1, and a^{-n} is defined as $1/a^n$. The function a^x has thus been defined for all integral values of x. That this function satisfies conditions (1) and (2) and that it is always positive, follows directly from its definition.

Lemma 1. If $a > 1$, $m > n$, then $a^m > a^n$;

       if $a < 1$, $m > n$, then $a^m < a^n$.

Proof. We use mathematical induction. We are given $a > 1$. Suppose $a^p > 1$, where p is a positive integer. Multiplying both sides of the last inequality by a, we get $a^{p+1} > a > 1$. Since $m > n$, $m - n$ is a positive integer. Therefore $a^{m-n} > 1$. Multiplying both sides by a^n we get the required result. The proof for the case that $a < 1$ is analogous.

Next we want to define a^x for rational values of x. In order to be able to do this we need another lemma.

Lemma 2. If $a > 0$, and p is a positive integer, there exists a unique positive number c such that $c^p = a$. We denote this number by $a^{1/p}$.

Proof. The function x^p is a continuous function of x. When x is equal to min (a, a^{-1}) it takes on a value less than or equal to a; when x is equal to max (a, a^{-1}) it takes on a value greater than or equal to a. By Theorem 6.4.3 there exists a number c such that $c^p = a$.

We must show that c is unique. Suppose there were two numbers c and d such that $c^p = d^p = a$. If $c < d$, then by mathematical induction $c^p < d^p$, which contradicts our hypothesis. Thus $a^{1/p}$ is uniquely defined.

For any rational number p/q we now define $a^{p/q} = (a^p)^{1/q}$, where q is a positive integer, p an integer. We must show that if $p/q = s/t$, then $a^{p/q} = a^{s/t}$. Suppose $a^{p/q} = a_1$, $a^{s/t} = a_2$. From this it follows that

$$a_1{}^q = a^p, \quad a_2{}^t = a^s, \quad \text{and that} \quad a_1{}^{pt} = a_2{}^{pt} = a^{ps}.$$

Hence by Lemma 2, $a_1 = a_2$.

The function a^x has thus been defined for all rational values x. It is easy to verify that a^r, where r is rational, still satisfies the properties (1) and (2) of the theorem and the monotonic property described in Lemma 1.

Lemma 3.

$$\lim_{n \to \infty} a^{1/2^n} = 1.$$

Proof. Because of the monotonic character of a^r, the limit exists. Let us designate it by b. Then

$$b^2 = \lim_{n \to \infty} a^{1/2^{n-1}} = b.$$

Hence b must be 1, 0, or ∞. If $a > 1$, then $1 < a^{1/2^n} < a$, and if $a < 1$, then $a < a^{1/2^n} < 1$. These inequalities exclude 0 and ∞ as possible values for b. Therefore $b = 1$, as was to be shown.

Lemma 4.

$$\lim_{r = 0} a^r = 1.$$

Proof. Lemma 3 and the monotonic character of a^r for r rational.

Lemma 5. The function a^r defined for all rational values is uniformly continuous in the bounded interval $-M \leqslant x \leqslant M$.

Proof. Let a positive number ϵ be given. We can, because of Lemma 4, find a positive number δ such that if

$$|r| < \delta, \quad \text{then} \quad |1 - a^r| < \epsilon/\max (a^M, a^{-M}).$$

Hence, for every r, and r' in $[-M, M]$, such that $|r - r'| < \delta$ we have

$$|a^r - a^{r'}| \leqslant \max (a^M, a^{-M}) |1 - a^{r-r'}| < \epsilon.$$

The hypotheses of the Theorem 6.5.1 are satisfied by the function a^r. Hence that theorem may be applied to a^r, and this proves Theorem 6.5.2.

6.6 Sequences of real functions. We shall now consider functions which are defined by means of limits of sequences.

Definition 6.6.1. If the range of a sequence is a subset of the set of real functions, the sequence is called a *sequence of real functions.* Thus if $\{u_k(x)\}$ represents a sequence of real functions, each entry $u_k(x)(k = 1,2,3,\ldots)$ is a real function.

The notion of convergence of a sequence $\{u_k(x)\}$ of real functions at a point x_0, is defined to be that of the convergence of the sequence of real numbers $u_k(x_0)$. This type of convergence of a sequence of functions is called *ordinary* or *pointwise* convergence. If for each x_0 in an interval (a,b) the sequence of real functions $u_k(x)$ has a limit whose value we may designate by $f(x_0)$, the set of limits $f(x)$ for all x in (a,b) constitutes the range of a function which is defined in (a,b) by the sequence $\{u_k(x)\}$. We shall designate this by writing $\lim_{k\to\infty} u_k(x) = f(x)$ for x in (a,b).

The concept of convergence of sequences can be given a more restrictive meaning when we deal with sequences of functions as will be shown in the next definition.

Definition 6.6.2. A sequence of functions $u_k(x)$ is said to *converge uniformly to the function* $f(x)$ in (a,b) if for every ϵ, which is greater than 0, there exists an integer $n(\epsilon)$ such that for every n greater than $n(\epsilon)$, and for every x in (a,b) it is true that

$$| u_n(x) - f(x) | < \epsilon.$$

The interval (a,b) may here be an open, semiopen, or closed interval.

Example. Let each entry of the sequence $\{u_k(x)\}$ be defined as follows.

$$u_k(x) = \begin{cases} kx & \text{if} \quad 0 \leqslant x < \dfrac{1}{k}, \quad (k=1,2,3,\ldots) \\[2mm] 1 & \text{if} \quad \dfrac{1}{k} \leqslant x \leqslant 1. \end{cases}$$

It is obvious that

$$f(x) = \lim u_k(x) = \begin{cases} 0 & \text{if} \quad x = 0, \\ 1 & \text{if} \quad 0 < x \leqslant 1. \end{cases}$$

It follows that for $\epsilon = \frac{1}{2}$, and for every N, there exists an x (i.e., $x = 1/(3N)$ will do) such that

$$| u_N(x) - f(x) | > \tfrac{1}{2}.$$

Hence the given sequence converges in the ordinary sense in the closed interval [0,1] but it does not converge uniformly in this interval. We note that the limit of the given sequence of continuous functions is a discontinuous function.

THEOREM 6.6.1. *Let $u_k(x)$ represent a uniformly convergent sequence of continuous real functions defined in an interval (a,b). [This interval may be open, semiopen, or closed.] Let $f(x)$ represent the function to which the given sequence converges uniformly. Then $f(x)$ is continuous in (a,b).*

Proof. Let a positive number ϵ be given. Since $f(x)$ is the limit of the given uniformly convergent sequence there exists an integer n_1 which depends only on ϵ, and not on x, such that for all n greater than n_1 and for all x in (a,b) it is true that

$$| f(x) - u_n(x) | < \frac{\epsilon}{3}.$$

Let x' be a given point in (a,b). We shall show that $f(x)$ is continuous at x'. Let n be a positive integer greater than n_1. Since $u_n(x)$ is continuous at x', there exists a positive number δ such that for all x in (a,b) for which $| x' - x | < \delta$ it is true that $| u_n(x') - u_n(x) | < \epsilon/3$. It follows that for all such x,

$$
\begin{aligned}
&| f(x) - f(x') | \\
&= | f(x) - u_n(x) + u_n(x') - f(x') + u_n(x) - u_n(x') | \\
&\leqslant | f(x) - u_n(x) | + | u_n(x') - f(x') | + | u_n(x) - u_n(x') | \\
&< \epsilon/3 + \epsilon/3 + \epsilon/3.
\end{aligned}
$$

This proves the theorem.

P. 6.6.1. Construct a nonuniformly convergent sequence of continuous functions on [0,1] converging to a function continuous on [0,1].

Chapter VII

INFINITE SERIES

7.1 Introduction. We shall now consider the problem of extending the notion of the sum of a finite number of terms to that of infinitely many terms.

Definition 7.1.1. By an infinite series, indicated by

$$a_0 + a_1 + \ldots + a_n + \ldots ,$$

or by $\sum a_i$, is meant the *sequence*

$$\left\{ \sum_{i=0}^{n} a_i \right\}, \quad \text{where} \quad n = 0, 1, 2, \ldots .$$

The nth term in this sequence is called the nth partial sum of the infinite series. We denote the nth partial sum of the series by s_n. The terms a_i of the series will be assumed, for this course, to be real numbers.

According to our definition, an infinite series is a sequence which is identified by the symbol for the series. Conversely, every sequence of numbers can be given as an infinite series. For let $\{x_n\}$ be a given sequence of numbers. We can denote it by $\sum (x_i - x_{i-1})$ if we define x_{-1} to be zero. The partial sums of this infinite series are obviously $x_0, x_1, x_2, \ldots .$

7.2 Convergent series. Since a series is a sequence, whose terms are the partial sums of the series, the definitions of convergence and divergence given for sequences (see Def. 5.2.1) apply also to series. For the sake of easier future references we repeat these definitions here as they apply to series.

Definition 7.2.1. A series $\sum a_i$ is said to be convergent if the sequence of its partial sums converges. The limit of this sequence is called the *sum* of the infinite series. If we denote it by s we shall write

$$s = \sum_{i=0}^{\infty} a_i.$$

Any series which is not convergent is called a *divergent series*.

We have thus associated with every convergent series a number called the sum of the series. We can reword the above definition in the following form. An infinite series $\sum a_i$ converges to the sum s if for every ϵ greater than 0 there exists an integer $n(\epsilon)$ such that for every n greater than $n(\epsilon)$

$$\left| s - \sum_{i=0}^{n} a_i \right| < \epsilon.$$

These definitions of the sum permit us only to verify whether a certain number s is the sum of an infinite series, but they are useless for testing the convergence of a series whose sum is not known. We have, however, a necessary and sufficient condition that a sequence in a complete space be convergent. This condition is that it be a Cauchy sequence. Restating this result in the terminology of series we get the following theorem.

Theorem 7.2.1. (*Cauchy criterion for series.*) *A necessary and sufficient condition for a series* $\sum a_i$ *to be convergent is that for every* ϵ *greater than 0 there exists an integer* $n(\epsilon)$ *such that for every* n *greater than* $n(\epsilon)$, *and every* m *greater than* $n(\epsilon)$ *it is true that*

$$\left| s_m - s_n \right| = \left| a_{n+1} + a_{n+2} + \ldots + a_m \right| < \epsilon.$$

As immediate consequences of this theorem we have the next four theorems.

Theorem 7.2.2. *If from a certain term on, all terms of a series vanish, the series is convergent to the finite sum of the nonvanishing terms. That is, if the series* $\sum a_i$ *is such that for all* $i > n$, $a_i = 0$, *then the series converges to* $a_0 + a_1 + \ldots + a_n$.

Theorem 7.2.3. *If the series* $\sum a_i$ *converges to* s, *then for every real number* b *the series* $\sum b a_i$ *converges to* bs.

Theorem 7.2.4. *If the series* $\sum a_i$ *and* $\sum b_i$ *converge to* a *and* b, *respectively, the series* $\sum (a_i + b_i)$ *converges to* $a + b$.

Theorem 7.2.5. *If a finite number of the terms of a convergent series are increased or decreased, the series remains convergent, its sum being changed by the net amount of increase or decrease of all the altered terms.*

P. 7.2.1. Write out the formal proofs of Theorems 7.2.4 and 7.2.5.

THEOREM 7.2.6. *A necessary condition for a series $\sum a_i$ to converge is that*

$$\lim_{n \to \infty} a_n = 0.$$

Proof. Let the sum of the series be s, and let s_n be the nth partial sum of the series. Then s_n is a Cauchy sequence. Hence for every given ϵ greater than 0, there exists an $n(\epsilon)$ such that for all n greater than $n(\epsilon)$ we have $\mid s_n - s_{n-1} \mid = \mid a_n \mid < \epsilon$.

7.3 Absolute convergence

Definition 7.3.1. A series $\sum a_i$ is said to be *absolutely convergent* if the series $\sum \mid a_i \mid$ converges.

THEOREM 7.3.1. *Absolute convergence of a series implies convergence of the series.*

Proof. Because of the convergence of $\sum \mid a_i \mid$ we have, by Theorem 7.2.1, that for every given positive ϵ there exists an $n(\epsilon)$ such that for n greater than $n(\epsilon)$ and m greater than n

$$\mid a_{n+1} \mid + \mid a_{n+2} \mid + \ldots + \mid a_m \mid < \epsilon.$$

But

$$\mid a_{n+1} + a_{n+2} + \ldots + a_m \mid \leqslant \mid a_{n+1} \mid + \mid a_{n+2} \mid + \ldots + \mid a_m \mid < \epsilon$$

if $n > n(\epsilon)$, $m > n(\epsilon)$. Hence by Theorem 7.2.1, $\sum a_i$ is convergent.

Definition 7.3.2. A convergent series, which is not absolutely convergent, is said to be *conditionally convergent*.

7.4 Bracketed series. We have extended the notion of the sum of a finite number of terms to that of an infinite number of terms. We shall next examine under what conditions the associative law, which holds for finite sums, can be extended to the addition of terms of an infinite series.

Definition 7.4.1. The terms of a series are *bracketed* if the terms of the series are partitioned into nonoverlapping groups of finitely many terms, and if each of these groups is replaced by the sum of its terms.

Example. The series

$$\sum_{n=1}^{\infty} \frac{(-1)^{n-1}}{n}$$

is bracketed if we write it as

$$\left(1 - \frac{1}{2}\right) + \left(\frac{1}{3} - \frac{1}{4}\right) + \left(\frac{1}{5} - \frac{1}{6}\right) + \ldots,$$

or as

$$\sum_{n=1}^{\infty} \frac{1}{(2n - 1)2n}.$$

Every bracketing of a series $\sum a_i$ consists in replacing it by a new series $\sum b_n$, where $b_0 = a_0 + a_1 + \ldots + a_{\lambda_1}$,

$$b_n = a_{\lambda_n+1} + a_{\lambda_n+2} + a_{\lambda_n+3} + \ldots + a_{\lambda_{n+1}}.$$

Here $n \geqslant 1$, and the sequence $\{\lambda_n\}$ is a strictly increasing sequence of nonnegative integers. The partial sum S_n of the bracketed series is equal to the partial sum $s_{\lambda_{n+1}}$ of the original series. Thus the sequence $\{S_n\}$ is a subsequence of the $\{s_n\}$. But every subsequence of a convergent sequence converges by P. 5.2.1. Hence we have the following result.

THEOREM 7.4.1. *If a convergent series is bracketed, the resulting bracketed series converges to the sum of the original series.*

That the converse of this theorem is not true is shown by the following example. The bracketed series $(1 - 1) + (1 - 1) + (1 - 1) + \ldots$ is obviously convergent, but the unbracketed series $1 - 1 + 1 - 1 + 1 - 1 + \ldots$ is divergent. We shall now give sufficient conditions under which brackets can be removed in a series without changing the convergence character of a series.

THEOREM 7.4.2. *If a convergent bracketed series $\sum b_n$, where*

$$b_0 = a_0 + a_1 + \ldots + a_{\lambda_1},$$

$$b_n = a_{\lambda_n+1} + a_{\lambda_n+2} + \ldots + a_{\lambda_{n+1}},$$

is such that no bracket contains more than a fixed number, say k, of terms, and if $\lim\limits_{n\to\infty} a_n = 0$, the unbracketed series $\sum a_i$ converges to the sum of the bracketed series.

Proof. Let S_n be the nth partial sum of the bracketed series, while s_n is the nth partial sum of the unbracketed series. Then $S_n = s_{\lambda_{n+1}}$. By hypothesis $\lim S_n$ exists. Let it be s. We must show that for every ϵ greater than 0 there exists an $n(\epsilon)$ such that for all n greater than $n(\epsilon)$ $|s_n - s| < \epsilon$. Let a positive ϵ be given. Since $\lim S_n = s$, there exists a number $n_1(\epsilon)$ such that for all n greater than $n_1(\epsilon)$,

$$|S_n - s| = |s\lambda_{n+1} - s| < \epsilon/2.$$

Since lim $a_n = 0$, there exists a number $n_2(\epsilon)$ such that for all n greater than $n_2(\epsilon)$, $|a_n < \epsilon/2k$, where k is the upper bound for the number of terms in each bracket. Hence for all n greater than sup $[n_1(\epsilon), n_2(\epsilon)]$ we have, if n is such that

$$\lambda_{n+1} \leqslant n < \lambda_{n+2},$$

$$|s_n - s| = |s_{\lambda_{n+1}} + a_{\lambda_{n+1}+1} + a_{\lambda_{n+1}} + 2 + \ldots + a_n - s|$$

$$\leqslant |s_{\lambda_{n+1}} - s| + k\epsilon/2k < \epsilon.$$

Example. The series

$$\sum_1^\infty \frac{1}{n(n+1)} = \sum_1^\infty \left(\frac{1}{n} - \frac{1}{n+1}\right)$$

converges and its sum is equal to the sum of the unbracketed series whose partial sums, S_n, are given by the following statements: $S_n = 1$, if n is odd; $S_n = n/(n+2)$ if n is even. Hence the sum of the series is 1.

P. 7.4.1. Evaluate the sum of

$$\sum_{k=0}^\infty \frac{1}{(\alpha+k)(\alpha+k+1)}$$

where $\alpha > 0$.

7.5 Rearrangement of terms (commutativity). If only a finite number of terms of a series are rearranged in a different order, the convergence character of the series will not be changed, nor will the sum of the series be changed. This follows from Theorem 7.2.5. Hence we need only to investigate the effect on a series of infinitely many rearrangements of its terms.

THEOREM 7.5.1. *If the terms of an absolutely convergent series are rearranged, the resulting series remains absolutely convergent and its sum is that of the original series.*

Proof. Let $\sum a_n$ be the given absolutely convergent series with sum s. Let $\sum b_k$ be a rearrangement of the given series. Then each b_k is equal to a certain a_n. Thus the b_k are determined in terms of the a_n by a simple map (Def. 1.4.6) $k = f(n)$ whose domain of definition and range are the nonnegative integers. We denote the inverse function by $n = g(k)$. In order to prove that $\sum b_k$ is absolutely convergent we must show that for every ϵ greater than 0 there exists a positive integer $n(\epsilon)$ such that for all k greater than $n(\epsilon)$ the sum

$$|b_k| + |b_{k+1}| + |b_{k+2}| + \ldots < \epsilon.$$

Let a positive ϵ be given. Since $\sum a_n$ is absolutely convergent, there exists a positive integer $m(\epsilon)$ such that for all n greater than $m(\epsilon)$ we have $|a_n| + |a_{n+1}| + \ldots < \epsilon$. Let $n(\epsilon)$ be the maximum of $f(n)$ on the finite set $0, 1, 2, 3, \ldots, m(\epsilon)$. Then for $k > n(\epsilon)$

$$|b_k| + |b_{k+1}| + \ldots = |a_{g(k)}| + |a_{g(k+1)}| + \ldots$$
$$\leqslant a_{m(\epsilon)+1} + a_{m(\epsilon)+2} + \ldots < \epsilon.$$

Next we must show that the sum of $\sum b_k$ is s. Let a positive number ϵ be given. Since $\sum b_k$ is absolutely convergent, there exists a positive integer $n_1(\epsilon)$ such that for all k greater than $n_1(\epsilon)$ it is true that $|b_{k+1}| + |b_{k+2}| + \ldots < \epsilon/2$. On the set $0, 1, 2, 3, \ldots, n_1(\epsilon)$, the function $g(k)$ has a maximum. Let it be $m_1(\epsilon)$. Let us assume that the sum of $\sum b_k = S$. Then

$$|S - s| = |S - \sum_0^{m_1(\epsilon)} a_n - (s - \sum_0^{m_1(\epsilon)} a_n)|$$
$$\leqslant |S - \sum_0^{m_1(\epsilon)} a_n| + |s - \sum_0^{m_1(\epsilon)} a_n|$$
$$= |S - \sum^* b_k| + |s - \sum_0^{m_1(\epsilon)} a_n|.$$

where $\sum^*$ is a finite sum of terms b_k whose subscripts include certainly all the terms less than or equal to $n_1(\epsilon)$. It follows that each term on the right is less than $\epsilon/2$, and thus $|S - s| < \epsilon$, as was to be shown.

P. 7.5.1. Find the sum of the series

$$\frac{7}{12} - \frac{25}{72} + \ldots + (-1)^{n-1} \frac{(3^n + 2^{2n})}{2(6^n)} + \ldots.$$

Justify your method.

We have considered rearrangements of terms of absolutely convergent series. For such series the last theorem proves that the order in which the terms are taken has no effect on the sum of the series. This means that the commutative law of addition holds for the terms of absolutely convergent series. We shall see, however, that this is not the case for conditionally convergent series.

Let $\sum a_i$ be a series of real numbers. We define

$$u_i = a_i \quad \text{if} \quad a_i > 0; \qquad v_i = -a_i \quad \text{if} \quad a_i < 0,$$
$$u_i = 0 \quad \text{if} \quad a_i \leqslant 0; \qquad v_i = 0 \qquad \text{if} \quad a_i \geqslant 0.$$

The series $\sum u_i$, and $\sum v_i$ are called the *positive series* and the *negative series* of $\sum a_i$, respectively.

THEOREM 7.5.2. *A necessary and sufficient condition for a series $\sum a_i$ to be absolutely convergent is that its positive series $\sum u_i$ and its negative series $\sum v_i$ both be convergent. If a series is conditionally convergent its positive and negative series are both divergent.*

Proof. We are given the three series $\sum a_i$, $\sum u_i$, and $\sum v_i$. The terms of the last two series are nonnegative. We denote the nth partial sums of the three series by A_n, U_n, and V_n, respectively. We thus have

$$A_n = U_n - V_n, \qquad \sum_0^n |a_i| = U_n + V_n \qquad (7.5.1)$$

Since the sequences $\{U_n\}$ and $\{V_n\}$ are nondecreasing sequences, they are convergent if they are bounded. Hence the following four cases can arise.

(1) $U_n \to$ number,[1] $\qquad V_n \to$ number,

(2) $U_n \to +\infty$, $\qquad V_n \to$ number,

(3) $U_n \to$ number, $\qquad V_n \to +\infty$,

(4) $U_n \to +\infty$, $\qquad V_n \to +\infty$.

In the first case $\sum |a_i|$ converges, and the sufficiency condition for the absolute convergence of $\sum a_i$ is thus established. If $\sum a_i$ is absolutely convergent, the second of eqs. (7.5.1) shows that U_n and V_n are bounded and hence convergent. This proves the necessity of the conditions stated in the theorem.

In the second and third cases, the series diverges to $+\infty$ and $-\infty$, respectively, as is shown by the first of eqs. (7.5.1).

If the series $\sum a_i$ is conditionally convergent, the only remaining case 4 must occur. The second of eqs. (7.5.1) then shows that $\sum |a_i|$ is divergent. This completes the proof of the theorem.

We shall now state some results concerning the rearrangement of terms in a conditionally convergent series.

---

[1] The arrow here is used to indicate that U_n converges to a number, while in the next line the arrow indicates that U_n diverges to $+\infty$.

THEOREM 7.5.3. *By a proper rearrangement of the terms of a conditionally convergent series it is possible to make the resulting series divergent, or convergent to any given number.*

Proof. Let $\sum a_i$ be a conditionally convergent series. Then in the notation introduced above, $\sum u_i$ and $\sum v_i$ are divergent. We rearrange the terms of the given series in the following way: We take enough positive terms a_i to give us a sum greater than 1. This is possible since the sum $\sum u_i$ of the positive terms diverges to plus infinity. Next we take the first negative term in $\sum a_i$. Then we add enough positive terms to make the sum of the chosen terms greater than 2. Then we take the second negative term of the a_i and so on. The resulting series cannot be convergent since a subsequence of its partial sums will be unbounded.

Next we prove the second part of the theorem. Let M be any number. Let us assume $M \geqslant 0$. An analogous proof will hold if M is negative. We rearrange the terms of the given series by taking first positive terms, in the order in which they occur, until their partial sum exceeds M for the first time. Then we select negative terms in the order in which they occur until we obtain for the first time a partial sum less than M. Then we take just enough positive terms in the order in which they occur to obtain a partial sum greater than M, then again negative terms, and so on. We shall show that this series converges to M, that is, we shall show that for every ϵ greater than 0 there exists an $n(\epsilon)$ such that for all n greater than $n(\epsilon)$ the partial sums s_n of our new series are such that $|M - s_n| < \epsilon$. Let a positive number ϵ be given. Since the original series converges, $\lim a_n = 0$. Hence there exists a positive integer m such that for all n greater than m, $|a_n| < \epsilon$. Let $n(\epsilon)$ be the subscript of the first partial sum in the new arrangement which includes all the terms a_i of the original series with i less than m. Then for every n greater than $n(\epsilon)$ the partial sums cannot differ from M by more than ϵ, since the manner of construction of the new series is such that no partial sum can differ from M by more than the largest absolute value of the a_i still available for selection in the original series. Thus for n greater than $n(\epsilon)$

$$|s_n - M| \leqslant |a_i| < \epsilon.$$

We have limited our discussion to series of numbers. The symbol for a series will have a meaning whenever the sequence of partial sums is defined. This implies that the terms a_i of a series must belong to a set for which addition is defined. In other words, the concepts of convergent and divergent series have a meaning in linear spaces. For the generalization of the concepts associated with absolutely convergent series, the space must be a normed linear space. The theorems of this section can all be generalized to such spaces. The theory of series of complex numbers is one such generalization.

7.6 Comparison tests for convergence. One of the most important problems in the theory and in the applications of infinite series is to determine whether a given series is convergent or divergent. The solution of this problem usually consists in finding tests, applicable to the given series, which will reveal the convergence character of the series. Two powerful tests for this purpose are the definition of convergence, and the Cauchy criterion (Theorem 7.2.1) for infinite series. They can be applied directly to some series. In order to simplify their application some systematic methods for determining the convergence or divergence of series have been devised. Most of these methods consist in comparing the given series with other series whose convergence character has been established directly. We speak of these methods as comparison tests. Since they apply mainly to series with nonnegative terms, they are essentially tests for absolute convergence or divergence.

THEOREM 7.6.1. *Let* $\sum b_i$ *be a series of nonnegative terms which is convergent. If each term* a_i *of another series* $\sum a_i$ *is in absolute value not greater than the corresponding term* b_i *of the convergent series, that is, if* $|a_i| \leqslant b_i$, *the series* $\sum a_i$ *is absolutely convergent.*

P. 7.6.1. Prove Theorem 7.6.1.

THEOREM 7.6.2. *Let* $\sum b_i$ *be a convergent series of positive terms. If*

$$\left| \frac{a_{i+1}}{a_i} \right| \leqslant \frac{b_{i+1}}{b_i},$$

for all nonnegative integers i, *the series* $\sum a_i$ *is absolutely convergent.*

Proof. We multiply the displayed inequalities of the theorem for $i = 0, 1, 2, \ldots, n - 1$. Then we obtain

$$\left| \frac{a_n}{a_0} \right| \leqslant \frac{b_n}{b_0} \quad \text{or} \quad |a_n| \leqslant \left| \frac{a_0}{b_0} \right| b_n.$$

The last inequality implies, on the basis of Theorem 7.6.1, that $\sum |a_i|$ is convergent if $\sum |a_0/b_0| b_i$ is convergent. But the latter series is convergent by Theorem 7.2.3, since $\sum b_i$ is convergent by hypothesis. This completes the proof of the theorem.

THEOREM 7.6.3. *Let $\sum b_i$ be a series of nonnegative terms which is divergent. If each term of the series $\sum a_i$ is not less than the corresponding term b_i of the divergent series, that is, if $a_i \geqslant b_i$, the series $\sum a_i$ is divergent.*

P. 7.6.2. Prove Theorem 7.6.3.

We shall next give a comparison test in which the partial sums of a series are compared to the value of an integral.

THEOREM 7.6.4. (INTEGRAL TEST.) *Let $\sum a_i$ be a series of positive terms. If there exists a nonincreasing function $f(x)$ defined for all $x, \geqslant k \geqslant 0$, such that $a_i = f(i)$ for i greater than k, then the infinite series $\sum a_i$ and the improper Riemann integral*

$$\int_k^\infty f(x)dx$$

will have the same convergence character; that is, if one converges the other converges; if one diverges, the other diverges also.

Proof. From the definition of $f(x)$ it follows that

$$a_{i+1} \leqslant f(x) \leqslant a_i \quad \text{if} \quad i \leqslant x \leqslant i+1.$$

Hence we have the inequalities

$$\sum_{k+1}^{p+1} a_i \leqslant \int_k^{p+1} f(x)dx \leqslant \sum_k^p a_i$$

Taking the limits of these sequences as p goes to infinity, we have the result stated in the theorem.

In order to be able to make use of the comparison tests established by Theorems 7.6.2 and 7.6.3, one needs to know some convergent and some divergent series. The following theorems give two such series whose convergence character can be established either directly from the definition of the sum of a series or by means of Cauchy's integral test.

THEOREM 7.6.5. *The geometric series $\sum_{k=0}^\infty r^k$ converges if $|r| < 1$, diverges if $|r| \geqslant 1$.*

P. 7.6.3. Prove this theorem in two ways.

Theorem 7.6.6. *The Dirichlet series* $\sum n^{-p}$ *is divergent for* $p \leqslant 1$ *and convergent for* $p > 1$. (Here p is a constant).

P. 7.6.4. Prove this theorem.

P. 7.6.5. Test for convergence or divergence the series

$$\sum_{k=1}^{\infty} \frac{1 \cdot 3 \cdot 5 \cdot \ldots \cdot (2k+1)}{2^{k+1}(k+1)!k}.$$

Hint. Make use of the fact that the geometric mean of two positive numbers is less than or equal to the arithmetic mean of these numbers.

P. 7.6.6. Establish the *ratio test*, that is, prove that if there exists a number N such that for all n greater than N $|u_{n+1}|/|u_n| \leqslant r < 1$, then the series $\sum u_n$ converges absolutely. If, however, there exists a number N such that for all n greater than N $|u_{n+1}|/|u_n| \geqslant 1$, then $\sum u_n$ diverges.

Also prove that if

$$\lim_{n \to \infty} \left| \frac{u_{n+1}}{u_n} \right| < 1,$$

then $\sum u_n$ converges absolutely, but if

$$\lim_{n \to \infty} \left| \frac{u_{n+1}}{u_n} \right| > 1,$$

then $\sum u_n$ diverges.

P. 7.6.7. Establish the *root test*, that is, prove that if there exists a number N such that for all n greater than N,

$$\sqrt[n]{|u_n|} \leqslant r < 1,$$

then $\sum u_n$ converges absolutely, but if there exists a number N such that for all n greater than N

$$\sqrt[n]{|u_n|} \geqslant 1,$$

then $\sum u_n$ diverges.

Also prove that if

$$\limsup_{n \to \infty} \sqrt[n]{|u_n|} \leqslant r < 1,$$

then $\sum u_n$ converges absolutely, but if

$$\limsup_{n \to \infty} \sqrt[n]{|u_n|} > 1,$$

then $\sum u_n$ diverges.

The method by which certain bracketed series can be summed (see P. 7.4.1) suggests a test for convergence of series. The series $\sum v_n$ where

$$v_n = \frac{1}{n(n+1)}, \qquad n = 1, 2, 3, \ldots,$$

can be written as the bracketed series

$$\frac{1}{2} + \sum_{n=2}^{\infty} [(n-1)v_{n-1} - nv_n].$$

The nth partial sum S_n of the original series is thus seen to be

$$S_n = \frac{1}{2} + \left(\frac{1}{2} - \frac{1}{3}\right) + \left(\frac{1}{3} - \frac{1}{4}\right) + \cdots$$
$$+ \left(\frac{1}{n} - \frac{1}{n+1}\right) = 1 - \frac{1}{n+1}.$$

The fact that the nth term v_n for n greater than 2 could be written

$$v_n = (n-1)v_{n-1} - nv_n \qquad (7.6.1)$$

made it possible to find the sum of the series. If we are interested only in a test for convergence of a series $\sum u_n$ of positive terms, it is sufficient to show that the partial sums of the series are bounded. This can obviously be done on the basis of a relation similar to the last displayed equation even if the equality sign is replaced by a less or equal sign. As a matter of fact it is sufficient to have a relation of the form

$$cu_n \leqslant a_{n-1}u_{n-1} - a_n u_n,$$

where $c > 0$, and $\{a_i\}$ is any sequence of positive numbers, to insure the convergence of $\sum u_n$. We state this result in the form of a theorem and give a formal proof for it.

THEOREM 7.6.7. (KUMMER'S TEST.) *Let $\sum u_i$ be a series of positive terms. If there exists a sequence $\{a_i\}$ of positive numbers, and a positive number c, such that for all n greater or equal to 2,*

$$a_{n-1} \frac{u_{n-1}}{u_n} - a_n > c,$$

then $\sum u_i$ converges.

If there exists a sequence a_i of positive numbers such that $\sum 1/a_i$ diverges, and

$$a_{n-1} \frac{u_{n-1}}{u_n} - a_n \leqslant 0,$$

then $\sum u_i$ diverges.

Proof. By hypothesis

$$cu_1 \leqslant a_0u_0 - a_1u_1$$

$$cu_2 \leqslant a_1u_1 - a_2u_2$$

$$\cdot \cdot \cdot \cdot \cdot \cdot \cdot \cdot \cdot \cdot \cdot \cdot$$

$$cu_n \leqslant a_{n-1}u_{n-1} - a_nu$$

Adding these equations, we get for the partial sums s_n of the given series the following bound.

$$s_n \leqslant \frac{a_0u_0 - a_nu_n}{c} + u_0$$

$$< \frac{a_0u_0}{c} + u_0.$$

This proves the first part of the theorem.

Next suppose that the inequalities stated in the second part of the theorem hold. Then

$$a_nu_n \geqslant a_{n-1}u_{n-1} \geqslant \ldots > a_1u_1.$$

Hence

$$u_n \geqslant (a_1u_1)\frac{1}{a_n}.$$

By hypothesis $\sum 1/a_i$ is divergent; hence by Theorem 7.6.3, $\sum u_i$ is divergent.

Kummer's test is more powerful than the ratio test. It reduces to the ratio test if the sequence $\{a_i\}$ is chosen with each $a_i = 1$. In this case

$$\frac{u_{n-1}}{u_n} \geqslant 1 + c,$$

or

$$\frac{u_n}{u_{n-1}} \leqslant \frac{1}{1+c} = r < 1.$$

Example. Consider the series of P. 7.6.5,

$$\sum u_k = \sum_1^\infty \frac{1 \cdot 3 \cdot 5 \cdot \ldots \cdot (2k-1)}{2^{k+1}(k+1)!k}$$

Let $a_n = n$. Then we find

$$(n-1)\frac{u_{n-1}}{u_n} - n = \frac{3}{2} + \frac{3}{2(2n-1)} > \frac{3}{2}.$$

Hence this series converges.

As a direct consequence of Kummer's test we have the following result.

THEOREM 7.6.8. (GAUSS'S TEST.) *Let $\sum u_n$ be a series of positive terms. If the ratio u_n/u_{n+1} can be written in the form*

$$\frac{u_n}{u_{n+1}} = 1 + \frac{h}{n} + \frac{B(n)}{n^2},$$

where $B(n)$ is a bounded function of n as n goes to infinity, then $\sum u_n$ converges if $h > 1$, diverges if $h \leqslant 1$.

P. 7.6.8. Prove this theorem. Hint. In Kummer's test let $a_n = n$ for the case when $h \neq 1$. For the case when $h = 1$ let $a_n = n \log n$.

P. 7.6.9. Test for convergence and divergence

$$\sum_{n=1}^{\infty} \frac{1(1 + c)(1 + 2c)\ldots(1 + nc)}{2(2 + d)(2 + 2d)\ldots(2 + nd)n}$$

where $c > 0$, $d > 0$. Consider the various cases.

7.7 Sets of test series. Any series whose convergence character is known, and which therefore can be used in a comparison test to determine the convergence character of another series, is called a *test series*. In order to facilitate the application of the comparison tests it is helpful to have sets of test series.

Definition 7.7.1. Let $\sum a_i$ and $\sum b_i$ be two convergent series. We say $\sum a_i$ converges *more slowly* (or at a slower rate) than $\sum b_i$ if $\lim_{n \to \infty} b_n/a_n = 0$. If $\sum a_i$ and $\sum b_i$ are two divergent series, we say $\sum a_i$ *diverges more slowly* than $\sum b_i$ if $\lim_{n \to \infty} a_n/b_n = 0$.

A set of test series is especially useful if it consists of two sequences of series, one of which represents a set of convergent series in which each series converges more slowly than each preceding one, while the other sequence consists of a set of divergent series in which each series diverges more slowly than each preceding series in this sequence. The following two sequences of series represent such a set of test series. (We designate $\log \log n$ by $\log^2 n$, $\log \log \log n$ by $\log^3 n$, and so on, while $\log n$ raised to the exponent p will be denoted by $(\log n)^p$. It will be understood that the summation index n in the indicated sums will have its lower limit large enough to make the denominators real and different from zero).

Set of Test Series

Sequence of convergent series, $p > 1$	Sequence of divergent series
$\dfrac{1}{n(\log n)^p}$	$\dfrac{1}{n \log n}$
$\dfrac{1}{n(\log n)(\log^2 n)^p}$	$\dfrac{1}{n(\log n)\log^2 n}$
$\dfrac{1}{n(\log n) \ldots (\log^{k-1} n)(\log^k n)^p}$	$\dfrac{1}{n(\log n) \ldots (\log^{k-1} n)(\log^k n)}$

P. 7.7.1. Establish the convergence character of these test series by means of the integral test, Theorem 7.6.4.

If one wants to prove the convergence of a series by means of the comparison test, one must compare the given series with a convergent series; if one wants to prove the divergence of a series by the comparison test, one must use a divergent series for a test series. The question naturally arises whether there does not exist a perfect comparison series for convergence, that is, whether there does not exist a convergent series which converges more slowly than any other. A similar question applies to the test series for divergence, that is, does there exist a divergent series which diverges more slowly than any other divergent series. The answer to these questions is given by the next theorem.

THEOREM 7.7.1. *If $\sum c_i$ is a convergent series, there exists a convergent series $\sum a_i$ such that $\lim_{n \to \infty} c_n/a_n = 0$, that is, there exists no convergent series which converges more slowly than any other convergent series. If $\sum d_i$ is a divergent series, there exists a divergent series $\sum b_i$ such that $\lim_{n \to \infty} b_n/d_n = 0$, that is, there exists no divergent series which diverges more slowly than any other divergent series.*

Proof. To prove the first part of the theorem, let

$$r_n = c_n + c_{n+1} + c_{n+2} + \ldots .$$

We define

$$a_n = \frac{c_n}{\sqrt{r_n}} = \frac{r_n - r_{n+1}}{\sqrt{r_n}}$$

$$= \frac{(\sqrt{r_n} - \sqrt{r_{n+1}})(\sqrt{r_n} + \sqrt{r_{n+1}})}{\sqrt{r_n}}$$

$$\leqslant 2(\sqrt{r_n} - \sqrt{r_{n+1}}).$$

Hence the partial sums of $\sum a_i$ are bounded, for

$$\sum_{i=0}^{n} a_i \leqslant 2(\sqrt{r_1} - \sqrt{r_{n+1}}),$$

and as n goes to infinity

$$\sum_{i=0}^{\infty} a_i \leqslant 2\sqrt{r_1}.$$

Thus $\sum a_i$ converges, but

$$\lim_{n \to \infty} \frac{c_n}{a_n} = \lim \sqrt{r_n} = 0.$$

To prove the second part of the theorem we set

$$s_n = d_0 + d_1 + \dots d_n,$$

and define

$$b_n = \frac{d_n}{\sqrt{s_n}} = \frac{s_n - s_{n-1}}{\sqrt{s_n}}$$

$$= \frac{(\sqrt{s_n} - \sqrt{s_{n-1}})(\sqrt{s_n} + \sqrt{s_{n-1}})}{\sqrt{s_n}}$$

$$\geqslant \sqrt{s_n} - \sqrt{s_{n-1}}.$$

This proves that

$$\sum_{i=1}^{n} b_i \geqslant \sqrt{s_n} - \sqrt{s_0},$$

and $\sum b_i$ diverges. But

$$\lim_{n \to \infty} \frac{b_n}{d_n} = \lim_{n \to \infty} \frac{1}{\sqrt{s_n}} = 0.$$

7.8 Series of real functions. If the terms a_i of an infinite series $\sum a_i$ are real functions of a variable x, we call the series a series of real functions and designate it $\sum a_i(x)$. The partial sums of such series are sequences of real functions. The limit of the partial sums, if it exists is a function of x.

Definition 7.8.1. If each $a_i(x)$ is a real function of x defined in the interval (a,b), the series $\sum a_i(x)$ is said to *converge uniformly to* $f(x)$ in (a,b) if the sequence of partial sums converges uniformly to $f(x)$ in (a,b).

As a direct consequence of this definition and Theorem 6.6.1 we have the result that if a series of continuous, real functions defined in (a,b) converges uniformly in (a,b), it converges to a function which is continuous in (a,b).

An important class of series of functions are the series of the form

$$\sum_{i=0}^{\infty} c_i x^i, \quad \text{or} \quad \sum_{i=0}^{\infty} c_i (x - h)^i$$

known as power series in x or in $(x - h)$, respectively. Since such series are extensively treated in most elementary books on the calculus, we leave the study of their properties as exercises for the student.

P. 7.8.1. (a) Find the interval of convergence of the series

$$\sum_{n=0}^{\infty} \frac{2^n \sqrt{2!} \sqrt[3]{3!} \sqrt[4]{4!} \dots \sqrt[n+1]{(n+1)!}}{(n+1)!} x^n.$$

(b) Find an interval of uniform convergence of this series. Is there a largest interval of uniform convergence for this series? If so, what is it?

P. 7.8.2. Construct a power series in x whose partial sums s_n are x^n. For what values of x will this series converge? In what interval will it converge uniformly?

CHAPTER VIII

MEASURE

8.1 Length of an interval. The length of an interval (open, closed, or semiopen; see Def. 1.7.6) whose end points are the real numbers a, b $(a < b)$ is defined to be the positive number $b - a$. For a degenerate interval $[a,b]$, with $a = b$, the length is zero. The set of all real numbers x such that $x > a$ is designated by $(a,+\infty)$, and is called an infinite interval extending to $+\infty$. The symbol $(-\infty,a)$ shall stand for the set of real numbers x such that $x < a$. This set is called an infinite interval extending to $-\infty$. The whole real axis will also be considered an infinite interval and will be designated $(-\infty,+\infty)$. The length of every infinite interval is denoted by $+\infty$. Thus the length of every interval is either 0, a positive number, or $+\infty$. This set of values will be designated by the term *nonnegative quantities*. Thus the length of every interval is a nonnegative quantity, the length of every finite interval is a nonnegative number, while the length of every finite nondegenerate interval is a positive number.

We have defined for every interval a nonnegative quantity. We may express this by saying that we have defined a set function on the set of all intervals to the set of nonnegative quantities, and that the length of a given interval is the value of this function for the particular interval. If I represents an interval, we designate the length of I by $L(I)$. We shall next list some properties of this function whose values are given by $L(I) = b - a$, or $L(I) = +\infty$.

The following properties of $L(I)$ are direct consequences of its definition.

(1) $L(I)$ is defined for every interval.

(2) $L(I) \geqslant 0$.

(3) $L(I_1) \geqslant L(I_2)$ if $I_1 \supseteq I_2$. (This property is frequently described by saying that the function $L(I)$ is a *monotone set* function.)

(4) If I is the sum of a finite number of mutually disjoint intervals,

that is, if

$$I = \sum_{j=1}^{n} I_j,$$

where $I_j I_k = 0$ (null set) for $j \neq k$, then

$$L(I) = \sum_{j=1}^{n} L(I_j).$$

(This property is known as that of *finite additivity*, and any set function possessing it is said to be *finitely additive*.)

(5) If I is the sum of a denumerable number of mutually disjoint intervals, that is, if

$$I = \sum_{j=1}^{\infty} I_j,$$

where $I_j I_k = 0$ (null set) for $j \neq k$, then

$$L(I) = \sum_{j=1}^{\infty} L(I_j).$$

(This property is known as that of *denumerably infinite additivity*, and any set function which possesses it is said to be *denumerably additive*. Set functions which possess properties 4 and 5 are also said to be *countably additive*.)

We shall show how some of these properties can be deduced from the definition of length, but leave the verification of the remaining properties as exercises for the student.

P. 8.1.1. Verify property (3) for $L(I)$, that is, prove that if $I_2 \subseteq I_1$, then $L(I_2) \leqslant L(I_1)$.

We shall now establish property (4) for $L(I)$.

Proof of the finite additivity of the length of an interval. We are given that

$$I = \sum_{j=1}^{n} I_j, \qquad I_j I_k = 0 \quad \text{if} \quad j \neq k,$$

and we must show that

$$L(I) = \sum_{j=1}^{n} L(I_j). \tag{8.1.1}$$

We may assume without loss of generality that the intervals lie on the axis of reals and that they have been labeled in such a way that I_j lies to the left of I_k if $j < k$. Since the length of an open, or semi-open interval is the same as that of a closed interval we may assume that the interval I is closed. Let $I = [a,b]$, $I_1 = [a,b_1)$, $I_2 = [b_1,b_2)$, $\dots$, $I_{n-1} = [b_{n-2},b_{n-1})$, $I_n = [b_{n-1},b]$. The sum of the lengths of the subintervals is given by our definition for the length of an interval as

$$(b_1 - a) + (b_2 - b_1) + \ldots + (b_{n-1} - b_{n-2}) + (b - b_{n-1}),$$

which by the associative law for the addition of real numbers reduces to $b - a$. This establishes the property for finite intervals. If the interval I is infinite, at least one of the finite number of subintervals must extend either to $+\infty$ or to $-\infty$. Hence the left-hand side and the right-hand side are both $+\infty$, and the property is established for all intervals.

P. 8.1.2. Prove that if an interval I contains the sum $\sum_{j=1}^{n} I_j$ of a finite number of mutually disjoint intervals, $L(I) \geqslant \sum_{j=1}^{m} L(I_j)$.

P. 8.1.3. Prove that if an interval I is contained in the sum of a finite number of intervals $I_j (j=1,2,\ldots,n)$, then

$$L(I) \leqslant \sum_{j=1}^{n} L(I_j).$$

The properties (1) to (4) of $L(I)$ are stated in terms of a finite number of intervals. They are therefore immediate consequences of the definition of $L(I)$. The property (5) of denumerably infinite additivity requires for its verification certain tools of the analysis of infinite point sets. We shall establish this property by means of the Heine-Borel covering theorem.

Proof of the denumerably infinite additive property of $L(I)$. We are given that

$$I = \sum_{j=1}^{\infty} I_j, \qquad I_j I_k = 0 \quad \text{for} \quad j \neq k,$$

and we must prove that

$$L(I) = \sum_{j=1}^{\infty} L(I_j).$$

We shall first establish the property for the case when I is a finite interval. Without loss of generality we may assume that I is a closed interval. Let us consider the sum $\sum_{j=1}^{n} I_j$. This is the sum of a finite set of intervals all contained in I. Hence the sum of their lengths is, on the basis of problem P. 8.1.2, or as a direct consequence of property (4) for $L(I)$, at most equal to the length of I. Thus each partial sum

$$\sum_{j=1}^{n} L(I_j) \leqslant L(I),$$

and hence

$$\sum_{j=1}^{\infty} L(I_j) \leqslant L(I). \tag{8.1.2}$$

Next we shall show that

$$\sum_{j=1}^{\infty} L(I_j) \geqslant L(I).$$

Let the end points of I_j be the real numbers a_j, b_j $(a_j < b_j)$, and let us denote the open interval (a_j, b_j) by J_j. Then $L(I_j) = L(J_j)$. We construct the following set G of intervals.

(1) The intervals J_j,

(2) The intervals $(a - \epsilon, a + \epsilon)$, $(b - \epsilon, b + \epsilon)$,

(3) The intervals $(a_j - \epsilon/2^j, a_j + \epsilon/2^j)$, $(b_j - \epsilon/2^j, b_j + \epsilon/2^j)$,

where $j = 1, 2, 3, \ldots$, while ϵ is a positive number. The set G constitutes an infinite set of open intervals covering I. According to the Heine-Borel theorem there exists a finite subset of intervals of G which cover I. But the sum of the lengths of these intervals, finite in number, will (by P. 8.1.3) be at least as large as the length of I. The sum of the lengths of all the intervals of the set G is therefore at least as large as the length of I. We thus have

$$\sum_{j=1}^{\infty} L(J_j) + 4\epsilon + 4\epsilon \sum_{j=1}^{\infty} \frac{1}{2}j = \sum_{j=1}^{\infty} L(I_j) + 8\epsilon \geqslant L(I).$$

Since this is true for every ϵ greater than 0, it follows that

$$\sum_{j=1}^{\infty} L(I_j) \geqslant L(I). \qquad (8.1.3)$$

Thus by eqs. (8.1.2) and (8.1.3),

$$\sum_{j=1}^{\infty} L(I_j) = L(I),$$

if I is a finite interval. If I is an infinite interval, we let I_0 be a subinterval of I. Then eq. (8.1.3) shows that

$$\sum_{j=1}^{\infty} L(I_j) \geqslant L(I_0).$$

Since I_0 is any interval contained in the infinite interval I, we can choose I_0 so that $L(I_0)$ may be as large as we please. Hence

$$\sum_{j=1}^{\infty} L(I_j) = +\infty = L(I).$$

We have thus proved that if an interval is the sum of a finite or denumerably infinite number of parts, the length of the total interval is equal to the sum of the lengths of the parts. We express this by saying that the length $L(I)$ is a *countably additive interval function*, or since an interval is a set of points, we say that $L(I)$ is a *countably additive set function*.

The concept of interval in E_1 has its analogue in E_2, where it represents a rectangle. Corresponding to the notion of length of an interval we have the concept of area. In E_3 the intervals are rectangular parallelepipeds and the notion of length generalizes to that of volume. Length, area, and volume may be designated by the terms measure. We have seen that this measure, when it stands for length, has the properties of being nonnegative, monotone, and countably additive. Our object in this chapter is to define, if possible, a "measure" with at least these properties for more general sets. If such a measure function is to be a generalization of the concept of length, area, and volume, it should reduce to $L(I)$ for intervals in E_1, to s^2 for a square of side s in E_2, to s^3 for a cube of edge s in E_3. For sets in E_n it should be invariant under Euclidean motion, that is, under translation and rotation.

8.2 Set functions and point functions

Definition 8.2.1. A function whose domain of definition is a class of sets is called a *set function*. If the range of such a function is a subset of the set of nonnegative real numbers we have a *nonnegative, real set function*. If the range of a set function is a subset of the set consisting of the set of nonnegative real numbers and $+\infty$, we say that we have a *nonnegative set function*. (Note that we have left off the adjective "real," for $+\infty$ is not a real number.)

Examples. (a) The lengths of intervals are the values of a nonnegative set function defined on the set of all intervals in E_1.

(b) The diameters $d(S)$ (see Def. 6.2.3) of sets are the values of a nonnegative real set function defined on all bounded subsets of a metric space.

(c) The cardinal numbers of finite sets are given by the values of a nonnegative real set function defined on the class of all finite sets. Since the values of this function are integers, we can say that it is an integer-valued set function.

We shall have occasions to use in the same discussions functions which are defined at each point of subsets of a space, and also set functions defined for the sets of classes of sets of the same space. We shall refer to the former functions as *point functions* to distinguish them from the latter.

Example. Let a bounded real-valued function, denoted by $f(x)$, be defined for all real numbers. This is a point function, for it sets up a correspondence between the individual points of the domain of definition E_1 and the elements of the range which is a subset of E_1. Let $F(S)$ denote the set function which associates with every subset S of E_1 the $\sup f(x)$ on S. This function $F(S)$ is a real set function defined for all subsets S of E_1. Another example of a set function is given by

$$G(S) = |\sup f(x) - \inf f(x)|$$

where S is any subset of E_1. This is a nonnegative real set function. If $f(x)$ had not been assumed to be bounded, the function given by $G(S)$ would have been a nonnegative set function, for its range might contain $+\infty$.

8.3 Postulational approach to the concept of measure. We have pointed out that the lengths of intervals are the values of a nonnegative function defined on the set of all intervals. Hence to generalize this notion to more general sets might be equivalent to defining a set function, say $m(S)$, which would possess certain pre-assigned properties similar to those satisfied by $L(I)$. We list now the properties which such a set function might be required to have.

Postulates for an ideal measure function $m(S)$.

(1) $m(S)$ shall be defined for every set S.

(2) $m(S) \geqslant 0$, that is, $m(S)$ shall be a nonnegative function, $m(S) = 0$ if S is the null set.

(3) $m(S)$ shall be countably additive, that is,

$$m(S) = \sum m(S_j) \quad \text{if} \quad S = \sum S_j, \quad \text{and} \quad S_j S_k = 0$$

(null set) if $j \neq k$.

(4) If $S \subseteq E_n$, then $m(S)$ shall be invariant under Euclidean motion. That is if T represents translation or rotation in E_n, then

$$m(S) = m(TS).$$

(5) $m(S)$ shall reduce to s^n if S is a "cube" of edge s in E_n.

It can be shown that such an ideal measure function cannot exist if one accepts Zermelo's axiom of choice. We shall give here a well-known example which proves this fact.

Example. Let I represent the closed interval [0,1]. We define two points x_1 and x_2 of I to be equivalent, $x_1 \sim x_2$, if their difference $x_1 - x_2$ is a rational number. It can be easily verified that this equivalence relation is reflexive, symmetric and transitive. Hence, by this relation the points of I are distributed among classes of equivalent points. We now construct a set S by selecting one and only one representative point out of each class of equivalent points. Here we are making use of Zermelo's axiom of choice. (The set S is of course nondenumerable, for if it were denumerable the points of I would be denumerable because each class of equivalent points contains only a denumerable number of points given by $s + r$, where s is an element of the class and r is any rational number.) We shall now list and establish the properties of the set S, which are pertinent for the construction of our example.

(1) The difference between two distinct elements, say s_1 and s_2, of S is always irrational. For if $s_1 - s_2$ were equal to a rational number, s_1 and s_2 would belong to the same class and hence could not both belong to S.

(2) For every point x of I there exists an element s of S such that $x - s$ is a rational number. For suppose there were no s of S satisfying this condition. Then the class of points equivalent to x would not be represented by any point in S. This contradicts the definition of S as the set which contains a representative point from each class of equivalent points.

In order to be able to establish two more essential properties of the set S, we must give some preliminary definitions. Since the set S and the interval I are subsets of the Euclidean space E_1, postulate (4) for an ideal measure should be satisfied by any ideal measure function which we might assign to S. In order to apply this postulate we must have a way to describe translation in I. For this purpose we make the following definition of addition in I. If x and y are two elements of I, we shall mean by the addition $x \oplus y$ ordinary addition of x and y modulo 1, that is

$$x \oplus y = \begin{cases} x + y & \text{if } x + y \leqslant 1, \\ x + y - 1 & \text{if } x + y > 1. \end{cases}$$

We designate by S_r the set which is obtained from S by the addition of the same rational number r to each element of S. Thus S_r consists of all points of I which are of the form $s \oplus r$, where s is an element of S. We can now state and establish two more facts which are pertinent for the construction of the example.

(3) If $r \neq r'$, then S_r and $S_{r'}$ have no points in common. For suppose $s_1 \oplus r = s_2 \oplus r'$. Then $s_1 - s_2 = r' - r$ modulo 1, that is, the difference between s_1 and s_2 would be a rational number, and by property 1, s_1 would be equal to s_2.

(4) The interval I is the sum $\sum S_r$ extended over all rational numbers r in I. To prove this let x be any point of I. By property 2, there exists in S

an element s such that $x - s = r_1$, where r_1 is a rational number. Let r be the element in I such that $r = r_1$ modulo 1. Then $x \epsilon S_r$, and hence $x \epsilon \sum S_r$.

We are now ready to show that S cannot be assigned a measure satisfying our postulates. Suppose we could assign a measure $m(S)$ to S. From postulate 3 and 5 it would follow that $m(S) = m(S_r)$ for every rational r. To show this we write S as the sum of two sets, S' and S'', where S' consists of all s of S such that $s \leqslant 1 - r$, while S'' contains all s of S such that $s > 1 - r$. From the definition of S_r it follows that $S_r = S_r' + S_r''$ where S_r' is obtained from S' by a translation through r, while S_r'' is obtained from S'' by means of a translation through $r - 1$. Thus since $S = S' + S''$, and $S' \cdot S'' = 0$ (null set), we have by postulate (3),

$$M(S) = m(S') + m(S'').$$

From postulates (4) and (3) it now follows that

$$m(S) = m(S') + m(S'')$$
$$= m(S_r') + m(S_r'') = m(S_r).$$

Next suppose $m(S) = 0$. Then since $I = \sum S_r$, and $S_r S_r' = 0$ (null set), we have by postulate (4),

$$1 = m(I) = \sum m(S_r) = 0,$$

which is a contradiction. If $m(S) = c > 0$, then

$$1 = m(I) = \sum m(S_r) = +\infty,$$

which is also a contradiction. Hence it is impossible to assign to this set S a measure which would satisfy the conditions which were imposed on an ideal measure function.

This example shows that if every set is to have a measure, the restrictions stated in postulates (2) to (5) are too severe. Even if the requirement of postulate (3) is weakened to that of finite additivity, there can exist sets in E_3 which do not have even such a less restrictive measure (see Hausdorff, *Grundzüge der Mengenlehre*, pp. 469–472). If we insist that a measure function is to satisfy the last four postulates, we must give up the demand of the first postulate that every set have a measure, and hence admit the possibility of the existence of so-called nonmeasurable sets. The above example establishes (but only on the basis of Zermelo's axiom of choice) the existence of a nonmeasurable set.

8.4 Outer measure in a metric space. We have seen that it is impossible to define an ideal measure for every set. There exist, however, set functions which can be considered as generalizations of the notions of length, area, and volume, for these functions are identical with the ideal measure functions for certain classes of sets known as "measurable sets."

Definition 8.4.1. A set function $m_0(S)$ defined on subsets of a metric space is called an *outer measure* if it satisfies the following postulates, which are known as *Caratheodory's postulates for outer measure.*

(1) $m_0(S)$ is defined for every set.

(2) $m_0(S) \geqslant 0$, and $m_0(S) = 0$ if S is the null set.

(3) $m_0(S_1) \leqslant m_0(S_2)$ if $S_1 \subseteq S_2$.

(4) For any finite or infinite sequence of sets S_1, S_2, S_3, ... , whether they have common points or not,

$$m_0(\textstyle\sum S_j) \leqslant \textstyle\sum m_0(S_j).$$

This is known as the *countably subadditive property* of $m_0(S)$.

(5) For any two sets at a positive distance (see Def. 6.2.4) from each other

$$m_0(S_1 + S_2) = m_0(S_1) + m_0(S_2).$$

Examples. (a) Let S be any set in the metric space E_1. We define $m_0(S) = 1$ if a given fixed point, say x_0, is an element of S. If $x_0 \not\subset S_1$, then $m_0(S) = 0$. It is easily seen that this set function $m_0(S)$ satisfies the postulates for an outer measure.

P. 8.4.1. Prove that the function defined in the preceding example satisfies the postulates of Def. 8.4.1.

P. 8.4.2. Construct examples of set functions which satisfy the postulates of an outer measure.

The definition of outer measure as given here specifies properties which have a meaning in any metric space. The properties of the invariance under Euclidean motions, and that of reducing to length, area, or volume (this property is known as that of *normalization*), which were mentioned as desirable properties for an ideal measure function, have no meaning in arbitrary metric spaces. These properties are connected with the special metric spaces E_n. Such specializations will be considered later.

8.5 Sets which are measurable with respect to a given outer measure. All sets considered in this section will be assumed to be subsets of a metric space in which an outer measure $m_0(S)$ has been defined. In order to simplify the notation we shall designate the complement of a set S by $S^\sim$ instead of by cS as we have done before.

Definition 8.5.1. A set S is said to be *measurable with respect to a given outer measure* $m_0(S)$ *or just measurable*, if for every set T,

$$m_0(T) = m_0(ST) + m_0(S^\sim T). \tag{8.5.1}$$

The measure of a measurable set S is denoted by $m(S)$, and is defined to be equal to its outer measure $m_0(S)$.

Since every set T can be written

$$T = ST + S^\sim T,$$

it follows from the subadditive property 4, Def. 8.4.1 of outer measure that

$$m_0(T) \leqslant m_0(ST) + m_0(S^\sim T). \tag{8.5.2}$$

Hence, in order to prove that a set S *is measurable we need only to show that for any set* T *of finite outer measure*

$$m_0(T) \geqslant m_0(ST) + m_0(S^\sim T), \tag{8.5.3}$$

for the inequalities (8.5.2) and (8.5.3) imply the equality (8.5.1). The inequality (8.5.3) is obviously satisfied by any set T whose outer measure is $+\infty$.

We call attention to the fact that the outer measure, and hence the measure, of sets is a nonnegative set function by postulate 2, Def. 8.4.1. Hence its values may be zero, any positive real number, or $+\infty$. We shall now derive results on measurable sets.

THEOREM 8.5.1. *The complement* $S^\sim$ *of a set* S *is measurable if and only if* S *is measurable.*

Proof. Equation 8.5.1, which defines measurable sets, is symmetric in S and $S^\sim$.

THEOREM 8.5.2. *If* S_1 *is measurable, and if* S_2 *is any other set which has no point in common with* S_1, *then*

$$m_0(S_1 + S_2) = m(S_1) + m_0(S_2).$$

Proof. We apply eq. (8.5.1) to the measurable set S_1 by letting the arbitrary set T be the set $S_1 + S_2$. Then we obtain the equation

$$m_0(S_1 + S_2) = m_0[S_1(S_1 + S_2)] + m_0[S_1^\sim(S_1 + S_2)]$$
$$= m_0(S_1) + m_0(S_2) = m(S_1) + m_0(S_2),$$

since $S_1 S_2$ is the null set, and $S_1^\sim S_2 = S_2$.

THEOREM 8.5.3. *The sum $S_1 + S_2$ of two measurable sets is measurable.*

Proof. Applying the definition of measurable sets first to S_1 and then to S_2, we obtain the equations

$$m_0(T) = m_0(S_1T) + m_0(S_1{}^\sim T)$$
$$= m_0(S_1T) + m_0(S_2S_1{}^\sim T) + m_0(S_2{}^\sim S_1{}^\sim T)$$
$$= m_0(S_1T) + m_0(S_2S_1{}^\sim T) + m_0[(S_1 + S_2)^\sim T],$$

since the product of the complements of two sets is equal to the complement of their sum (Theorem 2.3.1). Applying eq. (8.5.1) to S_1 with T replaced by $T(S_1 + S_2)$, we get the equations

$$m_0[T(S_1 + S_2)] = m_0[S_1T(S_1 + S_2)] + m_0[S_1{}^\sim T(S_1 + S_2)]$$
$$= m_0(S_1T) + m_0(S_1{}^\sim S_2T)$$

since $S_1(S_1 + S_2) = S_1$, and since $S_1S_1{}^\sim = 0$ (null set). Substituting the quantity on the left-hand side of the last displayed equation for its equal in the expression for $m_0(T)$ above, we get

$$m_0(T) = m_0[(S_1 + S_2)T] + m_0[(S_1 + S_2)^\sim T],$$

as was to be shown.

As a direct consequence of the last two theorems we have the next result.

THEOREM 8.5.4. *If S_1 and S_2 are two disjoint measurable sets,*

$$m(S_1 + S_2) = m(S_1) + m(S_2).$$

P. 8.5.1. Extend this result to any finite number of disjoint measurable sets.

THEOREM 8.5.5. *If S_1 and S_2 are two measurable sets, the product S_1S_2 is measurable.*

Proof. $S_1S_2 = (S_1{}^\sim + S_2{}^\sim)^\sim$, by Theorem 2.3.1. Hence S_1S_2 is measurable, by Theorems 8.5.1 and 8.5.3.

By mathematical induction it follows from the last three theorems that the *sum* and *the product of any finite number of measurable sets is measurable,* and that the measure of the sum of any finite number of mutually disjoint measurable sets is the sum of their measures (see P. 8.5.1). This last statement is equivalent to saying that the measure is a finitely additive function. These results are special cases of more general theorems which we shall establish later.

THEOREM 8.5.6. *If S_1 and S_2 are measurable sets, and if $S_2 \subseteq S_1$, the difference $S_1 - S_2$ is measurable.*

Proof. Since $S_1 - S_2 = S_2{\sim}S_1$, it follows from Theorems 8.5.1 and 8.5.5 that $S_1 - S_2$ is measurable.

P. 8.5.2. Prove that if $S_2 \subseteq S_1$, and S_1 and S_2 are measurable,

$$m(S_1 - S_2) = m(S_1) - m(S_2).$$

In order to establish the generalizations of the theorems on the sum and product of a finite number of measurable sets to infinite sequences of measurable sets, we must give some preliminary definitions.

Definition 8.5.2. Let $\{S_n\}$ be a sequence of sets. The *limit superior* (or *complete* limit) of the sequence of sets S_n is the set which consists of all those points which are elements of *infinitely many* of the sets S_n. In symbols

$$\limsup S_n = \prod_{m=1}^{\infty} \left(\sum_{n>m} S_n \right)$$

$$= (S_1 + S_2 + S_3 + \ldots)(S_2 + S_3 + S_4 + \ldots)(S_3 + S_4 + S_5 + \ldots)\ldots.$$

The *limit inferior* (or the *restricted* limit) of the sequence $\{S_n\}$ of sets is the set which consists of all those points which are elements of *all but a finite number* of the sets S_n. In symbols

$$\liminf S_n = \sum_{m=1}^{\infty} \left(\prod_{n>m} S_n \right)$$

$$= S_1 S_2 S_3 \ldots + S_2 S_3 S_4 \ldots + S_3 S_4 S_5 \ldots + \ldots.$$

If the limit superior of a sequence $\{S_n\}$ of sets is the same set as the limit inferior of the sequence of sets, this set is called the *limit of the sequence* $\{S_n\}$ of sets, and it is denoted by $\lim_{n\to\infty} S_n$ or simply by $\lim S_n$.

It follows from these definitions that every nondecreasing sequence of sets $S_1 \subseteq S_2 \subseteq S_3 \subseteq \ldots$ has a limit which is equal to the sum $\sum S_n$, every nonincreasing sequence of sets, $S_1 \supseteq S_2 \supseteq S_3 \supseteq \ldots$ has a limit which is equal to the product $\Pi\, S_n$.

P. 8.5.3. Find the limit superior and limit inferior of the sequence $\{S_n\}$ of sets where S_n, for n odd, consists of all those points of the xy-plane for which $y \geqslant (x^2 - 1)/n$, while for n even, S_n consists of those points of the xy-plane for which $y \leqslant (1 - x^2)/n$.

P. 8.5.4. Prove that if $S_1, S_2, \ldots, S_n$ are a finite number of disjoint measurable sets, and if T is any set, then

$$\sum_{k=1}^{n} m_0(S_k T) = m_0 \left(T \sum_{k=1}^{n} S_k \right).$$

Hint. To prove it for S_1 and S_2, apply eq. (8.5.1) to one of the sets S_1 or S_2 by letting $(S_1 + S_2)T$ take the place of the arbitrary set in that equation. Extend the result by mathematical induction.

We shall now extend the results on the sum and product of finite numbers of measurable sets to sequences of measurable sets.

THEOREM 8.5.7. If $S_1 \supseteq S_2 \supseteq S_3 \supseteq \ldots$ is a nonincreasing sequence of measurable sets, the limit set $S = \text{IIS}_k$ is a measurable set, and for every set of finite outer measure

$$m_0(TS) = \lim_{k \to \infty} m_0(TS_k).$$

Proof. Let T be any set of finite outer measure. We shall prove first that $\lim m_0(TS_k)$ exists and is equal to $m_0(TS)$. The sequence $m_0(TS_1), m_0(TS_2), m_0(TS_3), \ldots$ is a nonincreasing sequence of nonnegative real numbers. Hence this sequence has a limit, say λ. Since $S \subseteq S_k$ for every k, we have by postulate (3), Def. 8.4.1, that

$$m_0(TS) \leqslant m_0(TS_k) \quad \text{and} \quad m_0(TS) \leqslant \lambda. \qquad (8.5.4)$$

Next we show that $m_0(TS) \geqslant \lambda$. The set T can be broken up in the following way.

$$T = TS + TS_1^{\sim} + S_1 TS_2^{\sim} + S_2 TS_3^{\sim} + S_3 TS_4^{\sim} + \ldots. \qquad (8.5.5)$$

Therefore, by postulate (4), Def. 8.4.1,

$$m_0(T) \leqslant m_0(TS) + m_0(TS_1^{\sim}) + m_0(S_1 TS_2^{\sim})$$
$$+ m_0(S_2 TS_3^{\sim}) + \ldots. \qquad (8.5.6)$$

But each of the sets S_k is measurable. Hence, we have on the basis of eq. (8.5.1),

$$m_0(TS_1^{\sim}) = m_0(T) - m_0(TS_1), \qquad (8.5.7)$$
$$m_0(S_{k-1} TS_k^{\sim}) = m_0(S_{k-1} T) - m_0(S_{k-1} TS_k) \qquad (8.5.8)$$
$$= m_0(TS_{k-1}) - m_0(TS_k).$$

On the basis of these last two equations, the inequality (8.5.6) can be put into the following form.

$$m_0(T) \leqslant m_0(TS) + [m_0(T) - m_0(TS_1)] + [m_0(TS_1)$$
$$- m_0(TS_2)] + [m_0(TS_2) - m_0(TS_3)] + \ldots$$
$$= m_0(TS) + m_0(T) - \lambda.$$

Thus we have shown that

$$m_0(TS) \geqslant \lambda.$$

Combining this with the result expressed by eq. (8.5.4), we find that

$$m_0(TS) = \lim_{k \to \infty} m_0(TS_k) = \lambda.$$

We now proceed to show that S is measurable. Making again use of eq. (8.5.5), we have

$$TS^\sim = T - TS = TS_1{}^\sim + S_1 TS_2{}^\sim + S_2 TS_3{}^\sim + \ldots$$

and hence by postulate (4), Def. 8.4.1, that

$$m_0(TS^\sim) \leqslant m_0(TS_1{}^\sim) + m_0(S_1 TS_2{}^\sim) + m_0(S_2 TS_3{}^\sim) + \ldots .$$

Making use of eqs. (8.5.7) and (8.5.8), the last inequality can be written

$$m_0(TS^\sim) = [m_0(T) - m_0(TS_1)] + [m_0(TS_1) - m_0(TS_2)]$$
$$+ [m_0(TS_2) - m_0(TS_3)] + \ldots$$
$$= m_0(T) - \lambda.$$

Therefore
$$m_0(T) = m_0(TS^\sim) + m_0(TS),$$

as was to be shown.

THEOREM 8.5.8. *The product of denumerably many measurable sets is measurable.*

Proof. Let $S_1, S_2, S_3, \ldots$ be a denumerable collection of measurable sets. The sets

$$S_1, \quad S_1 S_2, \quad S_1 S_2 S_3, \quad S_1 S_2 S_3 S_4, \quad \ldots$$

constitute a nonincreasing sequence of measurable sets. Hence, by the preceding theorem the limit of the sequence, which is ΠS_k, is a measurable set.

THEOREM 8.5.9. *The sum of denumerably many measurable sets is measurable.*

P. 8.5.5. Prove Theorem 8.5.9.

P. 8.5.6. Let S_1 be measurable, S_2 be of finite outer measure. Prove that

$$m_0(S_1 + S_2) = m_0(S_1) + m_0(S_2) - m_0(S_1S_2).$$

We have shown that sets, which can be obtained from a denumerable collection of measurable sets by denumerably many operations involving the formation of sums, products, and the taking of complements, are measurable. The definitions of the limit superior and limit inferior of sequences of sets (Def. 8.5.2) involve only sums and products of a denumerable collection of sets. Hence we have the following result.

THEOREM 8.5.10. *The limit superior and the limit inferior of sequences of measurable sets are measurable sets.*

The above theorems show that certain operations applied to measurable sets will lead to measurable sets. They leave the existence of measurable sets still open, nor do they give any information in regard to the value of the measure of the limits of measurable sets in terms of the measures of these sets. The following theorems relate to the value of the measure of sets.

THEOREM 8.5.11. *If $S_1, S_2, S_3, \ldots$ is a sequence of mutually disjoint measurable sets, the measure of the sum $S = \sum_{i=1}^{\infty} S_i$ of the sets is the sum of the measures of these sets.*

Proof.

$$m(S) = m\left(\sum_{i=1}^{\infty} S_i\right) \geqslant m\left(\sum_{i=1}^{n} S_i\right) = \sum_{i=1}^{n} m(S_i),$$

where the last inequality follows from the result of P. 8.5.1. If the last sum diverges as n goes to infinity, $m(S) = +\infty$, and the theorem holds. If the limit of this sum exists and is equal to a number L, then $m(S) \geqslant L$. But by postulate (4), Def. 8.4.1, $m(S) \leqslant L$. Hence $m(S) = L$ as was to be shown.

THEOREM 8.5.12. *If $S_1, S_2, S_3, \ldots$ is a nondecreasing sequence of measurable sets, the measure of their sum S is the limit of their measures, that is,*

$$m(S) = \lim_{n \to \infty} m(S_n).$$

(We here admit $+\infty$ as the limit of a divergent sequence.)

P. 8.5.7. Prove this theorem. Hint: Express S as the sum of mutually disjoint sets.

THEOREM 8.5.13. *If $S_1 \supseteq S_2 \supseteq S_3 \supseteq \ldots$ is a nonincreasing sequence of measurable sets, the measure of their products $S = \Pi\, S_i$ is given by*

$$m(S) = \lim_{k \to \infty} m(S_k)$$

provided at least one of the set S_k has a finite measure.

Proof. Let us assume that S_n is of finite measure. We can represent S_n as the sum of mutually disjoint sets:

$$S_n = S + (S_n - S_{n+1}) + (S_{n+1} - S_{n+2}) + (S_{n+2} - S_{n+3}) + \cdots$$
$$= S + \sum_{p=0}^{\infty} (S_{n+p} - S_{n+p+1}).$$

Hence by Theorem 8.5.1,

$$m(S_n) = m(S) + \sum_{p=0}^{\infty} m[S_{n+p} - S_{n+p+1}],$$

or $\qquad m(S) = m(S_n) - \sum_{p=0}^{\infty} [m(S_{n+p}) - m(S_{n+p+1})]$

$$= \lim_{k \to \infty} m(S_k).$$

The hypothesis that at least one of the sets be of finite measure cannot be dropped, as is shown by the following example. Let S_1 be the set of all real numbers greater than 1; S_2 be the set of all real numbers greater than 2. In general let S_k consist of real numbers x such that $x > k$. If we let the measure of an interval be its length, then $m(S_k) = +\infty$ for $k = 1, 2, 3, \ldots$. Hence $\lim_{k \to \infty} m(S_k) = +\infty$, but since $S = \prod_{k=1}^{\infty} S_k$ is the null set, $m(S) = 0$.

The above theorems contain the most important properties of measurable sets. Let us summarize them here.

(1) The complement of a set is measurable if and only if the set is measurable.

(2) The sum $\sum S_k$ of a finite or denumerably infinite collection of measurable sets is measurable, and if no two S_k have a point in common,

$$m(\sum S_k) = \sum m(S_k).$$

(3) The product $\Pi\, S_k$ of a finite or denumerably infinite collection of measurable sets is measurable, and if one of the partial products $\prod_{k=1}^{n} S_k$ has a finite measure,

$$m(\Pi\, S_k) = \lim_{n \to \infty} m\left(\prod_{k=1}^{n} S_k\right).$$

Up to now, the existence of measurable sets has been left open. We shall now give examples of sets which are measurable for any given outer measure.

THEOREM 8.5.14. *Every set of outer measure zero is measurable.*

Proof. Let S be a set of outer measure zero and T be any set of finite outer measure. Since $T \supseteq S^\sim T$, we have

$$m_0(T) \geqslant m_0(S^\sim T).$$

We also have by postulates (2) and (3) of Def. 8.4.1 that

$$0 \leqslant m_0(ST) \leqslant m_0(S) = 0.$$

Therefore, $m_0(T) \geqslant m_0(ST) + m_0(S^\sim T),$

which proves that S is measurable.

Definition 8.5.3. Let P be a property defined for some points x of a set S. If there exists in S a subset Z of measure zero such that P holds on $S - Z$, the property P is said to hold *almost everywhere* on S, or *at almost all points of S*.

THEOREM 8.5.15. *Every open set G is measurable.*

Proof. Let G be an open set. We denote by G_k the set of all points whose distance from the complement of G is greater than $1/k$. Thus

$$x \epsilon G_k \quad \text{if} \quad \rho_x, = \rho(x, G^\sim), > 1/k,$$

where $\rho(x, A)$ stands for the distance from x to the set A. Consider the sequence $\{G_k\}$. It is a nondecreasing sequence of sets $G_1 \subseteq G_2 \subseteq G_3 \subseteq \ldots$. If we set $s_1 = G_1$, and $s_k = G_k - G_{k-1}$, for $k > 1$, then s_k consists of all those points of G whose distances ρ_x from $G^\sim$ satisfy the inequalities

$$\frac{1}{k} < \rho_x < \frac{1}{k-1}, \qquad k = 2, 3, 4, \ldots.$$

Any two s_k have no points in common, and

$$G = \sum_{k=1}^{\infty} s_k.$$

Let T by any set of finite outer measure. We must show that

$$m_0(T) = m_0(TG) + m_0(TG^{\sim}).$$

In order to establish this, we shall show that

$$m_0(T) \geqslant m_0(TG) + m_0(TG^{\sim}).$$

We show first that the infinite series

$$\sum_{k=1}^{\infty} m_0(Ts_k)$$

is convergent. We consider the two sequences, s_1, s_3, s_5, $\ldots$ and s_2, s_4, s_6, $\ldots$. The distance between s_k and s_{k+2} is greater than $1/[k(k+1)]$. Thus

$$m_0(s_1 T) + m_0(s_3 T) + m_0(s_5 T) + \ldots + m_0(s_{2k+1} T)$$
$$= m_0(s_1 + s_3 + s_5 + \ldots + s_{2k+1})T \leqslant m_0(T).$$

In a similar way, we can show that

$$m_0(s_2 T) + m_0(s_4 T) + \ldots + m_0(s_{2k} T) \leqslant m_0(T).$$

This shows that the partial sums

$$\sum_{k=1}^{n} m_0(s_k T)$$

are bounded by $2m_0(T)$, and hence the series $\sum m_0(s_k T)$ converges. Let a positive number ϵ be given. Then we can determine an N such that for all k greater than N it is true that

$$m_0(s_{k+1} T) + m_0(s_{k+2} T) + \ldots < \epsilon. \qquad (8.5.9)$$

Since $GT = G_k T + s_{k+1} T + s_{k+2} T + \ldots ,$

we have that

$$m_0(GT) = m_0(G_k T + s_{k+1} T + s_{k+2} T + \ldots)$$
$$\leqslant m_0(G_k T) + m_0(s_{k+1} T) + m_0(s_{k+2} T) + \ldots$$

by postulate (4), Def. 8.4.1. Hence

$$m_0(GT) \leqslant m_0(G_k T) + \epsilon \qquad (8.5.10)$$

by eq. (8.5.9). On the other hand, by postulates (5) and (3), Def. 8.4.1,

$$m_0(G^{\sim}T) + m_0(G_kT) = m_0(G^{\sim}T + G_kT)$$
$$= m_0[T(G^{\sim} + G_k)] \leqslant m_0(T).$$

From this and from inequality (8.5.10) we obtain

$$m_0(T) \geqslant m_0(GT) + m_0(G^{\sim}T) - \epsilon.$$

Since this is true for every ϵ greater than 0, we have the required result,

$$m_0(T) \geqslant m_0(GT) + m_0(G^{\sim}T),$$

which completes the proof of the theorem.

P. 8.5.8. Where would this proof break down if G were not an open set?

Since every closed set is the complement of an open set, it follows from our previous results that every closed set is measurable. Also all sets which can be obtained from open sets by taking sums, products, and complements a denumerable number of times are measurable. We state this as another fundamental result on measurable sets:

(4) All Borel sets are measurable (see Def. 4.9.2).

8.6 Measure of open intervals in E_n. The treatment in the last section was entirely postulational. The results were obtained on the basis of the definition of an outer measure in any metric space. We shall now show that those results can be realized in the Euclidean space E_n in such a way as to yield a measure which is a generalization of length, area, and volume.

Definition 8.6.1. Let $a_1, a_2, \ldots, a_n$, and $b_1, b_2, \ldots, b_n$ be $2n$ real numbers such that $a_k < b_k$, for $k = 1, 2, \ldots, n$. The point set $I = \{(x_1, x_2, \ldots, x_n)\}$ in E_n, where $a_k < x_k < b_k$ is called an *n-dimensional open interval*. It may also be called an open rectangular parallelepiped (in case $n \geqslant 3$) with edges parallel to the coordinate axes. If $b_k - a_k = s$, a constant for all k, then I is called a *cube* of edge length s with edges parallel to the axes. The point $(x_1', x_2', \ldots, x_n')$, where $x_k' = (a_k + b_k)/2$ for all k, is called the center of the interval, I. Two intervals with the same center are said to be concentric.

Definition 8.6.2. The *measure* $m(I)$ of an open interval I in E_n is defined to be the nonnegative number,

$$m(I) = \prod_{k=1}^{n} (b_k - a_k) = s_1 s_2 \ldots s_n, \qquad (8.6.1)$$

where $s_k = b_k - a_k$ represents the edge lengths of I.

We note that the measure of a one-dimensional open interval is its length, of a two-dimensional one its area, and of a three-dimensional one its volume.

We shall deal here mainly with open intervals. If, however, in the definition of an n-dimensional interval at least one, but not all of the "less" $(<)$ signs are replaced by a "less or equal" $(\leqslant)$ sign, the interval will be called a *semiopen* interval. If each of the inequalities $a_k < x_k < b_k$ in the definition for an open interval is replaced by $a_k \leqslant x_k \leqslant b_k$, we have the definition of a *closed* n-dimensional interval.

If an n-dimensional interval I is divided into two n-dimensional intervals I_1 and I_2 by deleting from I all points for which $x_k = c_k$, where k is one of the first n positive integers and c_k is a constant such that $a_k < c_k < b_k$, we say that *the n-dimensional interval I has been cut by a plane* [more precisely by an $(n-1)$-dimensional plane] *perpendicular to the x_k-axis into two n-dimensional intervals I_1 and I_2.*

THEOREM 8.6.1. *If an n-dimensional open interval I is cut by a finite number of planes $x_k = c_k^{(i)}$ perpendicular to the axis x_k*

(where $k = 1, 2, \ldots, n; \quad i = 1, 2, \ldots, p$)

into the open intervals $I_1, I_2, \ldots, I_q$, then

$$m(I) = m(I_1) + m(I_2) + \ldots + m(I_q).$$

Proof. Let I be cut by the plane $x_k = c_k$. Then the one-dimensional interval (a_k, b_k) on the x_k-axis is divided into the open intervals (a_k, c_k), and (c_k, b_k). The edge length $s_k = b_k - a_k$ of the original interval has been broken up into two parts $s_k = s_k^{(1)}$ and $s_k^{(2)}$, where $s_k^{(1)} = c_k - a_k$ and $s_k^{(2)} = b_k - c_k$ are the edge lengths of the new intervals. From eq. (8.6.1),

$$m(I) = s_1 s_2 \ldots s_{k-1}(s_k^{(1)} + s_k^{(2)}) s_{k+1} \ldots s_n$$
$$= s_1 s_2 \ldots s_{k-1} s_k^{(1)} s_{k+1} \ldots s_n + s_1 s_2 \ldots s_{k-1} s_k^{(2)} s_{k+1} \ldots s_n$$
$$= m(I_1) + m(I_2).$$

The proof can be completed by mathematical induction.

Whenever we say "interval" from now on we shall mean "n-dimensional interval" unless we specify otherwise.

THEOREM 8.6.2. *If a closed interval I^- is contained in a finite number of open intervals $I_1, I_2, \ldots, I_p$, then*

$$\sum_{j=1}^{p} m(I_j) \geqslant m(I)$$

where I is the maximum open interval contained in I^-.

Proof. Let the interval I_j be defined by the inequalities $a_k^{(j)} < x_k < b_k^{(j)}$, the interval I by $a_k^{(0)} < x_k < b_k^{(0)}$. We pass planes $x_k = a_k^{(j)}$ and $x_k = b_k^{(j)}$, for each j ($j = 0,1,2,\ldots,p$), and for all k ($k = 1,2,\ldots n$). Each of the intervals I_j is thus divided into subintervals, i.e., I_j is divided into $e_{j1}, e_{j2}, \ldots, e_{jq_j}$. By the last theorem the following relations hold for the measures of the open intervals with which we are concerned.

$$m(I_1) = m(e_{11}) + m(e_{12}) + \ldots + m(e_{1q_1}),$$

$$m(I_p) = m(e_{p1}) + m(e_{p2}) + \ldots + m(e_{pq_p}),$$

$$m(I) = m(e_{01}) + m(e_{02}) + \ldots + m(e_{0q}).$$

It is important to note that no two of the intervals e_{ji} have a point in common unless they coincide. Since, however, the intervals I_j cover the interval I, each e_{0j} must be contained in (and hence be identical to) at least one of the e_{ji} with $j \neq 0$. Suppose e_{01} is in I_{j_1}. We consider all e_{0i} which are contained in I_{j_1}. The sum of their measure is less than or equal to $m(I_{j_1})$. Next we consider the first of the sets $e_{01}, e_{02}, \ldots, e_{0q}$ which was not found to be in I_{j_1}. Suppose it is in I_{j_2}. We select all the e_{0i} which are not in I_{j_1} but are in I_{j_2}. The sum of their measures is at most equal to $m(I_{j2})$. We continue this process until none of the e_{0i} are left. We then have

$$m(I) = m(e_{01}) + m(e_{02}) + \ldots + m(e_{0q})$$

$$\leqslant m(I_{j_1}) + m(I_{j_2}) + \ldots + m(I_{j_t}) \leqslant \sum_{j=1}^{p} m(I_j).$$

THEOREM 8.6.3. *Let I be an open interval, and let ϵ and δ be any two given positive numbers. It is possible to cover the closure I^- of I by means of a finite number of open intervals, each of diameter less than δ, such that the sum of the measures of the intervals is less than $m(I) + \epsilon$.*

Proof. We divide the given interval I into subintervals by cutting it with planes perpendicular to the axes. By making a sufficient, but finite, number of such cuts, each of the resulting subintervals can be made so small that each of its edge lengths is less than $\delta/2n$, where n is the dimensionality of the space. Each of its subintervals will then have its diameter less than or equal to $\delta/2$. By Theorem 8.6.1,

$$m(I) = m(I_1) + m(I_2) + \ldots + m(I_q).$$

Next we cover each of the intervals I_j by a concentric interval I_j' such that the edge length s_k' of the new interval has a ratio r to s_k, (the corresponding edge length of I_j) which is greater than 1 but less than the smaller one of the numbers 2 and

$$\left[1 + \frac{\epsilon}{m(I)}\right]^{1/n}.$$

Then the diameter of each I_j' will be less than δ, and

$$m(I_j') = \prod_{k=1}^{n} s_k' = r^n \prod_{k=1}^{n} s_k = r^n m(I_j).$$

Hence the sum of the measures of the subintervals I_j' must satisfy the following inequality.

$$\sum_{j=1}^{q} m(I_j') \leqslant \left[1 + \frac{\epsilon}{m(I)}\right] \sum_{j=1}^{q} m(I_j)$$

$$= \left[1 + \frac{\epsilon}{m(I)}\right] m(I) = m(I) + \epsilon.$$

8.7 Lebesgue exterior measure in E_n. We have defined the measure of open intervals in E_n. In terms of the measures of such simple geometrical point sets we shall now define a set function which is an outer measure and which was used by Lebesgue to define a class of measurable sets.

Definition 8.7.1. The Lebesgue exterior measure of a *set S in E_n* is the greatest lower bound (we admit here $+\infty$ as such a value) of the sum of the measures of all denumerable sequences of open intervals which cover S. We denote the Lebesgue exterior measure of S by $m_e(S)$.

Here of course the measure of an open interval is given by Def. 8.6.2, and thus represents a length in the case the interval is one-dimensional, an area in case the interval is a rectangle, and a volume if we have a three-dimensional interval, namely a parallelepiped.

THEOREM 8.7.1. *If I is an open interval,*

$$m_e(I^-) = m_e(I) = m(I).$$

Proof. Let $\sum I_k$ be the sum of a denumerable number of open intervals which cover I^-. By the Heine-Borel theorem there exists a finite subset $\{I_j'\}$ of the intervals I_k such that every point of I^- is an interior point of at least one I_j'. By Theorem 8.6.2, the sum of the measures of these intervals I_j' is greater or equal to $m(I)$. Thus

$$m_e(I^-) \geqslant m(I).$$

Let $\epsilon, > 0$, be given. If I^- is the interval $a_k \leqslant x_k \leqslant b_k$ $(k = 1,2,\ldots,n)$, the interval

$$J = (a_k - \epsilon'/2 < x_k < b_k + \epsilon'/2)$$

covers I^- and has a measure equal to $\prod_{k=1}^{n} (s_k + \epsilon')$, where the s_k are the edge lengths of I. By choosing ϵ' small enough (for example, less than one and such that

$$\epsilon' < \epsilon/n! \sum_{i=1}^{n} s^{i-1},$$

where s is the maximum of the s_k of I) we can make

$$m(J) \leqslant m(I) + \epsilon.$$

Since this is true for every given positive ϵ,

$$m_e(I^-) = m(I).$$

We still have to show that $m_e(I) = m(I)$. Since $I \subseteq I^-$, $m_e(I) \leqslant m_e(I^-)$. But $m_e(I^-) = m(I)$, as we have just shown. It follows that

$$m_e(I) \leqslant m(I).$$

Let a positive number ϵ be given. We can choose a subinterval I_1 of I such that $m(I_1) > m(I) - \epsilon$. Then $m_e(I) \geqslant m_e(I_1^-)$, which by the established part of this theorem is equal to $m(I_1)$. We thus get the inequalities

$$m_e(I) \geqslant m_e(I_1^-) = m(I_1) > m(I) - \epsilon.$$

Since ϵ was an arbitrarily given positive number,

$$m_e(I) \geqslant m(I).$$

Hence, $m_e(I) = m(I)$, as was to be shown.

THEOREM 8.7.2. *The Lebesgue exterior measure of a set S is the greatest lower bound of the sum of the measures of all denumerable sequences of open intervals which cover S and whose diameters are less than any given fixed positive number δ.*

Proof. Let $m_\delta(S)$ be the greatest lower bound of the sum of the measures $\sum m(I_j)$ of all sequences of open intervals whose diameters are less than δ. Since such sequences of intervals constitute a subset of all the unrestricted sequences of intervals covering S, it follows that the greatest lower bound $m_\delta(S) \geqslant m_e(S)$, for the infimum of a subset is never less than the infimum of the whole set. If $m_e(S) = +\infty$, then $m_\delta(S) = +\infty$, and the theorem holds in this case. Suppose $m_e(S)$ is finite. Let ϵ greater than 0 be given. There exists a sequence of intervals $\{I_j\}$ such that

$$\sum m(I_j) < m_e(S) + \epsilon/2.$$

By Theorem 8.6.3 we can cover each I_j^- by a finite set of intervals I_{jk} each of diameter less than δ, such that

$$m(I_{j1}) + m(I_{j2}) + \ldots + m(I_{ji_1}) \leqslant m(I_j) + \frac{\epsilon}{2^{j+1}}.$$

The union of all the sets I_{ji} is a covering of S. The sum of the measures of these intervals is at most $\sum m(I_j) + \frac{\epsilon}{2} < m_e(S) + \epsilon$. Since this is true for every positive ϵ, it follows that $m_\delta(S) \leqslant m_e(S)$. This combined with the reversed inequality derived above completes the proof.

THEOREM 8.7.3. *The Lebesgue exterior measure is an outer measure as given by Definition 8.4.1.*

Proof. Properties 1, 2, and 3 of Def. 8.4.1 are direct consequences of the definition of Lebesgue exterior measure. We shall now establish the property 4, that is, we shall show that if

$$S = \sum_{k=1}^\infty S_k, \quad \text{then} \quad m_e(S) \leqslant \sum_{k=1}^\infty m_e(S_k).$$

If the series on the right diverges, the last inequality is obviously satisfied. Let us assume therefore that the series of nonnegative number $m_e(S_k)$ converges. Let a positive ϵ be given. We can cover S_k by a set of a denumerable number of open intervals I_k which are such that the sums of their measures will exceed $m_e(S_k)$ by less than $\epsilon/2^k$. This follows from the fact that $m_e(S_k)$ is the greatest lower bound (infimum) of all such sums of measures. The union of the coverings of all the S_k is a covering of S. Since there are at most denumerably many intervals S_k and each is covered by at most denumerably many intervals I_k, it follows that the totality of these intervals is at most denumerable. Thus

$$m(S) \leqslant \sum_{j=1}^{\infty} \sum_{i=1}^{\infty} m(I_{ji})$$
$$\leqslant \sum_{k=1}^{\infty} [m_e(S_k) + \epsilon/2^k]$$
$$= \sum_{k=1}^{\infty} m_e(S_k) + \epsilon.$$

Since this is true for every positive number ϵ,

$$m(S) \leqslant \sum_{k=1}^{\infty} m_e(S_k),$$

as was to be shown.

Next we show that property 5 of Def. 8.4.1 is satisfied. Let S_1 and S_2 be two sets in E_n which are at a positive distance, say δ, from each other. We must show that

$$m_e(S_1 + S_2) = m_e(S_1) + m_e(S_2).$$

If at least one of the quantities $m_e(S_1)$ or $m_e(S_2)$ is $+\infty$, then $m_e(S_1 + S_2) = +\infty$. This follows from the fact that every covering of $S_1 + S_2$ is a covering of S_1, and is also a covering of S_2. Next, suppose that $m_e(S_1)$ and $m_e(S_2)$ are finite. Then, by property 4 established above,

$$m_e(S_1 + S_2) \leqslant m_e(S_1) + m_e(S_2).$$

We cover $S = S_1 + S_2$ by a sequence of intervals of edge lengths less than $\delta/\sqrt{n}$, where n is the dimensionality of the space E_n. No such interval can cover points of S_1 and of S_2. Thus any covering of S is a combination of a covering of S_1 and of a covering of S_2. Hence the sum of the measures of the intervals covering $(S_1 + S_2)$ is equal to the sum of the measures of the intervals covering S_1 and those covering S_2. Since by Theorem 8.7.2 the Lebesgue exterior measure is given

by the greatest lower bound of the sum of the measures of all denumerable sequences of open intervals whose diameters are less than
a given fixed number, in our case less than $\delta/\sqrt{n}$, we obtain the
result that

$$m_e(S_1 + S_2) \geqq m_e(S_1) + m_e(S_2).$$

This inequality, combined with the one derived on the basis of property 4, yields the property 5.

We thus see that the Lebesgue exterior measure is an outer measure as defined in the preceding section. We can therefore speak of
sets measurable with respect to this outer measure.

Definition 8.7.2. A set which is measurable (Def. 8.5.1) with respect
to the Lebesgue exterior measure is said to be *Lebesgue measurable.*

All theorems derived in the last section for sets measurable with
respect to some outer measure hold true for Lebesgue measurable
sets. In particular, the properties 1, 2, 3, 4, listed in Sec. 8.5 are
satisfied by Lebesgue measurable sets.

THEOREM 8.7.4. *(Normalization property E.) The closed or open
cube*

$$0 \leqq x_k \leqq s \qquad (k = 1,2,\ldots,n)$$

has the Lebesgue measure s^n.

Proof. Since the cube is an interval, this theorem follows from
Theorem 8.7.1 and Def. 8.6.2.

THEOREM 8.7.5. *The Lebesgue exterior measure of a set S is the
greatest lower bound (infimum) of the measures of all open sets which
contain S.*

Proof. Let a positive number ϵ be given and let S be of finite outer
measure. By the definition of Lebesgue exterior measure of S, there
exists a denumerable set $\{I_\nu\}$ of open intervals which cover S and
which are such that

$$\sum_\nu m(I_\nu) \leqq m_e(S) + \epsilon.$$

The union $\sum I_\nu$ is an open set G whose measure is by property 4,
Def. 8.4.1, not greater than the sum of the measures of the I_ν. Hence

$$m(G) \leqq m_e(S) + \epsilon.$$

Next, if H is any open set containing S, then by property 3, Def. 8.4.1,

$$m_e(S) \leqslant m(H).$$

Thus, since G is open,

$$m_e(S) \leqslant m(G) \leqslant m_e(S) + \epsilon.$$

Since ϵ was an arbitrary positive number, the theorem is proved for sets of finite Lebesgue exterior measure. If $m_e(S)$ is $+\infty$, the result is obvious.

Definition 8.7.3. The Lebesgue *inner measure* $m_i(S)$ of a set S is the least upper bound (supremum) of the measures of all closed sets F which are contained in S.

It follows from property 3, Def. 8.4.1 of outer measure that $m_i(S) \leqslant m_e(S)$.

THEOREM 8.7.6. *A necessary and sufficient condition for a bounded set S to be Lebesgue measurable is that*

$$m_i(S) = m_e(S) = m(S).$$

Proof of necessity. Let S be a bounded, measurable set. Let I be an interval containing S. Then by the definition of inner measure we have that

$$\begin{aligned} m_i(S) &= \sup_{F \subseteq S} [m(F)] = \sup_{G \supseteq S^\sim} [m(I) - m(GI)] \\ &= m(I) - \inf_{G \supseteq S^\sim} [m(GI)]. \end{aligned}$$

Making use of Theorem 8.7.5, we get

$$m_i(S) = m(I) - m(IS^\sim).$$

Applying the definition of measurability to S we obtain

$$m_i(S) = m(I) - [m(I) - m(IS)] = m(S).$$

Proof of sufficiency. Let $\{G_k\}$ and $\{F_k\}$ be two sequences of open sets and closed sets, respectively, such that $F_k \subseteq S \subseteq G_k$, where $k = 1, 2, 3, \ldots$. Furthermore, let these sets be so chosen that

$$m(G_k) - \frac{1}{k} < m_e(S) = m_i(S) < m(F_k) + \frac{1}{k}.$$

The product $G = \Pi\, G_k$ and the sum $F = \sum F_k$ are measurable and $F \subseteq S \subseteq G$. But

$$m(G) = m_e(S), \quad \text{and} \quad m(F) = mt(S).$$

Since $m_e(S) = m_i(S)$ by hypothesis, the measure of $G - F$ is zero. But $G - F$ contains the set $S - F$. Hence $S - F$ is of exterior measure zero, and hence measurable (see Theorem 8.5.14). Since $S = F + (S - F)$, S is the sum of two measurable sets and is therefore measurable.

The property of invariance of the Lebesgue measure of sets in E_n is an important one, but we shall not establish it here. We mention only the fact that measurability of sets is preserved under linear transformations, but the values of the Lebesgue exterior, inner measure, and measure are each multiplied by the absolute value of the determinant of the transformation. A rigorous derivation of these results can be found in *Reelle Funktionen* by Carathéodory. (See references at the end of this chapter.)

8.8 Vitali's covering theorem

THEOREM 8.8.1. *Let S be a bounded measurable set in E_n, and let $\{C_\alpha\}$ be a (possibly nondenumerable) set of cubes such that every point of S is covered by cubes with arbitrarily small edge lengths. Then it is possible to select a sequence $C_1, C_2, C_3, \ldots$ from the set $\{C_\alpha\}$ such that:*

(1) *no two of the cubes $C_1, C_2, C_3, \ldots$ have a point in common;*

(2) *the sum $\sum_{j=1}^{\infty} \overline{C_i}$ covers the set S except for a set of measure zero.*

Proof. Let C be an open cube such that the distance from S to the complement of C is greater than some positive number, say 1. Of the given set $\{C_\alpha\}$ of cubes covering S we shall take into consideration only those which are contained in C. This restricted set of cubes still satisfies the hypotheses of the theorem. The least upper bound of the edge lengths of the cubes in this set exists and it is obviously greater than zero. Let it be L_1. We select now a cube C_1 such that its edge length $s_1 > L_1/2$. (We are here making use of Zermelo's postulate.) Let L_2 be the least upper bound of the edge lengths of all those given cubes contained in C which have no point in common with C_1. From among these cubes we select one, say C_2, whose edge length $s_2 > L_2/2$. We construct the sequence by an inductive process. Let $C_1, C_2, \ldots, C_{j-1}$ be chosen. Let L_j be the least upper bound of the edge lengths of all the given cubes in C which have no point in common with $C_1, C_2, \ldots, C_{j-1}$. From those cubes we select C_j such that its edge length $s_j > L_j/2$. We here assume that each of the L_j is positive, for if one of them were zero, the cubes $C_1, C_2, \ldots, C_{j-1}$ would cover every point of S except possibly those points of S which might be on the boundaries of these cubes, which constitute a set of measure zero in E_n. The theorem would therefore have been established. If all the L_j are positive, they constitute a nonincreasing sequence converging to zero, for

$$\sum_{j=1}^{\infty} (L_j/2)^n < \sum_{j=1}^{\infty} (s_j)^n \leqslant m(C),$$

since the C_j are nonoverlapping cubes all lying within the cube C.

Let E be the set of elements of S which are not contained in the sum $\sum_{i=1}^{\infty} C_i$. We must show that the measure of E is zero. Since S is measurable, and since the sum $\sum_{i=1}^{\infty} C_i$ is measurable, E is measurable, for it is the difference of two measurable sets. Let us assume that the measure $m(E) > 0$. We have shown above that the series $\sum_{j=1}^{\infty} (s_j)^n$ converges. Hence there exists an integer k such that

$$(s_k)^n + (s_{k+1})^n + (s_{k+2})^n + \ldots < \frac{m(E)}{(5\sqrt{n} + 1)^n}$$

where n is the dimensionality of the space E_n. Let us replace each of the cubes $C_k, C_{k+1}, \ldots,$ by concentric cubes $C_k', C_{k+1}', \ldots$ such that the edge length s_j' of C_j' is $(5\sqrt{n} + 1)s_j$. The sum of the measures of these new cubes is less than $m(E)$. Hence, these new cubes cannot cover all the points of E. Let x_0 be a point of E not covered by any of the $C_j', C_{j+1}', \ldots$. But x_0 is covered by the given $\{C_\alpha\}$ contained in C. Let C_0 be one of the given cubes which contains x_0 but does not intersect any of the finite number of cubes $C_1, C_2, \ldots, C_{k-1}$. Let the edge length of C_0 be s_0. Since the L_j converge to zero with increasing j, there exists an L_j which is less than s_0. The cube C_0 must have been excluded in the construction of the sequence $C_k, C_{k+1}, C_{k+2}, \ldots$. Hence, there must exist a first of these cubes, say C_{k_1}, which has a point in common with C_0. Hence, we have

$$s_0 \leqslant L_{k_1} \quad \text{and} \quad L_{k_1} < 2s_{k_1}.$$

But by hypothesis C_0 contains x_0, and C_k does not contain x_0. Since C_{k_1}' is concentric with C_{k_1}, and since C_{k_1} has at least one point in common with C_0 we see that x_0 has to be at a distance not greater than $5\sqrt{n}s_{k_1}/2$ from the center of C_{k_1}, and at the same time not less than $(5\sqrt{n} + 1)s_{k_1}/2$ from that center. This leads to the contradiction that $s_{k_1} = 0$. Hence $m(E) = 0$ as was to be shown.

8.9 Jordan content. A theory of measure was developed by Peano and Jordan which, although less useful than the more recent one of Lebesgue, has nevertheless played an important part in the development of the theory of integration. The fundamental difference between the earlier theory and the one due to Lebesgue is that in the former one the covering intervals (in terms of which the measure was defined) had to be finite in number, while in the latter theory infinite sets of covering intervals were admitted.

Definition 8.9.1. Let S be a set contained in a bounded interval I. Let S be covered by finite sets $\{I_j\}$ of intervals, that is, each point of S is to be an interior point of at least one of the intervals I_j. Let K be the infimum of the sum of the measures of the I_j for all possible such finite coverings of the set S. This number K is called the *exterior Jordan content of* S and is designated $C_e(S)$. Similarly, if $S^\sim$ is the complement of S, $C_e(S^\sim I)$ is defined to be the infimum of the sums of the measures of the intervals for all possible coverings of $S^\sim I$. If S is such that

$$C_e(S) + C_e(S^\sim I) = m(I),$$

then S is said to have a Jordan content $C(S)$, and $C(S)$ is defined to be $C_e(S)$. Sets which have a Jordan content are said to be *measurable Jordan.*

From this definition it follows that the union and intersection of a finite number of Jordan measurable sets are Jordan measurable.

P. 8.9.1. Show by an example that the sum of infinitely many Jordan measurable sets need not be Jordan measurable.

P. 8.9.2. Prove that the set $1/n$ where $n = 1, 2, 3, \ldots$, is Jordan measurable. What is its Jordan content?

P. 8.9.3. Prove that the set of rational numbers in $[0,1]$ is not Jordan measurable.

REFERENCES

Carathéodory, Constantine, *Reelle Funktionen*, B. G. Teubner, Leipzig and Berlin, 1918.

Schlesinger, L. and Plessner, A., *Lebesguesche Integrale und Fouriersche Reihen*, Walter de Gruyter & Company, Berlin and Leipzig, 1926.

Hausdorff, Felix, *Grundzüge der Mengenlehre*, von Welt & Company, Leipzig, 1914.

————, *Mengenlehre*, Walter de Gruyter & Company, Berlin and Leipzig, 1927.

CHAPTER IX

INTEGRALS

9.1 Introduction. In this section we give a geometrical interpretation of the main problem in the theory of integration of real functions. For the sake of simplicity we confine ourselves first to real functions of one real variable.

Let $y = f(x)$ represent a single-valued, nonnegative, real function defined on a subset E of the real axis E_1. The planar set of points

$$Q[x,y; \quad x \in E, \quad 0 \leqslant y < f(x)]$$

is called the *ordinate set of the given function*. The main problem in the theory of integration of real functions of one real variable is to determine the "area" of the ordinate sets of functions. The term "area" as used here depends on the definition of measure of planar sets. If by measure is meant the Jordan planar content, a satisfactory solution to the main problem of integration is furnished by Riemann's theory of integration. If, however, a measure is assigned to planar sets which are not Jordan measurable, and if there exist functions whose ordinate sets are of this type, the notion of integral must be modified. That there is a need for such a modification is shown by the following example.

Example. Let $y = f(x)$ represent the function which is defined in [0,1] and is zero for x rational, and 1 for x irrational. The ordinate set of this function is not Jordan measurable, and hence the Riemann theory of integration which was designed to give the Jordan content of ordinate sets cannot be expected to give an integral for this function. On the other hand, any theory of integration (in particular Lebesgue's theory) which is based on the concept of Lebesgue measure should provide an integral of value *one* for this function, since the Lebesgue measure of the ordinate set of this function is one as is easily seen.

The geometrical interpretation of integration as stated here can easily be extended to nonnegative real functions defined on a set E in E_n. If $z = f(P)$

represents such a function, the ordinate set of $f(P)$ is defined to be the set

$$Q[P,z; \quad P \in E, \quad 0 \leqslant z < f(P)]$$

which is a subset of E_{n+1}. Any theory of integration for such functions should furnish a previously defined $(n + 1)$ — dimensional measure (area, or volume if $n = 1$ and 2, respectively) for the ordinate sets of certain classes of functions.

For a detailed analysis of the relation which exists between measures and integrals the reader is referred to *Modern Theories of Integration* by H. Kestelman, and to the other references at the end of this chapter.

9.2 Riemann integrals

Definition 9.2.1. Let $f(x)$ represent a bounded real function defined in the interval $[a,b]$. Let the interval $[a,b]$ be subdivided into n intervals by the points $x_0, x_1, x_2, \ldots , x_n$, where

$$x_0 = a, x_n = b, \quad \text{and} \quad x_{i-1} < x_i, i = 1, 2, \ldots , n.$$

We shall call such a subdivision *a partition*, and designate it by the symbol σ. Let s_j be the length of the jth interval

$$I_j = (x_{j-1}, x_j).$$

Let M_j and m_j be the supremum and infimum, respectively, of the values of $f(x)$ in I_j. The *upper sum* $(\sum^- \sigma)$ as to σ of $f(x)$ in $[a,b]$ is defined as

$$\sum{}^- \sigma = \sum_{j=1}^n M_j s_j,$$

and the *lower sum* $(\sum_- \sigma)$ as to σ of $f(x)$ is defined by

$$\sum{}_- \sigma = \sum_{j=1}^n m_j s_j.$$

The *upper integral* of $f(x)$ on $[a,b]$ is defined as the infimum of $\sum^- \sigma$ for all possible subdivisions σ, and is denoted by

$$\overline{\int_a^b} f(x)dx.$$

The *lower integral* of $f(x)$ on $[a,b]$ is defined as the supremum of $\sum_- \sigma$ for all possible subdivisions σ, and is denoted by

$$\underline{\int_a^b} f(x)dx.$$

If

$$\overline{\int_a^b} f(x)dx = \underline{\int_a^b} f(x)dx,$$

then $f(x)$ is said to be *integrable according to Riemann*, and the *Riemann integral* of $f(x)$ on $[a,b]$ is defined as the value of the upper and lower integrals of $f(x)$ on $[a,b]$, and is denoted by

$$\int_a^b f(x)dx.$$

A function which has a Riemann integral on an interval is said to be *Riemann integrable on that interval*.

THEOREM 9.2.1. *A necessary and sufficient condition that a function $f(x)$ be Riemann integrable on $[a,b]$ is that for every positive number ϵ there exists a partition σ of $[a,b]$ such that*

$$\sum{}^- \sigma - \sum{}_- \sigma < \epsilon.$$

Proof of sufficiency. Let a positive ϵ be given. By hypothesis there exists a subdivision σ such that

$$\sum{}^- \sigma - \sum{}_- \sigma < \epsilon.$$

But by Def. 9.2.1,

$$\sum{}^- \sigma \geqslant \overline{\int_a^b} f(x)dx$$

$$\sum{}_- \sigma \leqslant \underline{\int_a^b} f(x)dx.$$

Therefore $\quad \overline{\int_a^b} f(x)dx - \underline{\int_a^b} f(x)dx \leqslant \sum{}^- \sigma - \sum{}_- \sigma < \epsilon.$

Since ϵ was arbitrary,

$$\overline{\int_a^b} f(x)dx = \underline{\int_a^b} f(x)dx,$$

and $f(x)$ is Riemann integrable on $[a,b]$.

Proof of necessity. Suppose $f(x)$ is Riemann integrable. Then

$$\overline{\int_a^b} f(x)dx = \underline{\int_a^b} f(x)dx = K,$$

where K is some number. Let a positive number ϵ be given. Since the integral of $f(x)$ on $[a,b]$ is the infimum of all upper sums $\sum{}^- \sigma$, there must exist a partition, say σ_1, such that

$$\sum^- \sigma_1 - K < \epsilon/2.$$

Also, there must exist a subdivision σ_2 such that

$$K - \sum_- \sigma_2 < \epsilon/2.$$

Hence $\qquad \sum^- \sigma_1 - \sum_- \sigma_2 < \epsilon.$

Let σ be a partition of $[a,b]$ formed by the totality of division points in σ_1 and in σ_2. Then it follows that

$$\sum^- \sigma_1 \geqslant \sum^- \sigma, \quad \text{and} \quad \sum_- \sigma_2 \leqslant \sum_- \sigma,$$

for the terms $M_j s_j$ of $\sum^- \sigma_1$ are replaced in $\sum^- \sigma$ by

$$M_j{}^{(1)} s_j{}^{(1)} + M_j{}^{(2)} s_j{}^{(2)} + \cdots + M_j{}^{(t)} s_j{}^{(t)}$$

where $\qquad \sum_{i=1}^{t} s_j{}^{(i)} = s_j,$

and each of the $M_j{}^{(i)}$ $(i = 1, \cdots, t)$ is not larger than M_j. A similar argument establishes the second displayed inequality. Therefore

$$\sum^- \sigma - \sum_- \sigma < \epsilon.$$

P. 9.2.1. Prove that if the saltus (or oscillation) $s(x)$ of a function is less than a positive number k at each point of a closed interval, there exists a positive number δ such that for every x_1 and x_2 such that $|x_1 - x_2| < \delta$, it is true that the saltus in the interval $[x_1, x_2]$ is less than k. Hint. Use the Heine-Borel theorem.

P. 9.2.2. Prove that if the Riemann integral of $f(x)$ on $[a,b]$ exists, it is equal to

$$\lim_{\max |x_i - x_{i-1}| \to 0} \sum_{i=1}^{n} f(\xi_i)(x_i - x_{i-1})$$

where ξ_i is any number such that $x_{i-1} \leqslant \xi_i \leqslant x_i$, and $(x_0, x_1, \ldots, x_n)$ is any partition of $[a,b]$, and conversely, if this limit exists, $f(x)$ is Riemann integrable.

THEOREM 9.2.2. *Let $f(x)$ be a real function defined at all points of $[a,b]$. Let S_k be the set of points x of $[a,b]$ at which the saltus of $f(x)$ is greater than or equal to k. A necessary and sufficient condition that $f(x)$ be Riemann integrable is that the Jordan content of S_k be zero for every positive number k.*

Proof. First, the condition is necessary. Let us suppose that for some $k, > 0$, the exterior Jordan content of S_k is greater than some positive number p. Then if σ is any subdivision whatsoever of $[a,b]$, the sum of the lengths of those intervals of σ which contain in their interiors points of S_k is at least p. The saltus in every such interval is at least k. Hence the upper sum as to σ exceeds the lower sum as to σ by at least pk, that is,

$$\sum{}^- \sigma - \sum{}_- \sigma \geqslant pk.$$

Since this is true for every subdivision, the function is not Riemann integrable by Theorem 9.2.1.

Secondly, the condition is sufficient. For let ϵ_1 be a given positive number. Then the Jordan content of the set S_{ϵ_1} (which is the set of points in $[a,b]$ where the saltus of $f(x)$ is greater or equal to ϵ_1) is by hypothesis zero. Hence, for every positive ϵ_2 there exists a finite set of open intervals I_j such that they cover the set S_{ϵ_1} and such that the sum of their lengths in less than ϵ_2. The saltus of $f(x)$ at any point of $[a,b]$ outside the I_j intervals is less than ϵ_1. Hence by P. 9.2.1 we can divide each of the closed intervals complementary to the I_j in $[a,b]$ into a finite number of intervals $I_j{}'$ such that the saltus of $f(x)$ in each of these subintervals is less than ϵ_1. The intervals I_j and $I_j{}'$ constitute a partition σ of $[a,b]$ such that

$$\sum{}^- \sigma - \sum{}_- \sigma < (M - m)\epsilon_2 + (b - a)\epsilon_1,$$

where M and m are the supremum and infimum, respectively, of $f(x)$ in $[a,b]$. Since ϵ_1 and ϵ_2 are arbitrary, it follows from Theorem 9.2.1 that $f(x)$ is Riemann integrable.

P. 9.2.3. Prove that the set S_k is closed. Here S_k is the set defined in the last theorem.

THEOREM 9.2.3. *Let $f(x)$ be a bounded real function defined in $[a,b]$. A necessary and sufficient condition that $f(x)$ be Riemann integrable is that the set of points of discontinuity of $f(x)$ be of Lebesgue measure zero.*

Proof of necessity. We establish first the necessity of the condition. Let D be the set of discontinuities of $f(x)$. We must show that if $f(x)$ is Riemann integrable, $m(D) = 0$. On the basis of the last theorem we have that for every $k > 0$ the Jordan content of the set S_k is zero, where S_k is the set of points x at which the saltus of $f(x)$ is greater than or equal to k. The set of discontinuities D can be broken up in the following way:

$$D = S_{1/2} + (S_{1/3} - S_{1/2}) + (S_{1/4} - S_{1/3})$$
$$+ \ldots + (S_{1/(n+1)} - S_{1/n}) + \ldots,$$

where each term is of content zero. Therefore we can cover the points of $S_{1/2}$ by means of a finite number of intervals of length-sum less than $\epsilon/2$; the set $(S_{1/3} - S_{1/2})$ can be covered by means of a finite number of intervals whose length-sum is less than $\epsilon/4$; in general, the set $(S_{1/(n+1)} - S_{1/n})$ can be covered by means of a finite number of intervals of length-sum less than $\epsilon/2^n$. The set D can thus be covered by means of a denumerable number of intervals of length-sum less than ϵ, and the exterior Lebesgue measure is therefore zero, and hence the Lebesgue measure of D is zero.

Proof of sufficiency. We must show that if $m(D) = 0$, then $f(x)$ is Riemann integrable. If $m(D) = 0$, the Lebesgue measure of S_k is zero for every $k > 0$. Hence S_k can be covered by means of $\aleph_0$ or fewer intervals of length-sum less than any preassigned positive number ϵ. Since S_k is closed (by P. 9.2.3) we can apply the Heine-Borel theorem, and can conclude that a finite number of the intervals of this very covering suffices to cover S_k. We thus have for every positive number ϵ a finite set of intervals which cover S_k and whose length-sum is less than ϵ. Therefore the Jordan exterior content, and also the content of S_k is zero for every positive k. Hence by the preceding theorem $f(x)$ is Riemann integrable.

Corollary 1 to Theorem 9.2.3. Every continuous function defined on a closed interval is Riemann integrable.

Corollary 2 to Theorem 9.2.3. Every bounded function with a finite or denumerable number of discontinuities is Riemann integrable.

Example. The function defined in Example (a), of Sec. 4.8 is discontinuous at every rational point in $[0,1]$ but is continuous at every irrational point of $[0,1]$. Hence that function is Riemann integrable.

THEOREM 9.2.4. *Every monotone function defined in a closed interval $[a,b]$ is Riemann integrable on $[a,b]$.*

Proof. We assume $f(x)$ to be monotone increasing, for if it were monotone decreasing we could apply the same proof to the increasing function $-f(x)$. The cardinal number of the set of points where the saltus of $f(x)$ is greater than a given positive number k is finite. For if it were infinite the saltus of the function on $[a,b]$ would be more than nk, where n is any given positive integer. But nk must be less than $f(b) - f(a)$. Therefore the totality of discontinuities is at most $\aleph_0$ and $f(x)$ is Riemann integrable.

P. 9.2.4. Construct a monotone function defined on $[0,1]$ which is continuous at every irrational point and discontinuous at every rational point.

Definition 9.2.2. A function $f(x)$ is said to be of *bounded variation on* $[a,b]$ if there exists a positive number P such that for every partition

$$(a = x_0, x_1, x_2, \ldots, x_n = b, \quad \text{with} \quad x_{i-1} < x_i),$$

$$\sum_{i=1}^{n} | f(x_i) - f(x_{i-1}) | < P.$$

The *total variation* of $f(x)$ over $\lfloor a,b \rfloor$ is the supremum for all partitions of

$$\sum_{i=1}^{n} | f(x_i) - f(x_{i-1}) |$$

P. 9.2.5. Give an example of a function which is bounded in $[0,1]$ but not of bounded variation in $[0,1]$.

P. 9.2.6. Show that every function of bounded variation can be represented as the sum of two monotone functions. Hence show that every function of bounded variation defined on a closed interval is Riemann integrable.

9.3 Properties of the Riemann integral. Before we list some of the important properties of the Riemann integral we need to define certain concepts which have a bearing on the nature of the integrals.

Definition 9.3.1. Let $f(x)$ be a single-valued function defined in an interval of which x_0 is an interior point. The *derivative of* $f(x)$ at the point x_0 is

$$\lim_{h \to 0} \frac{f(x_0 + h) - f(x_0)}{h}$$

if this limit exists. The derivative of $f(x)$ at x_0 is denoted by $f'(x_0)$.

Let $f(x)$ be a given function defined in $a < x < b$. If there exists a function $F(x)$ such that for all x in (a,b) $F'(x) = f(x)$, then $F(x)$ is called a *primitive or antiderivative* of $f(x)$ on (a,b).

As a direct consequence of Theorem 9.2.3 we have the result that if $f(x)$ is Riemann integrable on $[a,b]$, then $f(x)$ is Riemann integrable on every subset $[c,d]$ of $[a,b]$.

Definition 9.3.2. Let $f(x)$ be Riemann integrable on $[a,b]$ and let $[c,x]$ be a subinterval of $[a,b]$. Then the function

$$g(x) = \int_c^x f(x)dx$$

is called the indefinite integral of $f(x)$.

Thus far we have defined the Riemann integral of a function $f(x)$ on an interval $[a,b]$ with $a < b$. We now extend it by defining

$$\int_b^a f(x)dx = -\int_a^b f(x)dx,$$

and
$$\int_a^a f(x)dx = 0.$$

P. 9.3.1. (Rolle's theorem.) Prove that if $f(x)$ is continuous in $[a,b]$, $f(a) = f(b) = 0$, and $f'(x)$ exists at each point in (a,b), then there exists a number ξ such that $a < \xi < b$, and $f'(\xi) = 0$.

P. 9.3.2. (Theorem of the mean for derivatives). Prove that if $f(x)$ is continuous in $[a,b]$ and has a derivative at each point in (a,b), there exists a number ξ such that $a < \xi < b$, and

$$f(b) = f(a) + f'(\xi)(b - a).$$

P. 9.3.3. Prove that if $g(x)$ is defined on $[a,b]$, is the derivative of some function on $[a,b]$, and if $g(a)$ and $g(b)$ have opposite signs, there exists at least one number c such that $a < c < b$ and $f(c) = 0$. Deduce from this that a derivative function which is defined at each point of an interval takes on all values between any two of its values.

P. 9.3.4. Establish the following properties for the Riemann integral.

If $f(x)$ and $g(x)$ are Riemann integrable on $[a,b]$, the following statements are true.

(1) For every pair of real numbers α and β, $\alpha f(x) + \beta g(x)$ is Riemann integrable, and

$$\int_a^b [\alpha f(x) + \beta g(x)]dx = \alpha \int_a^b f(x)dx + \beta \int_a^b g(x)dx.$$

(2) For every triple of numbers c, d, and e in $[a,b]$,

$$\int_c^d f(x)dx + \int_d^e f(x)dx = \int_c^e f(x)dx.$$

(3) If $f(x) \leqslant g(x)$ on $[a,b]$, then

$$\int_a^b f(x)dx \leqslant \int_a^b g(x)dx.$$

(4) First theorem of the mean.

(a) If $m \leqslant f(x) \leqslant M$, then

$$m(b - a) \leqslant \int_a^b f(x)dx \leqslant M(b - a).$$

(b) If $f(x)$ is continuous on $[a,b]$, there exists a number ξ in (a,b) such that
$$\int_a^b f(x)dx = f(\xi)(b - a).$$

(c) If $f(x)$ and $g(x)$ are continuous on $[a,b]$ and if $g(x) \geqslant 0$ on $[a,b]$, there exists a number ξ such that $a < \xi < b$ and
$$\int_a^b f(x)g(x)dx = f(\xi)\int_a^b g(x)dx.$$

(5) The indefinite integral
$$F(x) = \int_a^x f(t)dt$$
is a continuous function of x where $a \leqslant x \leqslant b$.

(6) The indefinite integral $F(x)$ is of bounded variation on $[a,b]$. (Here and under 7, $F(x)$ has the same meaning as under 5.)

(7) $F'(x_0) = f(x_0)$ if $f(x)$ is continuous at x_0, where $a < x_0 < b$.

The reader is familiar with the fact that under certain conditions the indefinite integral, and hence the definite Riemann integral, can be evaluated by the use of the antiderivative. The conditions under which this is possible form the hypothesis of the fundamental theorem of the integral calculus. Before we state and prove that theorem for the Riemann theory of integration, we illustrate by example that there exist functions, even bounded functions, which have antiderivatives in a given interval but have no Riemann integral over that interval. On the other hand, there exist functions which have an indefinite Riemann integral over every subinterval of a given interval but have no antiderivative in any subinterval of the given interval.

Example of a bounded function which is the derivative of a function but which is not Riemann integrable. Every function of this nature has to be such that the set of points of discontinuities is not of Lebesgue measure zero. The well-known example which is given here was constructed by Volterra and dates back to 1881.

We construct in $[0,1]$ a nowhere dense perfect set (see Sec. 4.5) which is analogous to the Cantor ternary set, except that we make the sum of the lengths of the black intervals less than 1. Let (α,β) be any one of the black intervals. Let the set of white points in $(0,1)$ be denoted by E. We make use of the function

$$f(x,\alpha) = (x - \alpha)^2 \sin \frac{1}{x - \alpha}, \quad \text{if} \quad x \neq \alpha,$$
$$= 0 \quad \text{if} \quad x = \alpha.$$

This function has a derivative with respect to x at every point x, which is easily found to be

$$f'(x,\alpha) = 2(x - \alpha) \sin \frac{1}{x - \alpha} - \cos \frac{1}{x - \alpha}, \quad \text{if} \quad x \neq \alpha,$$
$$= 0 \quad \text{if} \quad x = \alpha.$$

The function $f'(x,\alpha)$ has an infinite number of zeros in the interval $(\alpha,(\alpha + \beta)/2]$. Let $\alpha + \gamma$ be the largest value of x in $(\alpha,(\alpha + \beta)/2]$ for which $f'(x,\alpha) = 0$. We now define $g(x)$ as follows:

$$g(x) = f(x,\alpha) \quad \text{if} \quad \alpha < x \leqslant \alpha + \gamma,$$
$$= f(\alpha + \gamma,\alpha) \quad \text{if} \quad \alpha + \gamma \leqslant x \leqslant \beta - \gamma,$$
$$= -f(x,\beta) \quad \text{if} \quad \beta - \gamma \leqslant x < \beta,$$
$$= 0 \quad \text{if } x \text{ is a point of } E.$$

The reader is advised to sketch the graph of $g(x)$ in one typical interval $[\alpha,\beta]$. At each point x_0 of $0 < x < 1$, the function $g(x)$ has a derivative, as we shall show. If x_0 is a point of the complement of E in $[0,1]$ then $g'(x_0)$ exists, for it is equal to $f'(x_0,\alpha)$ if $\alpha < x_0 \leqslant \alpha + \gamma$, is equal to zero if $\alpha + \gamma \leqslant x \leqslant \beta - \gamma$, is equal to $-f'(x_0,\beta)$ if $\beta - \gamma \leqslant x < \beta$. In order to find $g'(x_0)$ when x_0 is an element of E, we form the quotient

$$\frac{g(x_0 + h) - g(x_0)}{h}.$$

If we take the limit of this quotient as h approaches zero in such a way that $x_0 + h$ is always an element of E, the numerator of the displayed quotient is always zero. If $x_0 + h$ is an element of the complement of E, it follows from the definition of $g(x)$ that

$$\left| \frac{g(x_0 + h) - g(x_0)}{h} \right| \leqslant \left| \frac{h^2}{h} \right| = |h|.$$

Hence it follows that for each point of x_0 of E $g'(x_0) = 0$. But in every neighborhood of such a point x_0 there are endpoints of the intervals complementary to E. Hence in every neighborhood of each point of E the function $g'(x)$ takes on values of $+1$ and -1. This shows that $g'(x)$ is discontinuous at each point of E. Since E was constructed so that its Lebesgue measure would be greater than zero, $g'(x)$ is not Riemann integrable.

The function of Example (a), Sec. 4.8 is Riemann integrable and has an indefinite integral equal to zero over every subinterval of [0,1], but it does not have an antiderivative, as is obvious on the basis of P. 9.3.3.

We now state the *fundamental theorem of the integral calculus* which for the theory of Riemann integration takes the following form.

THEOREM 9.3.1. *If $f(x)$ is Riemann integrable on $[a,b]$ and if $f(x)$ also has an antiderivative $F(x)$ on $[a,b]$, then*

$$F(b) - F(a) = \int_a^b f(x)dx.$$

Proof. Let σ, given by $a = x_0, x_1, x_2, \ldots, x_n = b$, $x_{i-1} < x_i$, be an arbitrary partition of $[a,b]$. Then

$$F(b) - F(a) = \sum_{j=1}^n [F(x_j) - F(x_{j-1})].$$

Making use of the theorem of the mean for derivatives (see P. 9.3.2), we obtain from the last equation the result that

$$F(b) - F(a) = \sum_{j=1}^n f(\xi_j)(x_j - x_{j-1}).$$

Taking the limit as max $(x_j - x_{j-1})$ goes to zero, we can deduce on the basis of P. 9.2.2 the conclusion of the theorem.

P. 9.3.5. Show by means of an example that a bounded function defined on $[a,b]$ which is the limit of a sequence of Riemann integrable functions may itself not be Riemann integrable.

P. 9.3.6. Prove that a bounded, nonnegative function $f(x)$ defined on $[a,b]$ is Riemann integrable if and only if the ordinate set

$$Q[x,y; \quad x\epsilon[a,b]. \quad 0 \leqslant y < f(x)]$$

has a Jordan content.

9.4 Measurable functions of a single variable. Let $f(x)$ be a real function of a real variable defined on E. Let h and $k(h < k)$ be two real numbers. The subset of E which consists of those points x for which $h < f(x) < k$ will be designated by the symbol $E[h < f(x) < k]$. Analogously, the symbol $E[f(x) > h]$ shall indicate the set of elements x of E for which $f(x) > h$.

Definition 9.4.1. A function $f(x)$ is said to be *measurable* if for every pair of real numbers h and k, $h < k$, the set $E[h < f(x) < k]$ is measurable.

THEOREM 9.4.1. *If $f(x)$ is measurable and h and k are any two real number such that $h < k$, the set $E[h \leqslant f(x) < k]$ is measurable.*

Proof.

$$E[h \leqslant f(x) < k] = \prod_{n=1}^{\infty} E\left[\left(h - \frac{1}{n}\right) < f(x) < k\right].$$

The set $E[h \leqslant f(x) < k]$ has thus been represented as the intersection of a denumerable number of measurable set. Hence, it is measurable, by Theorem 8.5.11.

In a similar way it can be shown that the sets

$$E[h \leqslant f(x) \leqslant k] \quad \text{and} \quad E[k = f(x)]$$

are measurable if $f(x)$ is measurable.

THEOREM 9.4.2. *A function $f(x)$ is measurable if and only if the set $E[f(x) > m]$ is measurable for every real number m.*

Proof. If $E[f(x) > m]$ is measurable, the set $E[f(x) \geqslant m]$ is measurable, for it can be represented as

$$E[f(x) \geqslant m] = \prod_{n=1}^{\infty} E\left[f(x) > m - \frac{1}{n}\right].$$

By Theorem 8.5.11 this set is measurable. But

$$E[h < f(x) < k] = E[f(x) > h] - E[f(x) \geqslant k].$$

Since both of the last two sets are measurable, it follows from Theorem 8.5.6 that their difference is measurable. Therefore $f(x)$ is measurable.

Next, suppose $f(x)$ is measurable. Then $E[h < f(x) < k]$ is measurable for every h and k. Let $h = m$, and let k take on the values $h + 1, h + 2, h + 3, \ldots$. Then

$$E[f(x) > m] = \sum_{n=1}^{\infty} E[h < f(x) < h + n].$$

It follows from Theorem 8.5.9 that $E[f(x) > m]$ is measurable.

P. 9.4.1. Prove that if $f(x)$ is measurable, so is $-f(x)$.

P. 9.4.2. Prove that if $f(x)$ is measurable, E the domain of definition of $f(x)$ is a measurable set. Show also that the set $E[\,|f(x)\,| > k\,]$, where k is any nonnegative number, is measurable.

P. 9.4.3. Prove that every continuous function is measurable. Hint. If $f(x)$ is continuous, is the set of points $E[f(x) > h]$ an open set?

P. 9.4.4. (a) Give an example of a function which is not measurable.

(b) Prove that if $f(x)$ is measurable, the set $E[f(x) = k]$ is measurable for every k.

(c) Show by example that the converse of the statement in (b) is not true, that is, construct a function on, say $[0,1]$, such that $E[f(x) = k]$ is measurable for every k, but $f(x)$ is not measurable.

(d) Show by example that the measurability of $f(x)$ does not follow from the measurability of $f^2(x)$.

THEOREM 9.4.3. *The sum and the difference of two measurable functions defined on the same set E are measurable.*

Proof. Let $f(x)$ and $g(x)$ be two given measurable functions defined on the same set E. Let h be given, and let r be any rational number. Then the sets $E[f(x) > h - r]$ and $E[g(x) > r]$ are measurable sets, by Theorem 9.4.2. Hence the denumerable sum

$$S = \sum_r E[f(x) > h - r]E[g(x) > r]$$

taken over all rational numbers is measurable. We shall show that

$$S = E[f(x) + g(x) > h].$$

Let $x \in S$. Then $f(x) > h - r$, and $g(x) > r$. Adding these two inequalities, we find that

$$f(x) + g(x) > h, \quad \text{and} \quad x \in E[f(x) + g(x) > h].$$

Next, suppose $x \in E[f(x) + g(x) > h]$. Since the rational numbers are dense in the set of all real numbers, there exists a rational number, say r', such that $r' < g(x)$, but r' is so near to $g(x)$ that $f(x) + r' > h$. Hence

$$x \in E[f(x) > h - r'] \quad \text{and} \quad x \in E[g(x) > r'].$$

Thus $x \in S$, as was to be shown. It follows now from Theorem 9.4.2 that $f(x) + g(x)$ is measurable.

By P. 9.4.1, the function $-g(x)$ is measurable if $g(x)$ is measurable. It follows $f(x) - g(x)$ is measurable.

P. 9.4.5. Prove that the product of two measurable functions which are defined on the same set is measurable. Hint. Prove first that $f^2(x)$ is measurable if $f(x)$ is measurable.

P. 9.4.6. Prove that if $f(x)$ is defined on a measurable set and if the set of points of discontinuity of $f(x)$ is of Lebesgue measure zero, then $f(x)$ is measurable.

P. 9.4.7. Prove that if $g(x)$ is measurable and not equal to zero on E, then $1/g(x)$ is measurable.

P. 9.4.8. Prove that if $\{f_i(x)\}$ is a sequence of functions measurable on E, the $\lim_{n \to \infty} f_n(x)$ is measurable if it exists; if $\lim_{n \to \infty} f_n(x)$ does not exist, $\lim \sup_{n \to \infty} f(x)$ and $\lim \inf_{n \to \infty} f(x)$ are still measurable.

We have obtained the result that every continuous function is measurable, and that any function which is the limit of measurable functions is measurable. An important classification of functions which is due to R. Baire puts all continuous functions into the class *zero*. All functions which can be expressed as limits of sequences of continuous functions but which themselves are not continuous are put into class 1. In general the class n contains all functions which do not belong to any of the preceding classes but which can be expressed as limits of sequences of functions of the class $(n - 1)$. The results of this section establish the fact that every function which belongs to some class of Baire's classification is a measurable function.

Every continuous function of measurable functions is measurable, but there exist measurable functions of continuous functions which are not measurable. In this connection the reader is advised to see Carathéodory, *Vorlesungen über reelle Funktionen*, page 379.

9.5 Lebesgue integral for real functions of one real variable.

Definition 9.5.1. Let $y = f(x)$ be a bounded measurable real function defined on $[a,b]$. Let L be any real number less than the infimum of $f(x)$, and let U by any real number greater than the supremum of $f(x)$. Let the interval $[L,U]$ (on the y-axis) be divided into n parts by the partition J which is given by the points $y_0, y_1, y_2, \ldots, y_n$, where

$$y_0 = L, \quad y_n = U \quad \text{and} \quad y_{i-1} < y_i, \quad (i = 1,2,3,\ldots,n).$$

The *upper sum of $f(x)$ on $[a,b]$* as to J is defined to be

$$\sum{}^- J = \sum_{i=1}^n y_i m[E(y_{i-1} \leqslant f(x) < y_i)];$$

the *lower sum of $f(x)$ on $[a,b]$ as to J* is defined as

$$\sum{}_- J = \sum_{i=1}^n y_{i-1} m[E(y_{i-1} \leqslant f(x) < y_i)],$$

where $m[E]$ stands for the Lebesgue measure of the set E. The *upper Lebesgue integral of $f(x)$* on $[a,b]$ is the infimum of all upper sums of $f(x)$ on $[a,b]$ for all partitions J of $[L,U]$, while the *lower Lebesgue* *integral* of $f(x)$ on $[a,b]$ is the supremum of all *lower sums* of $f(x)$ on $[a,b]$ for all partitions J of $[L,U]$. We designate these upper and lower integrals

$$(L) \overline{\int_a^b} f(x)dx, \quad \text{and} \quad (L) \int_{\underline{a}}^b f(x)dx,$$

respectively. If the upper Lebesgue integral of $f(x)$ on $[a,b]$ is equal to the lower Lebesgue integral of $f(x)$ on $[a,b]$, their common value is called the Lebesgue integral of $f(x)$ on $[a,b]$, and is designated $L[f;a,b\,|$, or

$$(L) \int_a^b f(x)dx.$$

We shall also use the notation

$$\int_a^b f(x)dx$$

if it is clear from the context whether the Riemann or the Lebesgue integral is meant. When we want to call special attention to the fact that a certain integral is a Riemann integral we shall use the notation

$$(R) \int_a^b f(x)dx.$$

If $f(x)$ is bounded and has a Lebesgue integral on $[a,b]$ we say $f(x)$ is *Lebesgue integrable* on $[a,b]$.

THEOREM 9.5.1. *If $f(x)$ is bounded and measurable on $[a,b]$, then $f(x)$ is Lebesgue integrable on $[a,b]$.*

Proof. We must show that the infimum of all upper sums of $f(x)$ on $[a,b]$ is equal to the supremum of all lower sums of $f(x)$ on $[a,b]$. To do this we need only to show that there exists a partition J for which the difference between the upper sum and the lower sum is as small as we please. To this end let a positive number ϵ be given. Let J be a partition of $[L,U]$ of such a nature that the maximum $(y_i - y_{i-1})$ be less than $\epsilon/(b - a)$. Then

$$\sum{}^- J - \sum{}_- J = \sum_{i=1}^n (y_i - y_{i-1})m[E(y_{i-1} \leqslant f(x) < y_i)]$$

$$< \frac{\epsilon}{b - a} \sum_{i=1}^n m[E(y_{i-1} \leqslant f(x) < y_i)] = \epsilon.$$

P. 9.5.1. Give a function which is Lebesgue integrable but not Riemann integrable on $[a,b]$.

P. 9.5.2. Give a function $g(x)$ such that $|\,g(x)\,|$ is Lebesgue integrable but $g(x)$ is not.

P. 9.5.3. Prove that every function which is Riemann integrable on $[a,b]$ is also Lebesgue integrable on $[a,b]$. Hint. See Theorem 9.2.3 and P. 9.4.6.

P. 9.5.4. Prove that if $f(x)$ is Riemann and Lebesgue integrable on $[a,b]$, then

$$(R) \int_a^b f(x)dx = (L) \int_a^b f(x)dx.$$

P. 9.5.5. Prove that if $f(x)$ is a nonnegative Lebesgue integrable function such that

$$(L) \int_a^b f(x)dx = 0,$$

the sets $E(f(x) > 1/k)$, $k = 1, 2, 3, \ldots$ are all of measure zero.

P. 9.5.6. Prove that if a nonnegative Lebesgue integrable function is such that

$$(L) \int_a^b f(x)dx = 0,$$

then $f(x) = 0$ for all x in (a,b) except for a set of measure zero.

P. 9.5.7. Let $f(x)$ be a nonnegative bounded measurable function. Prove that the Lebesgue integral of $f(x)$ is the two-dimensional Lebesgue measure of the ordinate set of $f(x)$.

P. 9.5.8. Prove that if a bounded real function $f(x)$ is the limit of a monotone sequence $\{f_i(x)\}$ of functions which are Lebesgue integrable over $[a,b]$, then $f(x)$ is Lebesgue integrable over $[a,b]$ and

$$\int_a^b f(x)dx = \lim_{k \to \infty} \int_a^b f_k(x)dx.$$

P. 9.5.9. Show that Def. 9.4.1 is equivalent to defining the Lebesgue integral of $f(x)$ over $[a,b]$ as

$$\int_a^b f(x)dx = \lim_{\epsilon \to 0} \sum_{i=1}^n \eta_i m[E(y_{i-1} \leqslant f(x) < y_i)]$$

where $|\,y_i - y_{i-1}\,| < \epsilon$, and η_i is such that $y_{i-1} \leqslant \eta_i \leqslant y_i$.

We have defined the Lebesgue integral for functions which are defined at all points of a closed interval $[a,b]$. If $f(x)$ is defined on a bounded measurable set E which is a subset of some interval $[a,b]$, we can define the integral of $f(x)$ on E as follows. Let $F(x) \equiv f(x)$ on E. Let $F(x) \equiv 0$ on the complement of E. Then $F(x)$ is defined everywhere in the real continuum and hence everywhere in $[a,b]$. We define the integral of $f(x)$ on E as

$$\int_E f(x)dx = \int_a^b F(x)dx.$$

9.6 Lebesgue integral of unbounded functions over sets of finite measure. We have defined the Lebesgue integral for measurable functions under the conditions that the functions be bounded, and that the domain of definition be bounded. We shall now define Lebesgue integrals without these restrictions.

First we consider the case when the set E of the definition of $f(x)$ is still bounded but $f(x)$ is not necessarily bounded.

Definition 9.6.1. Let $f(x)$ be *measurable* on E, and let A and B be two real numbers such that $A < B$. We define a new function $f_{A,B}(x)$ on E thus.

$$f_{A,B}(x) = \begin{cases} A & \text{if} \quad f(x) < A, \\ f(x) & \text{if} \quad A \leqslant f(x) \leqslant B, \\ B & \text{if} \quad B < f(x). \end{cases}$$

The *Lebesgue integral of* $f(x)$ on E is defined as

$$\lim_{\substack{A \to -\infty \\ B \to +\infty}} \int_E f_{A,B}(x) dx$$

provided this limit exists.

If in the definition of $f_{A,B}(x)$ we let A be negative and B be positive, we get the following relations.

$$f_{A,B}(x) = f_{A,0}(x) + f_{0,B}(x),$$
$$| f(x) |_{A,B} = | f(x) |_{0,B} = -f_{-B,0}(x) + f_{0,B}(x).$$

These equations show that the Lebesgue integrals of $f(x)$ and $| f(x) |$ exist if and only if the following limits exist.

$$\lim_{A \to -\infty} \int_E f_{A,0}(x) dx, \qquad \lim_{B \to +\infty} \int_E f_{0,B}(x) dx.$$

9.7 Lebesgue integral over sets of infinite measure. We shall now remove also the second restrictions and define Lebesgue integrals over sets of infinite measure. Let E be a set of infinite measure. We denote by $E \cdot [a,b]$ the product (intersection) of E and $[a,b]$, where a and b are real numbers such that $a < b$.

Definition 9.7.1. Let $f(x)$ be a measurable (not necessarily bounded) function defined on E (not necessarily of finite measure). If $f(x)$ has a Lebesgue integral over $E \cdot [a,b]$ for every pair of real numbers a, b, and if

$$\lim_{\substack{a \to -\infty \\ b \to +\infty}} \int_{E \cdot [a,b]} |f(x)| \, dx$$

exists (has a finite real value), $f(x)$ is said to be *summable* over E. It is easily seen that if $f(x)$ is summable over E, then

$$\lim_{\substack{a \to -\infty \\ b \to +\infty}} \int_{E \cdot [a,b]} f(x) \, dx$$

exists. The value of this limit is denoted by

$$\int_E f(x) \, dx$$

and is called the *Lebesgue integral* of $f(x)$.

Definition 9.7.2. If a function (bounded or unbounded) defined on E (of finite or infinite measure) has a Lebesgue integral (by any one of Defs. 9.5.1, 9.6.1, or 9.7.1), then $f(x)$ is said to be *summable* (or Lebesgue summable) over E.

We note that if a bounded function $f(x)$ is summable over a bounded set E, then $f(x)$ is Lebesgue integrable over E.

P. 9.7.1. Give an example of a function $f(x)$ whose Riemann improper integral on $E(x; 0 \leqslant x < \infty)$ exists, but which is not summable, that is, the Lebesgue integral of $f(x)$ on E does not exist.

The definitions which were given for the Lebesgue integral can easily be extended to real functions defined on measurable sets of an n-dimensional Euclidean space, or even to functions defined on measurable subsets of any metric space in which a measure is defined.

9.8 Multiple integrals and Fubini's theorem. We shall now formulate the definition of a Lebesgue integral for functions of more than one variable. In analogy with previous definitions (Defs. 9.4.1, 9.5.1, P. 9.5.9) we give the next definitions.

Definition 9.8.1. Let

$$z = f(P) = f(x_1, x_2, \ldots, x_n)$$

represent a real function whose domain of definition is a subset of the n-dimensional Euclidean space E_n. The function $f(P)$ is said to be measurable if the n-dimensional set $E[P; z_{i-1} < f(P) < z_i]$ has an n-dimensional measure.

Definition 9.8.2. The *Lebesgue n-multiple integral on E* of a bounded, measurable, real function

$$z = f(P) = f(x_1, x_2, \ldots, x_n)$$

of n real variables is defined as

$$\int_E f(P)dx_1\, dx_2 \ldots dx_n =$$
$$\lim_{\epsilon \to 0} \sum_{i=1}^{p} \eta_i m E[P_i z_{i-1} \leqslant f(P) < z_i],$$

where $|z_i - z_{i-1}| < \epsilon$, and $z_{i-1} \leqslant \eta_i < z_i$.

In the cases that $n = 2$ and $n = 3$, these integrals are called double and triple integrals, respectively.

Under certain conditions n-multiple integrals can be evaluated by the successive, that is, repeated evaluation of single integrals. This result depends on an important theorem known as Fubini's theorem. We shall establish this theorem, but before we do this, we introduce some simplifying notations.

Let E be a set of finite n-dimensional measure, lying in E_n. We consider the intersection of this set E with an $(n-1)$-dimensional plane π_x perpendicular to one of the coordinate axes. The intersection of the set E with the $(n-1)$-dimensional plane π_x will be designated $E \cdot \pi_x$. We shall have to consider the $(n-1)$-dimensional measure of the set $E \cdot \pi_x$ and the n-dimensional measure of E. We shall assume that E lies between two planes π_a and π_b, where π_a and π_b are obtained by setting one of the coordinates equal to a and to b, respectively. The n-dimensional measure of E will be represented by $\mu(E)$ while the $(n-1)$-dimensional measure of $E\pi_x$ will be designated $m(E\pi_x)$.

Let K be a subset of the space E_n. A property P is said to hold almost everywhere in K, or for almost all points of K, if the points of K for which the property P does not hold constitute a set of n-dimensional measure zero.

THEOREM 9.8.1 (FUBINI'S THEOREM). *For almost all x in (a,b) the set $E \cdot \pi_x$ is an $(n-1)$-dimensional measurable set. The real function $m(E\pi_x)$ is Lebesgue summable over (a,b), and*

$$\int_a^b m(E\pi_x)dx = \mu(E).$$

Proof. We first establish this theorem for the more simple measurable sets such as open and closed sets. By making use of the structure of measurable sets we shall then extend it to the stated form.

If E is an n-dimensional interval the theorem is obvious. Hence in this case, since E is an interval I in E_n we have

(a) $$\mu(E) = \mu(I) = \int_a^b m(I\pi_x)dx.$$

If E is the sum of a finite number of nonoverlapping intervals I_1, $I_2, \ldots, I_k$, then

$$\mu(E) = \sum_{j=1}^k \mu(I_j) \quad \text{and} \quad m(E\pi_x) = \sum_{j=1}^k m(I_j\pi_x).$$

Integrating both sides of this equation and making use of (a) we obtain

(b) $$\int_a^b m(E\pi_x)dx = \sum_{j=1}^k \int_a^b m(I_j\pi_x)dx$$
$$= \sum_{j=1}^k \mu(I_j) = \mu(E).$$

Next, let E be any open set of finite measure. Then E can be represented by means of a monotone sequence of sets $E^{(1)}, E^{(2)}, E^{(3)}, \ldots,$ where each set $E^{(i)}$ is the sum of a finite number of nonoverlapping intervals. This follows from the fact that every open set can be represented as the sum of a denumerable number of open intervals $I^{(t)}$. Hence, if we let

$$E^{(i)} = \sum_{t=1}^i I^{(t)}, \quad \text{then} \quad E = \sum_{i=1}^\infty E^{(i)}.$$

It follows that $\mu(E) = \lim_{k\to\infty} \mu(E^k)$. Since, however,

$$E^{(1)}\pi_x \subseteq E^{(2)}\pi_x \subseteq E^{(3)}\pi_x \ldots,$$

and since $$E\pi_x = \sum_{k=1}^\infty E^{(k)}\pi_x,$$

it follows from Theorem 8.5.10 that

$$m(E\pi_x) = \lim_{k\to\infty} (E^k\pi_x).$$

But by (b), $$\mu(E^k) = \int_a^b m(E^k\pi_x)dx,$$

and hence

(c) $$\mu(E) = \int_a^b m(E\pi_x)dx.$$

Next, let E be a closed set. Then there exists an open set G which lies between the planes π_{a_1} and π_{b_1} and which contains E as a subset. Thus

$$E = G' - (G' - E) = G' - G'',$$

where G'' is an open set. Hence, $\pi_x E = \pi_x G' - \pi_x G''$, and

(d)
$$\begin{aligned}
\int_a^b m(\pi_x E)dx &= \int_a^b m(\pi_x G')dx - \int_a^b m(\pi_x G'')dx \\
&= \mu(G') - \mu(G'') \\
&= \mu(G' - G'') = \mu(E).
\end{aligned}$$

If E is the limit of a monotone nonincreasing sequence of open sets G_i, we may write

$$\begin{aligned}
\mu(E) &= \mu(\lim_{k \to \infty} G_1 G_2 \ldots G_k) \\
&= \lim_{k \to \infty} \mu(G_1 G_2 \ldots G_k)
\end{aligned}$$

by Theorem 8.5.13. Making use of the established case (c), when E is an open set, we conclude that

$$\mu(E) = \lim_{k \to \infty} \int_a^b m[(G_1 G_2 \ldots G_n)\pi_x]dx,$$

which by P. 9.4.8 yields

$$\begin{aligned}
\mu(E) &= \int_a^b \lim_k m[(G_1 G_2 \ldots G_n)\pi_x]dx \\
&= \int_a^b m(E\pi_x)dx.
\end{aligned}$$

A similar argument holds for the case that E is the limit of a monotone nondecreasing sequence of closed sets.

Next, let E be any measurable set of finite n-dimensional measure. There exists a set K which is the limit of a monotone nondecreasing sequence of closed sets contained in E, and there exists a set H which is the limit of a sequence of nonincreasing open sets containing E. Furthermore K and H are such that

$$K \subseteq E \subseteq H, \quad \text{and} \quad \mu(K) = \mu(E) = \mu(H).$$

It follows therefore that

(e)
$$K\pi_x \subseteq E\pi_x \subseteq H\pi_x,$$

(f)
$$m(K\pi_x) \leqslant m_i(E\pi_x) \leqslant m_0(E\pi_x) \leqslant m(H\pi_x).$$

By the preceding results that the theorem holds in the case that E is the limit of monotone sequences of open and closed sets, we obtain that

(g) $$\mu(E) = \int_a^b m(H\pi_x)dx = \int_a^b m(K\pi_x)dx.$$

Thus $$\int_a^b [m(H\pi_x) - m(K\pi_x)]dx = 0.$$

It follows from P. 9.5.6 that $m(H\pi_x) = m(K\pi_x)$ for almost all x in (a,b). Hence by (f), $m_i(E\pi_x) = m_0(E\pi_x)$ for almost all x in (a,b). From Theorem 8.7.6 it follows that the sets $E\pi_x$ are measurable for almost all x of (a,b). From equations (e) and (g) it now follows that

$$\mu(E) = \int_a^b m(E\pi_x)dx,$$

where $m(E\pi_x)$ is defined almost everywhere in (a,b).

Corollary. Let E be a measurable subset of E_n which lies between the $(n-1)$-dimensional planes E_a and E_b ($a < b$). If E is such that the real function $m(E\pi_x)$ is Lebesgue summable on $[a,b]$, then E is of finite Lebesgue measure.

Proof. Suppose E were not of finite measure. Then it would contain a subset S such that

$$\mu(S) > \int_a^b m(E\pi_x)dx.$$

But $$\mu(S) = \int_a^b m(S\pi_x)dx \leqslant \int_a^b m(E\pi_x)dx,$$

which contradicts the first inequality. Thus E must be of finite measure, and

$$\mu(E) = \int_a^b m(E\pi_x)dx.$$

This result has the nature of a converse to Fubini's theorem. In particular, if $m(E\pi_x)$ is zero almost everywhere in (a,b), the n-dimensional measure of E is zero. Conversely, if E is of n-dimensional measure zero, then since

$$\int_a^b m(E\pi_x)dx = 0,$$

the sets $E\pi_x$ are of $(n-1)$-dimensional measure zero for almost all x in (a,b).

9.9 Application of Fubini's theorem to multiple and repeated integrals. Let $z = f(x,y) = f(P)$ be a measurable nonnegative real function defined on a bounded measurable subset E of the xy-plane. We extend the domain of definition of $f(x,y)$ by setting $f(x,y)$ equal to zero on the complement of E. The Lebesgue integral

$$\iint_E f(x,y)dx\,dy$$

represents the Lebesgue 3-dimensional measure of the ordinate set

$$Q[P \in E; 0 \leqslant z < f(P)] \quad \text{in } E.$$

We shall designate this ordinate set simply Q, and its measure $\mu(Q)$. We next consider a plane π_x perpendicular to the x-axis. The intersection of the plane π_x with the ordinate set Q will be denoted by $Q\pi_x$. By Fubini's theorem

$$\mu(Q) = \int_a^b m(Q\pi_x)dx,$$

where a and b are two real numbers such that the set Q lies entirely between the planes $x = a$, and $x = b$. The set $Q \cdot \pi_x$ is a two-dimensional ordinate set of the function $z = f(x,y)$ where x is constant. These sets are thus known to be measurable for almost all x in (a,b), that is, for almost all x in (a,b), $f(x,y)$, as a function of y, is Lebesgue integrable. If furthermore we select two real numbers c, and d such that the set Q lies entirely between the planes $y = c$, and $y = d$ we have the result that

$$\int_c^d f(x,y)dy$$

exists for almost all x in (a,b). Hence

$$\iint_E f(x,y)dx\,dy = \int_a^b \left[\int_c^d f(x,y)dy \right]dx.$$

This equation expresses a double integral as a repeated integral.

If we had started with cuts perpendicular to the y-axis, we would have obtained the result

$$\iint_E f(x,y)dx\,dy = \int_c^d \left[\int_a^b f(x,y)dx \right]dy,$$

where $f(x,y)$ considered as a function of x is integrable for almost all values of y in (c,d).

If, conversely, it is known that $f(x,y)$ is integrable with respect to y from c to d for almost all values of x in (a,b), and if $f(x,y)$ is also integrable with respect to x from a to b for almost all y in (c,d), it follows from the corollary to Fubini's theorem that the ordinate set Q is of finite Lebesgue measure and that the repeated integrals are equal to $\mu(Q)$, and hence that the order of integration is immaterial.

These results can easily be extended to functions which are not of the same sign in their domain of definition. Let $f(x)$ represent such a function. We define two new functions $f^+(x)$ and $f^-(x)$ as follows:

$$
\begin{aligned}
f^+(x) &= f(x) \quad \text{if} \quad f(x) \geqslant 0, \\
&= 0 \quad\;\; \text{if} \quad f(x) < 0, \\
f^-(x) &= f(x) \quad \text{if} \quad f(x) \leqslant 0, \\
&= 0 \quad\;\; \text{if} \quad f(x) > 0.
\end{aligned}
$$

Then $f(x)$ can be expressed as $f(x) = f^+(x) + f^-(x)$. The results for $f(x)$ then follow from the validity of the results for $f^+(x)$ and $f^-(x)$.

9.10 Lebesgue integrals for Borel sets. The class of all Lebesgue measurable sets includes the class of all Borel sets as a proper subset (see Def. 4.9.2). Every measurable set is the sum of a Borel set and a set of measure zero. Since the Borel sets play an important role in the application of point set theory to mathematical statistics, we shall devote this section to integrals of functions defined on Borel sets.

Definition 9.10.1. Let S be a given set of finite measure $m(S)$ and let $f(x)$ be a bounded real function defined for all elements x of S. We denote the infimum of $f(x)$ by L and the supremum by U; thus $L \leqslant f(x) \leqslant U$ for all x in S. Let S be divided into a finite number of measurable sets S_i $(i = 1,2,\ldots,n)$ such that

$$S = S_1 + S_2 + \ldots + S_n, \qquad S_i S_j = 0 \quad \text{for} \quad i \neq j.$$

Such a partition of S into subsets will be called a partition p. Let the infimum of $f(x)$ in S_i be L_i, and the supremum of $f(x)$ in S_i be designated U_i. The *lower sum* of $f(x)$ on S as to the partition p is defined to be

$$\sum_{i=1}^n L_i m(S_i),$$

and is denoted by z, while the *upper sum* of $f(x)$ on S as to the partition p is given by

$$\sum_{i=1}^n U_i m(S_i),$$

and is indicated by Z.

It is easily seen that any partition of S superimposed on a given partition, that is, any partition of S obtained by subdividing some of the parts S_i will give a lower sum greater or equal to the lower sum of the original partition, and will also give an upper sum less than or equal to the upper sum of the original partition. Each lower sum is less than or equal to any upper sum. To prove this let z be an arbitrary lower sum corresponding to the partition p given by

$$S = \sum_{i=1}^{n} S_i, \qquad S_j S_i = 0 \quad \text{if} \quad i \neq j,$$

and let Z' be an upper sum corresponding to a partition p' given by

$$S = \sum_{j=1}^{m} S_{j'}, \qquad S_{j'} S_{i'} = 0 \quad \text{if} \quad i \neq j.$$

We now find the lower and upper sums for the partition p'' given by

$$S = \sum_{j=1}^{m} \sum_{i=1}^{n} S_i S_j' = \sum_{j=1}^{mn} S_j'',$$

where obviously $S_j' S_i'' = 0$ if $j \neq i$. This partition p'' is superimposed on each of the partitions p and p'. If z, z', and z'' represent the lower sums as to the partition p, p' and p'', respectively, and if Z, Z', Z'' are the corresponding upper sums we have

$$z \leqslant z'' \leqslant Z'' \leqslant Z'.$$

Hence, no lower sum can exceed an upper sum. Thus the lower sums have a least upper bound, a supremum, and the upper sums have a greatest lower bound, an infimum. The *lower integral* of $f(x)$ on S is the supremum of all lower sums, while the *upper integral* of $f(x)$ on S is the infimum of all upper sums of $f(x)$ on S. If the lower integral of $f(x)$ on S is equal to the upper integral of $f(x)$ on S, their common value is called the *Lebesgue integral* of $f(x)$ on the Borel set S.

THEOREM 9.10.1. *A necessary and sufficient condition for the Lebesgue integral of $f(x)$ to exist on a Borel set S is that for every positive number ϵ there exist a partition of the set S such that the difference between the corresponding upper sum Z and the lower sum z be less than ϵ.*

Proof. If the condition is satisfied, that is, if there exists a partition p such that $|Z - z| < \epsilon$, it follows

$$\left| \overline{\int_S f(x)dx} - \underline{\int_S f(x)dx} \right| \leqslant \left| Z - z \right| < \epsilon,$$

for the upper integral cannot exceed any Z, while the lower integral cannot be less than any z.

Conversely if $f(x)$ has a Lebesgue integral on S whose value is I, there must exist (by Def. 9.7.1) a partition p yielding a lower sum z such that $I - z < \epsilon/2$, for I is the least upper bound of all z. There must also exist a partition p' of S of such a nature that the corresponding upper sum Z' is such that $Z' - I < \epsilon/2$. Hence $Z' - z < \epsilon$. The partition obtained from the superposition of the partition p' on p will give a lower sum z'', and on upper sum Z'' such that $Z'' - z'' < \epsilon$.

We notice that this definition of integrals for Borel sets is perfectly analogous to the definition of the Riemann integral. In the latter case the set S is an interval which is divided into a finite number of subintervals S_i, and the lower and upper sums are formed just as they were formed here except that $m(S_i)$ designates the length of the ith subinterval of S. The Riemann definition is a particular form of the definition of an integral as given here. For if S is a finite interval $[a,b]$, any partition of this interval considered in the definition of the Riemann integral is a special case of the division of $[a,b]$ into Borel sets occurring in the Lebesgue definition. In this latter case subsets are admitted which are Borel sets of a more general nature than intervals. Since more partitions are admitted for the formation of lower and upper sums, the supremum of the set of lower sums may possibly be increased, and the infimum of set of upper sums may be diminished. We see therefore that the lower and upper integrals of a function $f(x)$ for the case of the Lebesgue definition lie between the corresponding integrals in the Riemann case. Thus if the Riemann integral of $f(x)$ exists, the Lebesgue integral must exist, and must have the same value as the former integral.

9.11 Set functions and point functions. The Lebesgue measure $m(S)$ is a function which is defined for every Borel set S. (It is of course also defined for measurable sets which are not Borel sets, but we shall consider in this section only Borel sets.) The Lebesgue measure is thus a set function which satisfies at least the following three conditions.

(a) $m(S) \geqslant 0$.

(b) $m(S)$ is denumerably additive, that is,
$$m(S_1 + S_2 + \ldots) = m(S_1) + m(S_2) + \ldots$$
if $S_i S_j = 0$ for $i \neq j$.

(c) $m(I)$, where I is an interval, is the length of I.

We next consider a set function $P(S)$ which shall satisfy the condition (a) and (b) but not necessarily (c). We shall call such a function a *P-measure*.

Definition 9.11.1. A set function $P(S)$ is said to be a *P-measure of S* if it is defined for every Borel set and if it satisfies the following conditions.

(1) $P(S) \geqslant 0$.

(2) $P(S)$ is denumerably additive.

(3) $P(S)$ is finite for every bounded set S. (The term P-measure is an abbreviation of the term probability measure.)

When the set S consists of all points having a given property we shall often replace the symbol S by the property describing S. Thus if S is the interval $[a,b)$ we may write

$$P(S) = P(a \leqslant \xi < b).$$

When S consists of a single point $\xi = a$, we indicate this as $P(S) = P(\xi = a)$.

For a set function the argument (independent variable) of the function is a set. The domain of definition of a set function is thus a class of sets. For a function which is defined on a set of points, the argument is represented either by the coordinates of point, such as $(x_1, x_2, \ldots, x_n)$ in E_n, or by a single letter, say x, or p representing the point. The domain of definition of such a function is a set of points, and we shall refer to them as *point functions*.

Let a set function $P(S)$ be defined in E_1. For the given set function, and a given constant k we define a point function $F(x,k)$ by setting

$$F(x,k) = \begin{cases} P(k < \xi \leqslant x) & \text{for } x > k, \\ 0 & \text{for } x = k, \\ -P(x < \xi \leqslant k) & \text{for } x < k. \end{cases}$$

It follows that for every given k, and for every finite interval (a,b),

$$F(b,k) - F(a,k) = P(a < \xi \leqslant b) > 0.$$

This shows that $F(x,k)$ is a nondecreasing function of x.

Let $P(S)$ be given, and let $F(x,k_0)$ and $F(x,k)$ be the point functions corresponding to $P(S)$ for two different values of the parameter k. If $k_0 < k$, we get

$$F(x,k) - F(x,k_0) = P(k_0 < \xi \leqslant k).$$

The right-hand side of this equation is a constant. If we designate $F(x,k_0)$ simply by $F(x)$, all point functions associated with $P(S)$ can be represented by

$$F(x,k) = F(x) + \text{constant}.$$

We can therefore state that for every given P-measure there exists a nondecreasing point function $F(x)$ such that for every finite or infinite interval we have

$$F(b) - F(a) = P(a < \xi \leqslant b).$$

P. 9.11.1. (a) If $P(S)$ is the Lebesgue measure, what is $F(x,k)$?

(b) If $P(S)$ is a P-measure defined as follows:

$P(S) = 0$ if the points $x = -4$, $x = -3$, $x = 2$ are not elements of S,

$P(S) = 1$ if $x = -4$ is an element of S,

$P(S) = 2$ if $x = -3$ is an element of S,

$P(S) = 1$ if $x = 2$ is an element of S,

sketch the associated point functions $F(x,0)$ and $F(x,4)$.

P. 9.11.2. (a) Show that if $P(S)$ is a P-measure, then $P(O) = 0$, where O is the null set.

(b) Show that every point function $F(x,k)$ which is associated with a P-measure, is continuous to the right.

(c) Show that for every point x such that $P(\xi = x) > 0$, the function $F(x,k)$ has a discontinuity of saltus equal to $P(\xi = x)$. Also show that for every point x such that $P(\xi = x) = 0$, the function $F(x,k)$ is continuous.

9.12 Lebesgue-Stieltjes integrals for functions of one variable. In the preceding section the notion of Lebesgue measure was generalized. We shall now show that by the use of a P-measure the theory of Lebesgue integration can also be generalized.

Definition 9.12.1. Let a fixed P-measure be given, that is, a function satisfying Def. 9.8.1. Let $g(x)$ be a given function of x, defined and bounded for all x belonging to a given set S of finite P-measure. We divide the interval S into a finite number of parts, $S_1, S_2, \ldots, S_n$, no two of which have a point in common. Let L and U be the infimum and supremum of $g(x)$ on S, and let L_i and U_i have analogous meanings for $g(x)$ in S_i, $(i = 1,2,\ldots,n)$. We form the *lower sum*

$$z = \sum_{i=1}^{n} L_i P(S_i)$$

and the upper sum $Z = \sum_{i=1}^{n} U_i P(S_i)$.

The *supremum* of the lower sums z for all possible partitions of S is called the *lower integral* and is designated

$$\int_{\underline{S}} g(x)dP(S),$$

while the infimum of the upper sums for all possible partitions of S is called the upper integral and is denoted by

$$\overline{\int_S} g(x)dP(S).$$

If $$\int_{\underline{S}} g(x)dP(S) = \overline{\int_S} g(x)dP(S),$$

we say that the Lebesgue-Stieltjes integral of $g(x)$ over S with respect to $P(S)$ exists and is equal to the common value of the lower and upper integrals. This integral is denoted by the symbol

$$\int_S g(x)dP(S), \quad \text{or by} \quad \int_S g(x)dF(x),$$

where $F(x)$ is a point function corresponding to $P(S)$.

We speak then of the Lebesgue-Stieltjes integral with respect to $P(S)$ or with respect to $F(x)$ according as we consider the P-measure to be given by $P(S)$ or $F(x)$.

In the particular case when $F(x) = x + c$, we have $P(S) = m(S)$ (the Lebesgue measure) and it is obvious that the above definition of the Lebesgue-Stieltjes integral reduces to the Lebesgue integral for Borel sets. Thus the Lebesgue-Stieltjes integral is obtained from the Lebesgue integral for Borel sets by replacing in the definition of the integral the Lebesgue measure by a more general P-measure.

Most properties of the Lebesgue integral are easily generalized to the Lebesgue-Stieltjes integral; no other modification of proofs are usually required than the replacement of the Lebesgue measure by a P-measure.

P. 9.12.1. Extend the definition of the Lebesgue-Stieltjes integral with respect to $F(x)$ to the case where $F(x)$ is a function of bounded variation. Hint. Make use of the fact that every function of bounded variation can be expressed as the sum of two monotone functions.

P. 9.12.2. If $P(S)$ is given by P. 9.11.1, evaluate

(a) $$\int_{(-5,3)} x^2 \, dP(S).$$

(b) $$\int_{(-4,0)} x^2 \, dP(S).$$

(c) $$\int_{(-4,2)} x^2 \, dP(S).$$

(d) $$\int_{(-4,2]} x^2 \, dP(S).$$

(e) $$\int_{(-5,3)} x^3 \, dP(S).$$

P. 9.12.3. (a) Let $P(S) = 1$ if $x = 0$ is an element of S.

$\qquad\qquad = 0$ otherwise.

Let $g(x) = 0$ if $x < 0$.

$\qquad\quad = 1$ if $x \geqslant 0$.

Does $$\int_{(-1,1)} g(x)dP(S)$$

exist? If so, what is its value?

(b) For the same P-measure, and for

$$f(x) = 1 \text{ if } x \leqslant 0,$$
$$= 0 \text{ if } x > 0,$$

does $$\int_{(-1,1)} f(x)dP \quad \text{exist?}$$

9.13 The Riemann-Stieltjes integral.

Definition 9.13.1. Let $g(x)$ and $f(x)$ be two bounded functions defined on $[a,b]$. Let a partition σ of $[a,b]$ be given by the points $x_0, x_1, \ldots, x_n$. We designate the maximum value of $|x_i - x_{i-1}|$ by Δ and call it the norm of the partition σ. The Riemann-Stieltjes integral of $g(x)$ with respect to $f(x)$ from a to b is the

$$\lim_{\Delta \to 0} \sum_{i=1}^{n} g(\xi_i) \, |f(x_i) - f(x_{i-1})|,$$

where S_i is any point of the ith subinterval. This limit, if it exists, is designated

$$\int_a^b g(x)df(x).$$

More precisely, this integral is said to exist and to have a value, say V, if for every positive number ϵ there exists a positive number δ such that for every partition σ such that the norm of σ is less than δ, and for every choice of the numbers ξ_i (from the ith interval) it is true that

$$\left| V - \sum_{i=1}^n g(\xi_i)[f(x_i) - f(x_{i-1})] \right| < \epsilon.$$

Let L_i, and U_i be the infimum and supremum of $g(x)$ in $[x_{i-1},x_i]$, respectively. The upper sum as to σ of $g(x)$ with respect to $f(x)$ is defined by the equation

$$\sum{}^- \sigma = \sum_{i=1}^n U_i[f(x_i) - f(x_{i-1})],$$

while the lower sum as to σ is given by

$$\sum{}_- \sigma = \sum_{i=1}^n L_i[f(x_i) - f(x_{i-1})].$$

THEOREM 9.13.1. *A necessary and sufficient condition that the Riemann-Stieltjes integral of $g(x)$ with respect to $f(x)$ from a to b exist is that for every positive ϵ there exist a positive δ such that for every partition σ whose norm is less than δ*

$$\left| \sum{}^- \sigma - \sum{}_- \sigma \right| < \epsilon.$$

P. 9.13.1. Prove Theorem 9.13.1.

THEOREM 9.13.2. *If $g(x)$ is continuous in $[a,b]$ and $f(x)$ is of bounded variation in $[a,b]$, the Riemann-Stieltjes integral of $g(x)$ with respect to $f(x)$ from a to b exists.*

P. 9.13.2. Prove Theorem 9.13.2.

P. 9.13.3. If $g(x) = 0$ for $x < 0$,

$$= 1 \text{ for } x \geqslant 0,$$

and $f(x) \equiv g(x)$, show that the Riemann-Stieltjes integral of $g(x)$ with respect to $f(x)$ from -1 to $+1$ does not exist, but that the Lebesgue-Stieltjes integral does exist over $(-1,1)$.

It is easily seen that if $g(x)$ and $f(x)$ have discontinuities at the same point, the Riemann-Stieltjes integral over an interval containing that point of discontinuity does not exist. By properly defining the functions $g(x)$ and $f(x)$ (for instance so that both are continuous to the right if this is possible) it may happen that the Lebesgue-Stieltjes integral may exist for such functions over an interval where they have a common point of discontinuity. If $g(x)$ is continuous and the set S is an interval, the Lebesgue-Stieltjes integral

$$\int_S g(x)df$$

reduces to a Riemann-Stieltjes integral.

The Riemann-Stieltjes integral reduces to an ordinary Riemann integral in the case that $f'(x)$ exists, and is Riemann integrable.

REFERENCES

Carathéodory, Constantine, *Vorlesungen über reelle Funktionen*, B. G. Teubner, Leipzig and Berlin, 1918.

Kestelman, H., *Modern Theories of Integration*, Oxford University Press, New York, 1937.

Schlesinger, L. and Plessner A., *Lebesguesche Integrale und Fouriersche Reihen*, Walter de Gruyter & Company, Berlin and Leipzig, 1926.

McShane, Edward James, *Integration*, Princeton University Press, Princeton, 1944.

Graves, Lawrence M., *The Theory of Functions of Real Variables*, McGraw-Hill Book Company, Inc., New York, 1946.

Jefferey, R. L., *The Theory of Functions of a Real Variable*, University of Toronto Press, Toronto, 1951.

CHAPTER X

THE INDEFINITE INTEGRAL
AND DERIVATIVES

10.1 Absolute continuity of a function. Before we can take up the study of certain properties of the "indefinite integral" as defined in the sequel, we need a concept which plays an important part in the theory to be developed. This concept is given by the next definition.

Definition 10.1.1. A real function of a real variable x is said to be *absolutely continuous* on a subset E of the linear continuum if for every positive number ϵ there exists a positive number λ such that for every set of nonoverlapping intervals

$$(x_1,x_1'), \quad (x_2,x_2'), \ldots , (x_n,x_n'),$$

where x_i, x_i' are points of E, and which are such that

$$\sum_{i=1}^{n} | x_i' - x_i | \leqslant \lambda,$$

it is true that $\sum_{i=1}^{n} | f(x_i') - f(x_i) | < \epsilon.$

Example. Let

$$g_n(x) = \begin{cases} 0 \text{ if } 0 \leqslant x \leqslant (2n+2)^{-1}, \\ (2n+2)x - 1 & \text{if} \quad (2n+2)^{-1} \leqslant x \leqslant (2n+1)^{-1}, \\ -2nx + 1 & \text{if} \quad (2n+1)^{-1} \leqslant x \leqslant (2n)^{-1}, \\ 0 & \text{if} \quad (2n)^{-1} \leqslant x \leqslant 1. \end{cases}$$

The function defined by $\quad f(x) = \sum_{n=1}^{\infty} g_n(x)$

is uniformly continuous in $[0,1]$ but is not absolutely continuous (see Fig. 10). In order to prove that this function is not absolutely continuous we need only to show that there exists a positive number ϵ such that for every positive number λ there exists a set of nonoverlapping intervals whose length-sum is less than λ, but which are such that the variation of $f(x)$ over these intervals is larger than ϵ.

189

We may choose ϵ to be *one*. Let λ be given. We select a positive integer N so that $1/N < \lambda$. Then the set of nonoverlapping intervals

$$(1/(N+1),\ 1/N)),\quad (1/(N+2),\ 1/(N+1)),\quad \ldots,\quad (1/(N+p),\ 1/(N+p-1))$$

has a length-sum less than λ for every p, but the variation of $f(x)$ over these intervals is greater than

$$\sum_{n=N}^{N+p-1}\frac{1}{n},$$

which can be made as large as we please, hence larger than one, by taking p large enough.

We notice that this function is not of bounded variation (see Def. 9.2.2). As a matter of fact, this function is not of bounded variation in every interval containing the origin.

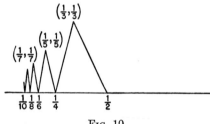

FIG. 10

Definition 10.1.2. A point x_0 of the closure of the domain of definition of $f(x)$ is said to be a *point of unbounded variation for $f(x)$* if $f(x)$ is of unbounded variation in every interval containing x_0.

P. 10.1.1. Construct a continuous function defined in $[0,1]$ for which each of the points $1/n$ $(n = 1,2,3,\ldots)$ is a point of unbounded variation.

P. 10.1.2. (a) Construct a function defined in $[0,1]$ for which each point in $[0,1]$ is a point of unbounded variation.

(b) Construct a continuous function on $[0,1]$ which has the property that each point of $[0,1]$ is a point of unbounded variation.

THEOREM 10.1.1. *If $f(x)$ is not of bounded variation in $[a,b]$, there exists at least one point of unbounded variation for $f(x)$.*

P. 10.1.3. Prove Theorem 10.1.1, and deduce the following.

Corollary. If $f(x)$ is absolutely continuous on $[a,b]$ then $f(x)$ is of bounded variation on $[a,b]$.

P. 10.1.4. Construct a function which is of bounded variation on [0,1] but which is not absolutely continuous, and thus prove that the converse of the last corollary is not true.

Definition 10.1.3. The λ-*variation* of a function $f(x)$ on (a,b) is the real function $V(\lambda)$, given by the equation

$$V(\lambda) = \text{supremum} \sum_{i=1}^{n} | f(x_i') - f(x_i) |$$

for all sets of nonoverlapping subintervals (x_i, x_i') of (a,b), which are such that

$$\sum_{i=1}^{n} | x_i' - x_i | \leqslant \lambda.$$

It is easily seen that if $f(x)$ is absolutely continuous on (a,b), then $\lim_{\lambda \to 0} V(\lambda) = 0$, and conversely, if $f(x)$ is such that the limit of the λ-variation of $f(x)$ is zero, $f(x)$ is absolutely continuous. We shall designate the limit $V(\lambda)$ by $V(0)$, and shall call it the *zero variation of* $f(x)$. With this notation we can say that the statement $f(x)$ is absolutely continuous on (a,b) is equivalent to saying that $V(0)$ of $f(x)$ is zero on (a,b).

10.2 Indefinite integrals over sets. Let $f(x)$ be a function defined on a measurable set E which is a subset of the n-dimensional Euclidean space E_n. We shall in the remainder of this chapter extend the domain of definition of $f(x)$ to the whole space by defining a new function which is identical to the given function on E, and which is equal to zero at all points of the complement of E. This extended function will also be designated $f(x)$. All functions will now be considered as defined in the whole space E_n.

Definition 10.2.1. If $f(x)$ and $g(x)$ are two functions which differ from each other only on a set of measure zero, that is, if $f(x) = g(x)$ almost everywhere, then $f(x)$ and $g(x)$ are said to be *equivalent functions.*

Definition 10.2.2. Let $f(x)$ be a measurable function summable over every set S of finite measure. The set function

$$F(S) = \int_S f(x) dx$$

defined for every set S of finite measure is called the *indefinite integral of* $f(x)$.

We see that certain point functions lead to set functions by the process of integration. We shall see later that the passage from a set function $F(S)$ to a point function $f(x)$ will be accomplished by the process of differentiation.

The point function $f(x)$ can be interpreted as a density function, while the set function $F(S)$ can be considered a mass function. For the particular case when the space E_n is the linear continuum, that is, when $n = 1$, and when the sets S are intervals, the indefinite integral

$$\int_S f(x)dx = \int_a^b f(x)dx,$$

and the general notion of the indefinite integral reduces to the elementary one.

THEOREM 10.2.1 (UNIQUENESS OF THE INDEFINITE INTEGRAL). *If $f_1(x)$ and $f_2(x)$ are two functions such that their indefinite integrals are equal, that is, $f_1(x)$ and $f_2(x)$ are such that for every set S of finite measure*

$$\int_S f_1(x)dx = \int_S f_2(x)dx,$$

then $f_1(x)$ and $f_2(x)$ are equivalent functions.

Proof. The function $f(x)$ which is equal to $f_1(x) - f_2(x)$ has an indefinite integral which is zero for every set S. The function $f^+(x) = \max [0, f(x)]$ has the same property, for if S is any set of finite measure, and S^- is the set where $f(x) \leqslant 0$, then $f^+(x) \equiv 0$ on S^-. The set $S - SS^-$ is of finite measure, and

$$\int_S f^+(x)dx = \int_{SS^-} f^+(x)dx + \int_{S-SS^-} f^+(x)dx$$

$$= \int_{S-SS^-} f(x)dx = 0,$$

where the last integral is zero by the hypothesis that $f_1(x)$ and $f_2(x)$ have the same indefinite integral. Thus the nonnegative function $f^+(x)$ has a vanishing integral. It follows from P. 9.4.8 that $f^+(x)$ is zero almost everywhere. Similarly it can be shown that $f^-(x)$, which is given by $\max [0, -f(x)]$, is zero almost everwhere. Hence $f_1(x) = f_2(x)$ almost everywhere.

10.3 Properties of the indefinite integral. As a direct consequence of Def. 10.2.2, we have the

THEOREM 10.3.1. *The indefinite integral is an additive set function, that is, if S_1 and S_2 are any two disjoint sets of finite measure,*

$$F(S_1 + S_2) = F(S_1) + F(S_2).$$

In order to describe some further properties of the indefinite integral we extend the notion of absolute continuity to set functions.

Definition 10.3.1. The λ-variation of a set function $\phi(S)$ is a real function $\tau(\lambda)$ defined by the statement

$$\tau(\lambda) = \text{supremum} \mid \phi(S) \mid$$

taken over all sets of measure $m(S) \leqslant \lambda$.

This function $\tau(\lambda)$ for a given set function is obviously a non-decreasing function of λ for $\lambda > 0$, and since it is nonnegative, the limit of $\tau(\lambda)$ as λ goes to zero exists. We shall designate this limit by $\tau(0)$, and call it the zero variation of $\phi(x)$.

Definition 10.3.2. An *additive* set function for which the zero-variation $\tau(0)$ is zero is said to be an *absolutely continuous* set function.

This definition can be reworded as follows. An additive set function is said to be absolutely continuous if its value, say $G(S)$, approaches zero as a limit as the measure of the set S goes to zero.

Definition 10.3.3. A set function $G(S)$ is said to be continuous if its value $G(S)$ approaches zero as a limit as the *diameter* of the set S goes to zero, that is, $G(S)$ is a continuous set function if for every positive number ϵ there exists a positive number δ such that for every set S of diameter less than δ it is true that $G(S) < \epsilon$.

We note that every absolutely continuous set function is continuous, but that the converse is not true.

P. 10.3.1. Give an example of an additive set function which is continuous, but is not absolutely continuous.

One of our aims in this section is to prove that the indefinite integral is absolutely continuous. That it is an additive set function we already know, we need only to show that its zero variation is zero. Before we can show this we need some preliminary results.

Lemma 10.3.1. Let $\phi(S) = \phi_1(S) + \phi_2(S)$ where $\phi_1(S)$ and $\phi_2(S)$ are set functions. Let $\tau_1(\lambda)$, and $\tau_2(\lambda)$ be their λ-variations, respectively, and let $\tau(\lambda)$ be the λ-variation of $\phi(S)$. Then

$$\tau(\lambda) \leqslant \tau_1(\lambda) + \tau_2(\lambda) \quad \text{and} \quad \tau(0) \leqslant \tau_1(0) + \tau_2(0).$$

P. 10.3.2. Prove this lemma.

Lemma 10.3.2. *If* $f(x)$ *has an indefinite integral,* $f(x)$ *can be represented as the sum of a bounded measurable function and a function summable over the whole space.*

Proof. Let

$$f^+(x) = \max\,[0,f(x)], \quad f^-(x) = \max\,[0,-f(x)].$$

Each of these functions is summable if $f(x)$ is summable. It is thus sufficient to establish our lemma for nonnegative functions. Let S_k be the set which consists of those points x for which $f(x) > 2^k$. Obviously $S_1 \supseteq S_2 \supseteq S_3 \supseteq \ldots$. Each of these sets is measurable by hypothesis. We shall show that at least one of these sets is of finite measure. Suppose every S_k were of infinite measure. Then there would exist in S_1 a subset T_1 such that $m(T_1) = \frac{1}{2}$ and on which $f(x) > 2$. In the complement of T_1 there would exist a set T_2 such that $m(T_2) = 1/2^2$, and $f(x) > 2^2$ in T_2. Proceeding in this manner we could construct a sequence of disjoint sets $T_1, T_2, T_3, \ldots$ such that $m(T_k) = 2^{-k}$ and such that $f(x)$ would be at least 2^k in T_k. The set

$$T = \sum_{k=1}^{\infty} T_k$$

would be a measurable set. By hypothesis $f(x)$ has a definite integral over T. But

$$\int_T f(x)dx \geqslant \sum_{k=1}^{\infty} \int_{T_k} f(x)dx.$$

The right-hand side, however, diverges, while the left-hand side is a fixed number. We have thus reached a contradiction. It follows that at least one of the sets S_k, say S_{k_0}, is of finite measure. Let

$$f_1(x) = \begin{cases} f(x) & \text{if } x \in S_{k_0}, \\ 0 & \text{if } x \notin S_{k_0}, \end{cases} \qquad f_2(x) = \begin{cases} 0 & \text{if } x \in S_{k_0}, \\ f(x) & \text{if } x \notin S_{k_0}. \end{cases}$$

Obviously $f(x) = f_1(x) + f_2(x)$. We also have that $f_2(x) < 2^{k_0}$ is bounded and measurable, while $f_1(x)$ is summable over the whole space, since it vanishes outside a set over which it is summable.

Lemma 10.3.3. *If* $f(x)$ *is bounded and measurable, the indefinite integral* $F(S)$ *of* $f(x)$ *is an absolutely continuous set function, that is,* $\tau(0)$ *for* $F(S)$ *is zero.*

Proof. Let U be an upper bound of $|f(x)|$. If S has a measure less than or equal to λ, then

$$| F(S) | = \left| \int_S f(x)dx \right| \leqslant U\lambda.$$

Hence $\quad \tau(\lambda) \leqslant U \cdot \lambda, \quad$ and $\quad \tau(0) = \lim_{\lambda \to 0} \tau(\lambda) = 0.$

This, together with Theorem 10.3.1, establishes this lemma.

Lemma 10.3.4. If $f(x)$ is summable then the indefinite integral $F(S)$ is such that $\tau(0)$ of $F(S)$ is zero.

Proof. Without loss of generality we may assume that $f(x) \geqslant 0$. Let

$$f_k(x) = \max [f(x),k].$$

From Def. 9.6.1 it follows that for every positive number ϵ we can find an integer k such that

$$\int [f(x) - f_k(x)]dx < \frac{\epsilon}{2}.$$

Next let S be any set of measure less than $\epsilon/2k$. Then

$$| F(S) | = \int_S f(x)dx = \int_S f_k(x)dx + \int_S [f(x) - f_k(x)]dx$$

$$\leqslant \frac{\epsilon}{2} + \frac{\epsilon}{2} = \epsilon.$$

On the basis of Theorem 10.3.1 and these lemmas we have the following result.

THEOREM 10.3.2. *The indefinite integral is an absolutely continuous set function.*

We shall next establish the converse of this theorem.

THEOREM 10.3.3. *Every absolutely continuous set function is the indefinite integral of some point function.*

This theorem will be established on the basis of several lemmas which follow.

Lemma 10.3.5. Every absolutely continuous set function $G(S)$ vanishes for every set of measure zero.

This is a direct consequence of the definition of absolute continuity for set functions (Def. 10.3.2).

Lemma 10.3.6. Every absolutely continuous set function $G(S)$ is a denumerably additive set function, that is,

$$G\left(\sum_{k=1}^{\infty} S_k\right) = \sum_{k=1}^{\infty} G(S_k)$$

if the sets S_k ($k = 1,2,3, \ldots$) are disjoint measurable sets whose sum is of finite measure.

Proof. We must show that the infinite series on the right converges and that the limit of its partial sums is equal to $G(S)$, where

$$S = \sum_{k=1}^{\infty} S_k.$$

The set S can be represented as

$$S = S_1 + S_2 + \ldots + S_n + R_n.$$

Since S is by hypothesis of finite measure, $\lim_{n \to \infty} m(R_n) = 0$. Because of the finite additivity of $G(S)$ (see Def. 10.3.2),

$$G(S) = G(S_1) + G(S_2) + \ldots + G(S_n) + G(R_n).$$

Since $G(S)$ is an absolutely continuous set function,

$$| G(R_n) | \leqslant \tau [\, m(R_n)\,],$$

which goes to zero as n goes to infinity. Thus the partial sums of the series $\sum_{k=1}^{\infty} G(S_k)$ converge to $G(S)$.

Definition 10.3.4. Let $G(S)$ be a set function. We define an *upper derivative* $D^-(G,x)$ and a *lower derivative* $D_-(G,x)$ at a point x by the equations

$$D^-(G,x) = \limsup \frac{G(C_x)}{m(C_x)},$$

$$D_-(G,x) = \liminf \frac{G(C_x)}{m(C_x)},$$

where the limits are taken as the side s of the cube C_x which contains x goes to zero. (Here x does not have to be the center of the cube C_x, but may be anywhere in the closure of C_x.) If $D^-(G,x) = D_-(G,x)$, their common value is called the derivative of the set function $G(x)$ and is denoted by $D(G,x)$. Here we admit $+\infty$ and $-\infty$ as possible values of $D(G,x)$.

Lemma 10.3.7. *The upper derivative $D^-(G,x)$ and the lower derivative $D_-(G,x)$ are measurable point functions.*

Proof. The proof will be given for the upper derivative. Let a be a real number, and let S be the set where $D^-(G,x) > a$. We must show that the set S is measurable. Let S_n and T_n have the following meaning.

$$S_n = \text{the set of } x\text{'s for which } D^-(G,x) > a + \frac{1}{n},$$

$$T_n = \text{the set of } x\text{'s for which } D^-(G,x) \geqslant a + \frac{1}{n},$$

where $n = 1, 2, 3, \ldots$. Obviously $S_1 \subseteq T_1 \subseteq S_2 \subseteq T_2 \subseteq \ldots$, and

$$\sum S_n = \sum T_n = S.$$

Let k and n be two positive integers. We consider all cubes C of edge-lengths less than $1/k$ for which

$$\frac{G(C)}{m(C)} > a + \frac{1}{n}.$$

From the definition of S_n it follows that each x of S_n is contained in an infinite number of such cubes whose sides are arbitrarily small. By Lindelöf's covering theorem there exists a denumerable set of cubes, say $C_{n,k}^{(1)}$, $C_{n,k}^{(2)}$, $\ldots$ which covers S_n. We designate the measurable sum of these cubes $C_{n,k}$, and form the set

$$C_n = \prod_{k=1}^{\infty} C_{n,k}.$$

This set C_n is measurable and contains S_n as a subset. Let x be an element of C_n. Then x is an element of every set $C_{n,k}$, where x is fixed and $k = 1, 2, 3, \ldots$. Hence for each k there exists at least one cube, say $C_{k'}$, which contains x and which is such that

$$a + \frac{1}{n} < \frac{G(C_{k'})}{m(C_{k'})} \leqslant \sup_{s < 1/k} \frac{G(C_x)}{m(C_x)}$$

where s is the edge-length of the cube C_x. Since this is true for each k,

$$a + \frac{1}{n} \leqslant \inf_{k \to \infty} (\sup) \frac{G(C_x)}{s < 1/k} = D^-(x).$$

This shows that x is also an element of T_n. Hence $S_n \subseteq C_n \subseteq T_n$, and S can be represented as the sum of the measurable sets C_n. This proves that S is measurable.

P. 10.3.3. Prove that $D_-(G,x)$ is measurable.

Lemma 10.3.8. *If $G(S)$ is an absolutely continuous set function whose upper derivative $D^-(G,x)$ is such that at every point of a set S of finite measure $D^-(G,x) \geqslant a(\leqslant a)$, then $G(S) \geqslant am(S)(\leqslant am(S))$.*

Proof. We shall establish only $G(S) \geqslant am(S)$. Let a positive number ϵ be given. We cover S with an open set T such that $m(T) < m(S) + \epsilon$. Next we consider cubes C such that $G(C) \geqslant am(C)$. From the hypothesis that at each point x of S $D^-(G,x) \geqslant am(S)$ it follows that each point of S is covered by a sequence of such cubes C whose edge-lengths tend to zero and which are contained in T. On the basis of Vitali's covering theorem we know that there exists a sequence of nonoverlapping such cubes, say $C_1, C_2, C_3, \ldots$ which cover S except for a set E of measure zero. Thus

$$S - E \subseteq \sum C_i \subseteq T.$$

Since $G(S)$ is an additive set function, we have

$$\begin{aligned}
G(S) - G(E) &= G(S - E) \\
&= G(\sum C_i) - [G(\sum C_i) - G(S - E)] \\
&= \sum G(C_i) - G[\sum C_i - (S - E)] \\
&\geqslant am(\sum C_i) - G[\sum C_i - (S - E)].
\end{aligned}$$

Since $G(S)$ is an absolutely continuous set function, and since E is of measure zero, $G(E) = 0$. We also have that

$$\sum C_i - (S - E) \subseteq T - (S - E)$$

and $\quad \left| G[\sum C_i - (S - E)] \right| \leqslant \left| G[T - (S - E)] \right|$

$$= \left| G(T - S) \right| \leqslant \tau[m(T - S)] = \tau(\epsilon),$$

Also since $m(\sum C_i) \geqslant m(S)$,

$$G(S) \geqslant am(S) - \tau(\epsilon).$$

Since ϵ was an arbitrary positive number, $G(S) \geqslant am(S)$.

P. 10.3.4. Establish the second part of Lemma 10.3.8.

We are now ready to give the

Proof of theorem 10.3.3. We must show that every absolutely continuous set function $G(S)$ is the indefinite integral of some point function. As a matter of fact, we shall show that such a point function is any point function which is equivalent to $D^-(G,x)$, or $D_-(G,x)$. As a side result we shall find that $D^-(G,x) = D_-(G,x)$ almost everywhere.

Let $G(S)$ be the given absolutely continuous set function. Let S

be a bounded set of finite measure. We denote the subset of S on which $D^-(G,x) > 0$ by S_+, and the subset of S on which $D^-(G,x) \leqslant 0$ by S_-. We shall show that $D^-(G,x)$ is summable, that it has a finite Lebesgue integral over S_+, and that

$$\int_{S_+} D^-(G,x)dx = G(S_+).$$

If S_n stands for the set of x for which $nh < D^-(G,x) \leqslant (n+1)h$ with $h > 0$, and if S_∞ represents the set where $D^-(G,x)$ is infinite, then

$$S_+ = S_\infty + S_0 + S_1 + S_2 + \dots .$$

The function $D^-(G,x)$ is summable over each set S_n, and

$$hnm(S_n) \leqslant \int_{S_n} D^-(G,x)dx \leqslant h(n+1)m(S_n).$$

From the preceding lemma it follows that

$$0 \leqslant hnm(S_n) \leqslant G(S_n) \leqslant h(n+1)m(S_n).$$

The series $h \sum n \cdot m(S_n)$ is convergent, since $\sum G(S_n) \leqslant G(S)$. Hence the series $h \sum (n+1)m(S_n)$ is also convergent, and the function $D^-(G,x)$ is summable over

$$S_0 + S_1 + S_2 + \dots = S_+ - S_\infty.$$

Furthermore $\quad \left| \int_{S_n} D^-(G,x)dx - G(S_n) \right| \leqslant hm(S_n).$

Thus $\quad \left| \int_{S_+ - S_\infty} D^-(G,x)dx - G(S_+ - S_\infty) \right| \leqslant hm(S_+)$

for all h, that is,

$$\int_{S_+ - S_\infty} D^-(G,x)dx = G(S_+ - S_\infty) = G(S_+) - G(S_\infty).$$

But for every given a, $D^-(G,x) > a$ for all x in S_∞. Hence by Lemma 10.3.8,

$$m(S_\infty) < \frac{G(S_\infty)}{a}$$

for every $a > 0$. Thus $m(S_\infty) = 0$, and $G(S_\infty) = 0$. This proves that

$$\int_{S_+} D^-(G,x)dx = G(S_+).$$

In an analogous manner it can be shown that $D^-(G,x)$ is summable over S_-, and hence over $S = S_+ + S_-$. Any set of finite measure can be represented as the sum of nonoverlapping bounded sets. And the theorem is thus extended to unbounded sets of finite measure. It follows that every absolutely continuous set function $G(S)$ is equal to the indefinite integral of its upper derivative $D^-(G,x)$. In a similar way it can also be shown that $G(S)$ is equal to the indefinite integral of its lower derivative $D_-(G,x)$. Hence

$$\int_S D^-(G,x)dx = G(S) = \int_S D_-(G,x)dx$$

for every set S of finite measure. It follows now from the theorem on the uniqueness of the indefinite integral (Theorem 10.2.1) that $D^-(G,x) = D_-(G,x)$ almost everywhere.

As a corollary to the above result we have the next theorem.

THEOREM 10.3.4. *If $G(S)$ is an absolutely continuous set function, then*

$$\lim_{s \to 0} \frac{G(C_x)}{m(C_x)}$$

exists almost everywhere. Here s is the edge-length of a closed cube C_x containing the point x. This limit defines a derivative $D(G,x)$, and $G(S)$ is the indefinite integral of this derivative.

This result might be called the *fundamental theorem of the Lebesgue integral calculus.* In the next section we shall specialize it to the case of functions of a single variable.

10.4 The one-dimensional indefinite integral. We consider interval functions defined for all open, closed, or half-open intervals in the one-dimensional space E_1. Definitions 10.3.1, 10.3.2, and 10.3.3 apply verbatim to interval functions except that the word "set" must be given the particular meaning of interval.

THEOREM 10.4.1. *Every absolutely continuous interval function $G(I)$ determines to within an arbitrary constant an absolutely continuous point function $F(x)$ such that for any interval $I = (a,b)$ (open, closed, or half-open)*

(1) $G(I) = F(b) - F(a)$.

Conversely, every absolutely continuous point function $F(x)$ determines uniquely an absolutely continuous interval function satisfying (1).

Proof. Let $\phi(I)$ be a given absolutely continuous interval function, and let a be a constant. We define $F(x)$ as follows.

$$F(x) = \begin{cases} \phi(I_x) & \text{where } I_x = (a,x), \ x \geqslant a, \\ -\phi(I_x) & \text{where } I_x = (x,a), \ x < a. \end{cases}$$

It is readily seen that for every interval (x,x'),

$$\phi(I) = F(x') - F(x).$$

Let us consider a set $\{I_j\}$ $(j = 1,2,\ldots,n)$ of nonoverlapping intervals such that $I_j = (x_j,x_j')$ and

$$\sum_{i=1}^{n} |x_i' - x_i| \leqslant \lambda.$$

Then
$$\sum |F(x_i') - F(x_i)| = |\Sigma_1| + |\Sigma_2|$$
$$= 2\tau(\lambda),$$

where Σ_1 stands for the sum over those I_j for which each difference $F(x_j') - F(x_j)$ is positive, while Σ_2 represents the sum over the remaining intervals. We see that the variation $V(\lambda)$ (see Def. 10.1.3) for the point function $F(x)$ goes to zero as λ goes to zero, since $\tau(\lambda)$ goes to zero for the absolutely continuous interval function ϕ. This shows that every absolutely continuous interval function determines an absolutely continuous point function. It is easily shown, as it was done in Sec. 9.11, that any two such point functions can differ by at most a constant.

Conversely, let $F(x)$ be an absolutely continuous point function. The interval function whose value is given for every interval $I = (a,b)$ by

$$\phi(I) = F(b) - F(a)$$

is an absolutely continuous interval function. This follows from the fact that for every set of nonoverlapping intervals $\{(I_j\}$,

$$I_j = (x_j,x_j') \quad \text{such that} \quad \sum |x_j' - x_j| \leqslant \lambda,$$

it is true that

$$\tau(\lambda) = |\phi(\sum I_j)| \leqslant |\sum \phi(I_j)| \leqslant \sum |\phi(I_j)|$$
$$= \sum |F(x_j') - F(x_j)| = V(\lambda).$$

Combining these results with those of Theorem 10.3.4 we obtain the next result which might be called the *fundamental theorem for the Lebesgue integral calculus.*

THEOREM 10.4.2. *Every absolutely continuous point function $F(x)$ defined everywhere in E_1 determines almost everywhere a real point function $f(x)$ which is given by*

$$\lim_{\substack{h_1 \to 0 \\ h_2 \to 0}} \frac{F(x + h_2) - F(x - h_1)}{h_2 + h_1} = f(x),$$

where h_1 and h_2 are nonnegative, and $h_1 + h_2 \neq 0$. Furthermore $f(x)$ is such that

$$F(b) - F(a) = \int_a^b f(x)dx$$

for every interval (a,b).

We note that at each point x for which $f(x)$ is finite it is equal to the derivative of $F(x)$ as given by Def. 9.3.1.

10.5 Unilateral derivatives

Definition 10.5.1. The *upper right, lower right, upper left,* and *lower left* derivatives of a *real function* $F(x)$ of a real variable x are defined as

$$D^+F(x) = \limsup_{h \to 0^+} \frac{F(x + h) - F(x)}{h},$$

$$D_+F(x) = \liminf_{h \to 0^+} \frac{F(x + h) - F(x)}{h},$$

$$D^-F(x) = \limsup_{h \to 0^-} \frac{F(x + h) - F(x)}{h},$$

$$D_-F(x) = \liminf_{h \to 0^-} \frac{F(x + h) - F(x)}{h},$$

respectively.

If all four derivatives are equal, their common value is called the *derived function of $F(x)$*. We admit here $+\infty$, and $-\infty$ as possible values for limit superior, limit inferior. If the derived function is finite it becomes the derivative of $F(x)$ as given by Def. 9.3.1.

Corresponding to the point function $F(x)$ we define the interval function $\phi(I)$ whose value for every interval (a,b) is given by

$$\phi(I) = \phi(a,b) = F(b) - F(a).$$

In terms of this interval function the four one-sided derivatives of $F(x)$ can be expressed as

$$D^+F(x) = \lim_{h \to 0} \sup \frac{\phi(x, x + h)}{h},$$

$$D_+F(x) = \lim_{h \to 0} \inf \frac{\phi(x, x + h)}{h},$$

$$D^-F(x) = \lim_{h \to 0} \sup \frac{\phi(x - h, x)}{h},$$

$$D_-F(x) = \lim_{h \to 0} \inf \frac{\phi(x - h, x)}{h},$$

where $h > 0$. Each of these limits has the form

$$\lim_{s \to 0} \frac{\phi(I_x)}{m(I_x)}$$

where s is the length of the interval I_x, whose left or right end point is x. We see that the limits here are taken under more restrictive conditions than those in Def. 10.3.3. Hence these limits will lie between $D^-(\phi, x)$ and $D_-(\phi(x))$ as defined earlier. Thus the derived function of a point function $F(x)$ will exist whenever the interval function $\phi(a, b) = F(b) - F(a)$ has a derivative $D(\phi, x)$ as given by Def. 10.3.3.

For a more detailed analysis of the properties of the derivatives of continuous or measurable functions the reader is referred to the bibliography given at the end of Chapter 9.

INDEX

(Numbers refer to pages)

205